Praise for *Big Broth*

A must-read account of the collapse of health care freedom in the United States. *Big Brother in the Exam Room* is essential reading for every patient and doctor looking to fight back against the intrusive government health care behemoth.

—**Dan Bongino,** *New York Times* BEST-SELLING AUTHOR OF *THE FIGHT*

Big Brother in the Exam Room is what happens when the federal government pays for over half of the health care in the US. As the responsible party for the majority of health care, the government gets to decide how much they're willing to pay for care, where it can be delivered, and by whom, and the "hoops that must be jumped through" for doctors to participate and to get paid. Every regulation and every federal requirement that gets between patients and their doctors, such as electronic medical records, brings us one step closer to a single-payer system and one step further away from individual freedom over health care decisions by patients.

—**Hal Scherz, MD,** FOUNDER OF DOCS 4 PATIENT CARE AND SECRETARY OF THE DOCS 4 PATIENT CARE FOUNDATION

We've grown so accustomed to rapid technological change that we often forget it comes with a cost. In health care, that cost could be your privacy, your freedom, and your health. In *Big Brother in the Exam Room*, Twila Brase offers an eye-popping exposé on how a government mandate for electronic health records—along with a privacy law that leaves Americans more vulnerable than they know—put all three at risk. A must-read for all those who have a stake in true health care reform.

—**Ed Morrissey,** SENIOR EDITOR FOR HOTAIR.COM

Brase shines a bright light on how the government foisted electronic health records (EHRs) onto the health care system to further control the practice of medicine, subordinating individualized patient care. *Big Brother in the Exam Room* is a must-read for anyone who cares about physician autonomy and patient care.

—**Naomi Lopez Bauman**, Director of Health Care Policy, Goldwater Institute

Big Brother in the Exam Room reads like a real-life version of *Nineteen Eighty-Four* or *Fahrenheit 451*. It's a chilling tale of steady encroachments on freedom and privacy, tending toward the suppression of the doctor-patient relationship itself. It's a handbook for medical subversives, optimistic citizens determined to preserve a genuinely human art of healing in a world overrun with bureaucratic centralizers, and idiot systematizers. In these deftly researched pages, we glimpse a future in which physicians are mere cogs and patients an afterthought. Happily, the story doesn't end there. The deft and fearless Ms. Brase offers a message of hope and an outline of sanity.

—**Dean Clancy**, Former Senior Health Policy Advisor in Congress and the White House

Twila Brase presents a compelling case that describes not only how electronic health records have been surreptitiously imposed on our health care system and eroded our right to privacy, but also how they have caused the opposite of what their proponents claimed. Health care costs are higher than ever, while too many patients are receiving less care. I highly recommend *Big Brother in the Exam Room* to anyone with an interest in reforming our health care system.

—**Rudy A. Takala**, Associate Editor for *The Hill*

Twila Brase is not only one of the most informed members of the health care profession, she writes the backstory of the transformation of health care (and thus the country) with the skill of an investigative reporter. With clarity and understanding, *Big Brother in the Exam Room* provides essential content to the health care debate.

—**Nancy Schulze**, founder, Congressional Wives Speakers, and board member, Physicians for Reform

What could possibly be dangerous about government-mandated electronic health records? Like most Americans, you probably think nothing. But once you've read Twila Brase's exceptionally well-researched and reasoned account of the origins and effects of EHR, you'll see that your privacy, your money, and even your life are endangered by this reckless electronic experiment. *Big Brother in the Exam Room* must not only be read, but studied.

—**Howard Root**, retired CEO of Vascular Solutions, Inc. and author of *Cardiac Arrest*

Twila Brase has been sounding the alarm about the perils of government data dredging at least since the HIPAA "Privacy" Rule was enacted. *Big Brother in the Exam Room* shows how the EHR, while destroying privacy, also has the opposite of the promised effects on efficiency, reliable record-keeping, and clinical errors. EHRs are clearly a danger to your health as well as your doctor's mental health.

—**Jane Orient, MD**, executive director, Association of American Physicians and Surgeons

Consent is the essence of medical privacy and the doctor-patient relationship back to the Hippocratic Oath. Unconsented medical experiments inherently violate these relationships and the Nuremberg principles. HIPAA is such an "experiment" among electronic medical records by removing the consenting relationship back to the Oath and imposing "coerced authorization" on patients and the health system. *Big Brother in the Exam Room* deserves careful consideration for its dissection of the deforming aspects of depriving individuals of their rights to medical privacy and consent. A simple sentence inserted in health legislation, "patient consent is required for all use, sharing, and treatment with medical information," could reverse this tawdry course and help restore health and integrity to medical care in the US. *Big Brother in the Exam Room* guides the way.

—**Richard Sobel**, author of "The HIPAA Paradox: The Privacy Rule That's Not" and *Citizenship as Foundation of Rights: Meaning for America*

In my work as legislative director for Ron Paul and as president of his Campaign for Liberty, I have benefited from Twila Brase's insights on the threats to privacy posed by the federal government's takeover of health care. I recommend her *Big Brother in the Exam Room* to anyone wishing to understand how socialized or corporatized medicine threatens our civil, as well as our economic, liberties.

—**Norm Singleton**, former legislative director for Congressman Ron Paul

Is the requirement for electronic health records intended to improve patient care or to serve insurance companies' interest in payment oversight and "compliance"? In *Big Brother in the Exam Room*, Twila Brase raises important questions that have been largely overlooked in the debates over health care legislation.

—**Edward Hasbrouck**, investigative journalist, author, and consultant for The Identity Project

Through meticulous research and the full range of sources, Twila Brase has made a very important contribution to the field of health care policy. Doctors, patients, and all who believe knowing how their private health care information is being collected and used is important need to read *Big Brother in the Exam Room*.

—**Eric Novack, MD**, orthopedic surgeon and chairman, US Health Freedom Coalition

PRAISE FOR BIG BROTHER IN THE EXAM ROOM

Twila Brase's book is a must-read for all Americans—physicians and patients alike. *Big Brother in the Exam Room* provides a comprehensive historical review and thoughtful evaluation of facts. Twila is a recognized expert on HIPAA and the ensuing multitude of rapid-fire federal laws and regulations crafted in DC to achieve top-down control by government entities and their cronies. She warns America about the inherent dangers of the government takeover of our medical care achieved through the forced and hasty adoption of the untested, undebated, unconsented electronic health record, which resulted in unprecedented losses of money, individual liberty, and life itself.

I pray the American people will take note, engage, and stop this pathological process—particularly members of the medical profession who are begrudgingly adopting EHRs, at first through monetary reward and now through monetary penalty and threat of the complete loss of autonomy and the ability to practice medicine in the United States at all.

—**Kris Held, MD**, co-founder of AmericanDoctors4Truth.org

The right to autonomy and privacy, which are natural rights acknowledged in the US Constitution and recognized internationally as human rights, are being violated in doctors' offices every day in America. Written by health-freedom advocate Twila Brase, who tells it like it is, *Big Brother in the Exam Room* is a hard-hitting, well-referenced book about how government-operated electronic health records tracking systems are a real threat to liberty and what you can do to protect yourself.

—**Barbara Loe Fisher**, co-founder and president, National Vaccine Information Center

Finally, a book that takes the approach to health IT that my early medical mentor, cardiothoracic surgery pioneer Victor P. Satinsky, MD, took towards medicine: "Critical thinking, always, or your patient's dead." The approach to health IT to date has usually been one of industry-led marketing puffery and "ignore-the-downsides, full-steam-ahead" hyperenthusiasm. The result has been loss of privacy and security, increased (not decreased) risks and costs, and loss of physician-patient autonomy to the computer—and the computer's bureaucratic masters. In *Big Brother in the Exam Room*, author Twila Brase "tells it like it is," namely, that the dreams of cybernetic medical utopia need to be dampened by the harsh master of medical reality.

—**Scot Silverstein, MD**, medical informatics specialist and independent EHR forensics expert

Twila Brase is brilliant in dissecting the quantum growth of data collection and how it can affect the civil rights of all Americans. *Big Brother in the Exam Room* is vital to anyone who wants to understand the troubling threat to our personal freedoms that has infested our health care industrial complex.

—**Warren Limmer**, Minnesota state senator

Technology makes countless parts of our lives better. So it can and should be with digitized medical records and the aggregation of medical data. In *Big Brother in the Exam Room,* leading medical-privacy advocate Twila Brase shows, however, that when government rather than individual choice determines what electronic medical records physicians will use and who can access your medical information, progress becomes elusive.

—**Michael F. Cannon**, Cato Institute

Twila Brase pulls back the curtain on government-mandated electronic health records, exposing the risks they pose to both patients and practitioners. This carefully researched book, *Big Brother in the Exam Room*, equips readers to advocate for the safety and health care privacy Americans expect and deserve.

—**Dr. Linda Solie**, psychologist and author of *Take Charge of Your Emotions*

PRAISE FOR BIG BROTHER IN THE EXAM ROOM

Big Brother in the Exam Room lays out how politicians, and all parts of the "health industry," teamed up to impose a sweeping system of surveillance that puts outsiders in charge of medical decisions, endangers patients, and is expanding to monitor private lives far from the exam room. Twila Brase's steps back to freedom should be implemented at every level as soon as possible. Read this book and then act as if your life depends on it.

—**Bob McEwen**, former member,
US House of Representatives, Ohio

In *Big Brother in the Exam Room,* Twila Brase exposes the alarming truth about government-mandated electronic health records. Her detailed documentation and refusal to let either political party off the hook demonstrate the integrity of her indictment. Dangers and threats hidden in plain sight are now finally revealed—opening the door to real reform.

—**David Kupelian**, best-selling author, journalist,
and managing editor of WND.com

BIG BROTHER
IN THE
EXAM ROOM

The Dangerous Truth about Electronic Health Records

TWILA BRASE, RN, PHN

ISBN 13: 978-1-59298-706-1

Library of Congress Catalog Number: 2018904492

Printed in the United States of America
First Printing: 2018
22 21 20 19 18 5 4 3 2 1

Cover and interior design by James Monroe Design, LLC.

BEAVER'S POND PRESS

Beaver's Pond Press, Inc.
7108 Ohms Lane
Edina, MN 55439–2129
(952) 829-8818
www.BeaversPondPress.com

To order, visit www.BigBrotherintheExamRoom.com
or call the Citizens' Council for Health Freedom at 651-646-8935.
Reseller discounts available.

Dedicated to Martin N. Kellogg, a man of integrity and wit who joined me to co-found Citizens' Council for Health Freedom. We have worked together for more than two decades to follow Micah 6:8: "What does the Lord require of you but to do justice, and to love kindness, and to walk humbly with your God?" Thank you for your leadership, your friendship, and your enduring support.

Contents

Foreword

While almost all the public discussion about health care in the past few years has centered on the regulations, subsidies, and mandates of Obamacare, very little attention has been given to the foundation for the whole enterprise—the national mandate on physicians, hospitals, and other health care providers to adopt federally dictated health information systems. In *Big Brother in the Exam Room*, Twila Brase corrects that error and digs deeply into the history and consequences of this requirement. What she finds should alarm anyone concerned about patient safety and privacy.

She finds a system that was poorly thought out and adopted with the flimsiest of evidence. It was imposed by a bipartisan clique that used the hysteria of the 2008 recession to create a "command and control" takeover of the entire health care system. The effort was fueled by a self-interested industry that enriched itself on the nearly $40 billion of taxpayer dollars that have been appropriated. It has resulted in worse care, rising costs, less competition, and destruction of the trusted relationship between patients and physicians. All this despite the near unanimous protests of the people actually responsible for clinical care.

Fortunately, Brase concludes the book with a vivid picture of how absurd all this would be if applied to any other area of the economy and provides a powerful path for state legislatures, providers, and the American people to extricate ourselves from this nightmare. Our future is in our own hands—all we have to do is seize it.

—**Greg Scandlen**, founder of Consumers for Health Care Choices and author of *Myth Busters: Why Health Reform Always Goes Awry*

Preface

The watched are never free.

Consider the world's most powerful dictators and secret police. Stalin required children to report their parents' conversations.[1] The Stasi in East Germany kept detailed files, which have recently been made available to those once kept under surveillance.[2] Hitler used IBM's Hollerith machine, which has been on display at the Holocaust Museum in Washington, DC.[3] Russia's Vladimir Putin has Sorm, a national system of eavesdropping on electronic communications.[4]

Surveillance is and has always been a tool of control. That's why America's Founding Fathers put privacy protections in the US Constitution, as part of the Bill of Rights. However, the emergence of new surveillance-enabled technologies today—such as computers, smartphones, digital driver's licenses, and biometric scans—create new tracking and analytic powers. Unless Americans remain watchful and engaged, their freedom can be taken away, one law and one technology at a time.

In 2009, Congress mandated the use of government-certified electronic health records (EHRs). Certified EHR technology (CEHRT) means the EHR is built not to improve patient care but to do what the government wants it to do: government reporting, patient and doctor profiling, data analytics, health services research, linking to a national medical-records system, population health, standardized treatment protocols, compliance tracking, and much more. The government calls this *Meaningful Use* of the EHR. Doctors and hospitals that refuse to install a government-certified EHR and refuse to demonstrate Meaningful Use receive reduced Medicare payments. As a result, this surveillance technology is now present in virtually every doctor's office and every hospital room. In the years since 2009, the federal government has mandated specific uses of the EHR in three stages and Congress prohibited "information blocking" between EHR systems.

Patients face this intrusive system because they don't pay their own medical bills. Third parties—the government, employers, and health plans—pay for most medical care. America's third-party payer system began with employer-sponsored coverage in the 1940s and expanded into Medicare, Medicaid, Obamacare, and more. As Americans handed over their responsibility for medical bills to third parties they gradually lost choices, privacy, control, and freedom. The payers, not the patients, hold the purse strings and the power. These third parties do not have the same interest in the patient's health, recovery, and quality of life as the patient does. As a friend of mine once quipped, "If someone else who doesn't love you is in charge of buying your food for the rest of your life, you will eat much differently than if you buy it on your own." In short, "He who pays the piper picks the tune."

The digitized EHR facilitates outside control of dollars, data, and decisions. With billions of dollars in their hands, third parties claim a right to decide who gets the dollars and what the dollars pay for. They decide how much of a patient's medical record must be disclosed before they'll agree to pay part or all (or sometimes none) of the patient's medical bills. The government-certified EHR was designed exactly for this purpose—billing, reporting, and data analytics—not patient care.

It doesn't have to be this way. Medical care can be confidential, affordable, and free from outside interference. For example, The Wedge of Health Freedom (JoinTheWedge.com) facilitates *first-party* payment. Patients pay doctors directly for care.[5] Wedge practices accept only cash, check, or credit card, but they welcome all patients, whether insured, uninsured, or publicly subsidized. They sign no contracts with the government or health plans, keeping their overhead expenses low. Thus, it is no surprise that inside The Wedge, patient data is not shared without the patient's express consent, medical treatment is tailored to each patient's individual needs, and the cost of care is affordable. There's no third party increasing the cost. This concept is not revolutionary. A first-party payer system is how Americans buy everything else they need from cars to computers to phones and homes. It's how they used to pay for medical care. It's how they can pay for it again.

The subject of this book is the *government EHR*, although I won't often refer to it that way. This book is about the government-controlled, government-mandated, and government-certified electronic health record. It's not about the free-market EHR many doctors purchased before the mandate—and were forced to give up. Those free-market EHRs worked for the doctor. The government-certified EHR works for the government.

The government EHR enables government control over private medical decisions. Ralph Grams, MD, a professor of medical informatics, says the EHR mandate will centralize power in the federal government and "move our entire economy into a socialized system with czars and unelected dictators in control."[6] He says rationing of care will be enforced through this "federally controlled EHR."

He's right. As you'll see in this book, the EHR in doctor's offices today is a command-and-control surveillance system meant to put medical treatment decisions under the scrutiny and control of government agencies and their health plan collaborators. Taxpayers have paid more than $30 billion to put this system in place—but they have no idea what it is or what it's doing to their care, their choices, and the confidentiality of their private information.

Citizens in countries run by tyrants understand the danger. During my visit to Romania nine months after the November 9, 1989 fall of the Berlin Wall, a young adult was taking a group of us on a walking tour of the town. Suddenly he stopped and pointed to the tallest building, which looked no more than four stories high. There, he said, is where his father raced as soon as he heard Nicolae Ceaușescu, president of the Socialist Republic of Romania, and his wife had been captured as they tried to escape the country in December 1989.

The young man's father didn't hesitate. He ran. Along with a few friends, he entered the government building left wide open by fleeing state workers and made a beeline to the top floor. They opened the windows, they opened the file cabinets, and they began to throw all the manila folders down to the street below. The folders held the surveillance details of every person in town. The young man watched as the folders were set on fire. Everyone's data was destroyed. Had his father waited, some worried bureaucrats may have returned and locked the building. In one blazing bonfire, these men took back their privacy, and with it, their freedom.

My efforts to protect patient privacy began in 1996. One day, when our health freedom organization was still in its infancy, I received an anonymous letter.

It contained a proposed amendment and the notice of a conference committee hearing at the Minnesota State Capitol. It made little sense to me because the amendment was so short, and I didn't have a copy of the related bill. Out of curiosity, I attended the hearing. There I found a full-fledged battle in progress, led by a soon-to-retire Democrat who was determined to add consent requirements for researcher access to medical records. Various health care lobbyists in the room were trying to stop the amendment. After a few hearings, in which our organization took the side of patient consent, the bill passed with the amendment.

But the lobbyists came back the next year, after the legislator had retired. The law was modified in 1997 to allow research without consent if it was *internal* to the organization holding the patient's data. Only researchers *external* to the organization were (and still are) required to get consent. However, the modification allowed "implied consent." If a patient is sent two letters asking for consent to participate in a research project and doesn't respond one way or the other to either letter—even if the patient never receives or opens the letters—consent is implied.[7] Hospitals, clinics, and others can share the patient's data with external researchers without express patient consent. We testified against this language, but to no avail.

That was the first of many battles to come, at both the state and national levels. I've had the opportunity to testify in support of patient privacy rights before legislatures in Pennsylvania and New Mexico as well as Minnesota. I also testified in 1998 in Chicago at the first of a series of scheduled US Department of Health & Human Services hearings on the creation of a unique patient identifier, and the only (to my knowledge) hearing held after it made front-page news in the *New York Times*.[8] Congress promptly prohibited funding to develop this national patient ID, but a 2017 federal law authorizes the development of a national strategy to identify patients. See section IV.

While our organization, Citizens' Council for Health Freedom (CCHF), has had many successes related to privacy, often bipartisan in nature, in every state and across the nation our country is still collectively moving in the wrong direction. The systems of health surveillance are growing, not shrinking.

Patients have lost data ownership rights and control of their private medical information. Physicians are sharing data under laws that force them to do it or be penalized. Corporations are reaping billions from the privacy onslaught. And state and federal agencies are building one database after the next while preparing a national medical-records system for 24/7 access to the private medical, genetic, lifestyle, and behavioral details of every American. When Congress forced doctors to set up government-certified EHRs in exam rooms nationwide, it compromised confidentiality, jeopardized patient safety, infringed on medical ethics, and let the government unconstitutionally interfere in medical treatment decisions.

Tragically, the public has no idea that the HIPAA privacy rule eviscerated their privacy rights rather than protected them—and therefore doesn't rise up and demand patient consent requirements be restored. They have no idea that the clinic's "patient portal," which many patients like, is government-mandated as part of Meaningful Use and used to capture patient-generated data.[9] They have no idea that the portal and the move to mobile personal health records (which are only a subset of patient data in the EHR) may be part of a campaign to build public acceptance of the surveillance system, encourage Americans to regularly add personal data to it, and make the government EHR feel indispensable.

You may not support privacy rights. You may be a fan of big data analytics and artificial intelligence. You may be fine with researchers sifting through your medical records and dissecting your genetic code without your consent. You may even support government control of treatment decisions. You have a right to those views. But no one has the right to force other patients to give up their right to privacy and informed consent. And no one has the right to deny other patients a fresh, unbiased second opinion. Some patients have lived for years after their first doctor said nothing could be done—but a second doctor without access to the first doctor's assessment offered an alternative treatment and acted on the patient's behalf. This is the kind of freedom and privacy that saves lives.

Over the past two decades, I've watched freedom fall as privacy rights are destroyed by third parties who claim a right to patient data for reasons such as "quality" measurement, public health, care coordination, "evidence-based medicine," the greater good, population health (see section V), and beneficence and justice.

As this book demonstrates, both Democrats and Republicans are responsible.

Outsiders should not be given patient data without consent whether identified, de-identified, or anonymized. The doctor-patient privilege is as important to the practice of medicine as the attorney-client privilege is to the practice of law. Confidentiality is key to a trusted patient-doctor relationship, enabling patients to make the disclosures necessary for accurate and timely medical care. Surveillance does the opposite.

But the resulting third-party payers, who are now in the driver's seat, claim a right to access patient data and the right to use that data to control the doctor's treatment decisions. They also claim the Constitution doesn't protect citizens from government access to medical data held by third parties (see section IV). After this book's conclusion, you'll find a brief timeline of the federal laws that led to today's third-party control.

This book does not cover every element of EHRs and health information technology, nor is it the final word on what's happening across America. Health information technology and health information exchange is a rapidly moving target. Just ask my editors! By the time this book is published certain facts will have changed, but the trajectory will have remained the same—away from privacy, away from freedom.

Big Brother is perfectly happy in the exam room. He won't leave willingly. Significant citizen engagement, physician resistance, and legislative action are required. But it could be as simple as pulling the plug on the EHR and going back to paper, as the Illinois Pain Institute did in 2015.[10]

Some people say privacy is lost forever, that this battle for patient and doctor freedom has no chance of success. These comments are meant to dissuade and demoralize. Ignore them. Once Americans understand the critical relationship between privacy and freedom, I believe they'll take steps to secure the rights they've lost. The final section includes a list of action steps specific to policy makers, practitioners, and patients.

There is no freedom without privacy. There is no freedom under Big Brother.

I wrote this book to connect these two dots—freedom and privacy—and to show Americans:

- The national surveillance system now under construction as a result of third-party payment
- The pressures doctors face to conform to computerized treatment protocols
- The endless checklists that interfere with patient care and cause physician burnout
- The penalties for failure to "meaningfully use" EHRs
- HIPAA and other unconstitutional infringements on privacy
- How EHRs are putting the practice of medicine under government control
- How EHRs are endangering patients

Inside are real-life stories of dangers and difficulties, comments from frustrated physicians, warnings from oversight agencies, quotes from industry insiders, examples of surveillance systems enabled by the EHR, privacy polls and EHR studies, obvious and hidden costs, and more. To make sure readers see how many data-reporting hoops America's highly skilled physicians are forced to jump through to get paid, several federal regulatory details are included.

If you want the CliffsNotes version of this book, read the introduction and the rest of the history section, the "steps back" section, and the afterword. Otherwise, flip through these pages and read whatever captures your attention—or start at the beginning and read through to the end. I also highly recommend the "clinical chaos" section. Wherever you start and however you continue, I suspect it won't take long before you begin to see what's at stake for patients, privacy, and freedom.

I hope this book will open many eyes to the serious dangers Americans face as patients and citizens. I also hope it serves as a call to action. May this book empower you, and doctors and patients everywhere, to banish Big Brother from the exam room and never let him back in.

Twila Brase, RN, PHN
June 1, 2018

Acknowledgments

No one writes a book alone.

I thank everyone who read the manuscript, proofed the text, checked the footnotes, raised questions, sought clarification, and suggested changes. This book is better because of its readers—who, in line with the message of the book, like their privacy. They shall remain anonymous. Thank you also to those who gave it a personal endorsement. Your statements of support have added weight and urgency to my call to action.

I also want to thank every concerned doctor and patient who has stepped up to publicly discuss or write about their personal experiences under the government's EHR mandate. I have included many of their comments. I hope sharing their experiences gives the reader not only a sense of the dangers patients face, but also a snapshot of the dilemmas practitioners experience every day as they try to do what they love: take care of the patients who need them.

And thank you to the Beaver's Pond Press staff, who edited, proofed, and designed the book inside and out. I couldn't be more pleased.

To my family and friends who supported this nearly six-year endeavor—and to the board of directors of Citizens' Council for Health Freedom (CCHF), who gave me time and sometimes a faraway, quiet place to get it done—thank you! I'm also grateful for the dedicated and excellent CCHF staff, who tried as much as possible to give me uninterrupted days in the final push to get the manuscript out the door (and weren't sure it would ever happen)—and for CCHF's donors and supporters. You are truly the wind beneath our wings.

And finally, and most especially, I'm thankful to Jesus Christ, my LORD and my God, the author and originator of freedom, without whom this book would never have been written.

I

The History of the EHR Mandate

Introduction

Today's electronic health record (EHR) is not what it seems. The computerized system in exam rooms and at the bedside was not made for patients. It was not made for doctors. It was not made with patient care in mind. This government-imposed EHR was designed for data collection, data reporting, and outside control of the practice of medicine by government and third-party payers. When Congress forced doctors and hospitals to buy and use EHRs for the purpose of conducting surveillance and imposing control, it had no idea how the mandate would impact doctors or patients.

Now we know. This experiment, foisted on patients and doctors without their consent, is being used to redesign the delivery of care and deconstruct the patient-doctor relationship for the political, social engineering, and financial benefits of others, including government agencies, health plans, the data industry, and more.

All Americans have been affected. Some have been injured. Others have died. Overwhelmed physicians are giving up and retiring early. Harm to patients and the practice of medicine has been thoroughly documented by practitioners and researchers. And private data from every possible aspect of personal lives is being entered into this new surveillance system for outside analysis and use.

Federal officials designed the EHR as an operating system for national health care. The mandate to buy and use it, passed by Congress in 2009, forces clinics and hospitals to install a computerized system that tracks every treatment, collects detailed information on every patient and doctor, and enables outside control of every medical decision. Physicians who refuse to buy and use a government-certified EHR; who refuse to collect, report, and share patient data electronically; or who engage in so-called "information blocking" face financial penalties.

"It is interesting to look at the role of the doctor in this 'brave new world,'" writes informatics professor Ralph Grams, MD, discussing the criteria to receive EHR incentive payments. "If you look down the list of features that are considered worthy of financial reward (twenty-three basic categories) you will note that only one criterion deals with clinical decision support." He notes that the other twenty-two items are secondary to the doctor and used to feed the government patient "data that is needed for cost controls and physician monitoring. What they are doing is promoting the automation of a paper medical record where the doctor fills in all the blanks and becomes the clerical front-end of this electronic surveillance system called the EHR."[1]

Grams goes on to warn, "When you look further at the EHR criteria, you will see that the majority of the criteria deal with billing, data transfer and data mining capabilities. The real goal of this EHR project is not to control costs or enhance patient care: it is data mining, the control of the physician population, and the ultimate rationing and control of patient services."[2] Richard Morris, MD, writes, "Why is government so set on this mandate? Because it wants to mine your data for public health information. But for the physicians who have to use these systems every day, who judge their potential on patient needs rather than pleasing Big Brother, the negatives at present are too great."[3]

Even for its stated purposes of patient safety, reduced costs, and improved care, the EHR is unproven. In 2009, after looking at four years of Medicare patient data (10.2 million hospital admissions), researchers at the University of Minnesota reported only two infections were averted per year as a result of the EHR. The researchers "found little evidence that health IT improved quality."[4] In March 2018, a study of EHRs and heart failure (HF) found "no association between degrees of EHR implementation and several quality metrics" including death. The authors wrote, "EHR may not be sufficient to improve HF quality or related outcomes."[5]

In 2016, the federal government admitted in the *Federal Register*, "At present, evidence on EHR benefits in either improving quality of care or reducing health care costs is mixed." And while one cited report claimed that a majority of studies evaluating the effect of health information technology on health care quality, safety, and efficiency were "at least partially positive," government officials stated: "Other recent studies have not found definitive quantitative evidence of benefits." Tellingly, although the administration asked for such evidence in a 2016 proposed rule, officials reported, "No commenters provided evidence concerning EHR benefits in reducing the costs or increasing the value of EHR-supported health care."[6]

The congressional mandate to move from paper charts to complex health information technology (health IT) systems was pushed to passage with "little hard evidence about how computer-based workflows and automated, data-driven analytics systems would impact "critical patient care," reports the blog *HealthITAnalytics*.[7] The goal was to redesign systems of care and use health IT for clinical and administrative support.[8] But as Nancy Leveson, a safety engineering expert at Massachusetts Institute of Technology told the blog *HuffPost* (formerly the *Huffington Post*): "People just assume that computers will make things safer . . . While they can be designed to eliminate certain kinds of hazards, they increase others and sometimes they introduce new types of hazards."[9]

This is not news to those health care practitioners and regulators who have been "deeply concerned that health IT could produce more problems than it solves," reports *HealthITAnalytics*.[10] Hayward Zwerling, MD, a board-certified internal medicine physician and a self-identified "geek" who says he created one of the older electronic medical records (EMRs), says scientific proof that benefits exceed risks must be "overwhelming" before physicians are willing to recommend a medical therapy be utilized for the entire population. But regarding health IT (he uses the acronym HIT), Zwerling writes,

> In the case of HIT, society has assumed a great risk (e.g., great cost, disruption and restructuring of physician practice patterns and many, potential unknown "side effects") without a priori demonstrating the putative benefits.
>
> As a profession which is grounded in science, I think it is time that physicians mandate a pause in the Federal Government's promotion of "certified" EMRs until there are numerous, unbiased and scientifically rigorous trials which convincingly demonstrate that the widespread use of HIT

will benefit society by either improving the quality of health-care or reducing the cost of healthcare.[11]

The hazards of nationwide implementation are real. In his dissent from a committee health IT report, Richard Cook, MD, a member of the Institute of Medicine's Committee on Patient Safety and Health IT, shares a devastating real-life story of a child injured in utero from a data-entry order and warns:

> [H]ealth IT can *and does* cause significant harm to patients. At least a few U.S. citizens—perhaps more than a few—have died or been maimed because of health IT. The extent of the injuries generated by health IT is unknown because no one has bothered to look for them in a systematic fashion . . .
>
> The development of health IT is marked by an optimism about the effects of IT that are unwarranted and naive. And the willingness to embrace this optimism to the extent of making large-scale investments in these systems and only later asking what their impact might be on patient safety borders on recklessness.[12]

The federal government is fully aware of the dangers. Jeffrey Shuren, director of the Center for Devices and Radiological Health at the Food and Drug Administration, testified in February 2010: "In the past two years, we have received 260 reports of HIT-related malfunctions with the potential for patient harm including 44 reported injuries and 6 reported deaths. Because these reports are purely voluntary, they may represent only the tip of the iceberg in terms of the HIT-related problems that exist."[13]

Despite these known dangers, in 2009, as part of the economic stimulus bill, the American Recovery and Reinvestment Act (ARRA), Congress mandated that every physician and most health care institutions use EHRs by January 1, 2014, or face significant financial penalties (long-term care facilities were excluded from the mandate).[14] The EHR must be government-certified and used "meaningfully," a prescriptive term defined by the federal government, to maintain full reimbursement for services provided to Medicare patients.[15]

As a result of the mandate, 72 percent of office-based physicians were using some type of electronic health records in 2012, up from about 35 percent in 2007.[16] Researchers at the University of Michigan and Harvard University wrote in *Health Affairs*, "There are likely very few other policies that have driven such substantial change in such a short period."[17] But as Arthur Allen reports in *Politico*, "The information technology tsunami has hit so fast that most of us haven't had time to think about what we might be sacrificing by trying to ride it. And that's particularly true when it comes to the delivery of health services."[18]

By early 2012, more than seven hundred vendors were producing 1,750 distinct government-certified EHR products.[19] Later that year it was reported that more than one thousand certified EHR vendors were in the marketplace.[20] None of them were required to work together, and because doctors and hospitals were forced to buy them, the EHRs didn't have to align with the way medicine is practiced or the critical workflow that surrounds the care of patients.

The purpose of a medical record is patient care, but the purpose of the government-certified EHR is something entirely different. As Grams points out, EHRs are designed primarily to transfer control of medical decisions to outsiders. The EHR allows nonphysicians, like the secretary of the US Department of Health & Human Services, the administrator of Medicare, managed-care corporations, and hospital administrators to influence, restrict, and control medical-treatment decisions. Margalit Gur-Arie, co-founder of BizMed and a software engineer, concurs:

> Whether we want to admit it or not, the facts of the matter are that health IT and EHRs, in particular, have turned from humble tools of the trade to oppressive straight jackets for the practice of medicine. Somewhere along the way, the roles were reversed, and clinicians of all stripes are increasingly becoming the tools used by technology to practice medicine. A common misconception is that EHR designers produce lousy software because they don't understand how medicine is practiced. The real problem is that many actually do, and the practice of medicine is precisely what they aim to change.[21]

Scot Silverstein, MD, an authority in health IT, says EHRs are "medical meta-devices." In a 2014 podcast with Meaningful HIT News, he said these systems are no longer "electronic filing cabinets." He called them "enterprise-wide command and control systems through which all medical transactions have to pass, controlling clinicians and clinical resources. They are beyond just a medical device. They're really command and control systems."[22]

A 2016 Physicians Foundation survey of 17,236 physicians found only 11 percent of doctors think EHRs have improved patient interaction, while 60 percent say EHRs have detracted from their interaction with patients.[23] Silverstein has been sending up warnings about EHRs since at least 2010, after a relative died due to EHR-related interference in communication. In January 2011, Silverstein shared a blog post titled "Healthcare IT Delirium":

> On top of an irrational exuberance . . . largely unsupported by the literature . . . the technology is experimental, its roll-out is a grand national experiment in social reengineering of medicine, there is no patient informed consent, nobody is in control, and nobody is taking responsibility for regulating the domain despite known risks. The results will very likely reflect the Wild West free-for-all that is now extant.
>
> This is crazy stuff.
>
> There's very little else I can do about it at this point, having tried writing, speaking, and political venues.
>
> This will affect **your** healthcare, not just mine (at least I know what to look out for).
>
> I suggest litigators stay closely attuned to hospital morbidity and mortality incidence (and incidents).[24]

Patient safety was not the focus of the mandate in the ARRA.

Forcing clinics and hospitals to buy and use government-certified EHRs—and leave their autonomy and inexpensive, easy-to-use paper medical charts behind—was the first step of the Obama administration's plan to remake the American health care system. Shortly after the mandate became law, Catherine Szenczy, vice president and chief information officer of MedStar Health in Columbia, Maryland, said

ARRA's medical IT component is the "foundation for health care reform."[25] Adrian Gropper, MD, claimed, "Obama is smart. His signing of the Health Information Technology for Economic and Clinical Health (HITECH) Act (as part of the stimulus package) recognizes the importance of Health IT as the foundation for health care reform and cost savings."[26]

In an exposé in the *Washington Post*, Robert O'Harrow Jr. concurs: "The inclusion of as much as $36.5 billion in spending to create a nationwide network of electronic health records fulfilled one of Obama's key campaign promises—to launch the reform of America's costly health-care system."[27] It also filled the pockets of the data industry, which had long pushed Congress to mandate the EHR, and created three new billionaires in the process, Politico Pro reported in 2014. Peter Orszag, a director of the Congressional Budget Office and Office of Management and Budget during the Obama administration and a key architect[28] of the Affordable Care Act (ACA, aka Obamacare), said HITECH funding for EHRs "is a key first step toward a high-performing health-care system."[29]

The reality stuns.

"I think that all EHRs today sort of suck, at least from a provider point of view," says Ed Park, chief operating officer of athenahealth. "Part of the issue here is that EHRs have multiple masters—more than half of EHR functionality is there to support the lawyers and the insurance companies, not the providers of care."[30] According to *Medical Economics*, the EHR has become "the third wheel in the exam room, getting in the way of physicians making meaningful connections with their patients."[31] Don Rucker, national coordinator of health information technology in the Trump administration says, "Everybody else has used computers to create less work for themselves. . . . We've used computers to create more work for ourselves."[32] And Howard Green, MD says his office has nicknamed their system "The PDS" (Practice Destroying Software). "It's gotten so bad for our patients and staff that our doctors must spend the first part of every history and physical exam apologizing for the inefficiencies and disruption of the practice due to the interference of EMR."[33]

"The unproven claim that EMRs would prevent medical errors, make medical records more accessible, result in more efficient healthcare delivery by eliminating redundancy, and do just about everything short of curing cancer, is simply false," writes Hal Scherz, MD, founder of the Docs 4 Patient Care Foundation. "There is currently no electronic interface that is more effective or more compassionate than your doctor with a pen. The need to complete all of the fields in an EMR actually detracts from patient care. The only reasons for the EMR currently, is to monitor compliance, fulfill certain criteria to justify payment and to comply with government requirements. When a truly useful system is created, every doctor will wait in line to purchase it."[34]

What about patient privacy and personal autonomy? What about the surveys, a few of which are included in this book, that show support for patient and parent consent requirements? Read on and remember: He who holds the data makes the rules. As Robert A. Heverly, writing in the *Los Angeles Times* more than a decade ago, warned:

> In the past, government could collect information, but it couldn't necessarily use it all. Human intervention was required to make connections between pieces of information. When government wanted to tyrannize its citizens, it gathered information and placed it in Manila file folders. Perhaps some of these files were centrally located under the control of a person charged with determining the importance of that information. Yet the government had only so many resources; there were only so many people who could be tyrannized at one time. People reviewed people, and people could do only so much. The danger of mass tyranny was not based on information itself, but on the leg power of government.
>
> But today computers allow different government agencies to share information; information collected for one purpose is now reviewed for others. Computers analyze according to their programs, spitting out potential relationships between facts and figures. Tyranny, as much as if not more than freedom, is facilitated by the computer.[35]

Heverly is correct. According to the federal Agency for Healthcare Research and Quality, the following are considered the primary advantages of interoperable EHRs, which communicate across health care systems and between EHRs created by various manufacturers:

- Structured data in EHRs "automatically extracted" for quality-measurement.
- Access to a "trove of clinical data," including information on physician orders, laboratory and imaging results, medications prescribed, progress notes, processes of care, and clinical outcomes of patients.
- Longitudinal patient data aggregated from multiple sources over time "into a single location."[36]

The EHR has already enabled a lucrative market for patient data. Adam Tanner writes in *Scientific American*, "Many doctors, nurses and patients are unaware that the information they record or divulge in an electronic health record or the results from lab tests they request or consent to may be anonymized and sold."[37]

It doesn't have to be this way. State legislators and the American people have the power to put an end to the intrusion and control. However, they should not expect any help from HIPAA, the so-called federal privacy rule.

Nicolas P. Terry, professor of law at Indiana University writes, "The HIPAA privacy rule is a misnomer."[38] The HIPAA privacy rule permits broad data sharing with third parties without patient consent—unless a state privacy law forbids it. Stronger state privacy laws supersede HIPAA's no-privacy rule. In short, state legislators can pass real privacy laws that must be followed. But many state legislators, believing that HIPAA protects privacy, have enacted state laws that conform their state's medical privacy laws to the HIPAA no-privacy rule, thereby undoing any privacy protections that were in state law or professional codes of conduct and authorizing broad sharing of patient data through the federal law and its intrusive rule.

"HIPAA is often described as a privacy rule. It is not," writes Richard Sobel. "In fact, HIPAA is a disclosure regulation, and it has effectively dismantled the long-standing moral and legal tradition of patient confidentiality."[39] And thus, because few states protect patients from HIPAA, patient data is digitized, analyzed, and shared regularly through the EHR.

Patients haven't given their consent to participate in this dangerous experiment in the delivery of their medical care. Americans haven't consented to give up their freedom or to submit to government controls over their private medical decisions. The government EHR is intrusive, unproven, costly, and replete with autonomy, data-security, constitutional, ethical, and patient-safety concerns. As this book will demonstrate:

- Deaths and injuries have resulted from the EHR.
- Patients and doctors are under digital surveillance.
- Outsiders and automation increasingly control the practice of medicine.
- Constitutional rights against government intrusion are ignored.
- Frustrated doctors are making plans to exit medicine, or becoming employees.
- The EHR mandate threatens the financial stability of clinics and hospitals.
- Data breaches and ransomware attacks on EHRs have skyrocketed.
- Comprehensive "EHR dossiers" on Americans are now possible.
- No one is safe from the government EHR—and every patient is in harm's way.
- The goal is government control.

In and of itself, digitized data does not endanger patients. If computerized medical records had been allowed to develop slowly and in accordance with the workflow of patient care and the needs of physicians, the story would have been a happy one. A market to meet their needs would have developed.

Some physicians designed their own computerized systems long before the mandate and love them. Some refuse to switch to the government version, which is designed to do what the government wants it to do instead of what the doctor and patient need it to do. These doctors choose to take the financial penalties, or exit out of Medicare, Medicaid, and all insurance contracts. They go free so their medical records can match the flow of patient care and achieve the purpose of medicine: treatment of their patients. They go free so they can sleep at night.

Today's computerized systems aren't tailor-made for the practice of medicine and patient care. The government EHR has been constructed and imposed without public debate or patient consent for many purposes other than treatment of patients—and often with the precise purpose of interfering in patient care.

Most Americans don't understand that their private medical information is no longer confidential, that third parties are using the EHR to control their doctors, that patients and practitioners are being profiled and tracked through data mining, or that the experimental government EHR systems are endangering patient lives.

This book aims to open a public discussion that's long overdue.

Key Definitions

The focus of this book is the government *electronic health record (EHR)* that has been imposed by Congress. Although not everyone uses the acronym the same way or consistently (some still refer to it as EMR), it's instructive to read the federal government's definition of it. According to the US Department of Health & Human Services (HHS):

> An **electronic medical record (EMR)** is a digital version of the paper charts in a doctor's office. They contain primarily the notes and information collected by and for the clinicians in that office. An **electronic health record (EHR)** is built to share information with other health care providers, such as laboratories and specialists. They contain information from all the clinicians involved in the patient's care and authorized clinicians can access the information they need, to provide care to that patient.[40] (Emphasis added.)

That's true, but the EHR allows many others who are not "authorized clinicians" to get access for purposes other than to "provide care." As the Office of the National Coordinator for Health Information Technology (ONC) states, "The EHR can also support the collection of data for uses other than clinical care, such as billing, quality management, outcome reporting, and public health disease surveillance and reporting."[41]

The EHR is complex. According to *Trend Watch*, an American Hospital Association (AHA) publication, "The EHR system is not a single technology product. Hospitals must integrate dozens of disparate information systems to bring all relevant patient information together at the point of care."[42]

As a helpful tool to distinguish between the two best-known electronic versions of your private data, and the subject of this book, think of the H in EHR as "hundreds of viewers" and the M in EMR as "me and my doctor."

Other related terms may confuse because they are not always used the same way. For example, with *health information exchange* and *health information organization*, you may have to use contextual cues. The following definitions and explanations should help, but consider marking this page for consultation as you read.

Health information exchange (HIE): there are two separate but related definitions, which can be confusing. The first is a verb. The second is a noun. As explained by HIMSS: "The term 'HIE' can mean either the verb (the electronic exchange of health-related data) or the noun (organizations dedicated to the secure exchange of health-related data)."[43] HIMSS continues: "Health Information Exchanges (HIEs) are being developed as the infrastructure for data sharing between providers and to support access to the complete patient record across providers in many geographic regions of the country. HIEs will ultimately provide the vehicle for data sharing among provider practices and health systems through the Nationwide Health Information Network (NwHIN)."[44] HIEs include exchanges set up by states and funded initially with federal grants under the 2009 HITECH Act.[45] Both types of exchanges are often referred to with the acronym HIE, but context clarifies whether it's the verb or the noun form of health information exchange.

Health information organization (HIO) is a term that has often been used interchangeably with health information exchange. The National Alliance for Health Information Technology (NAHIT) defines HIE solely in the verb form ("electronic movement of health-related information among organizations according to nationally recognized standards") and includes the following two definitions:

Health Information Organization (HIO): An organization that oversees and governs the exchange of health-related information among organizations according to nationally recognized standards.

Regional Health Information Organization (RHIO): A health information organization that brings together health care stakeholders within a defined geographic area and governs health information exchange among them for the purpose of improving health and care in that community.[46]

In late 2013, there were more than two hundred active RHIOs in the United States, providing "an HIE to health care stakeholders in a specific region."[47] Confused? NAHIT states "HIE is process. HIO is an oversight organization and RHIO is a type of HIO."[48] But sometimes HIE appears as a noun.

Health information technology (health IT or HIT), as defined by the federal government, is "the application of information processing involving both computer hardware and software that deals with the storage, retrieval, sharing, and use of health care information, data, and knowledge for communication and decision making."[49] This can include the EHR and the EMR, as well as computerized disease registries, electronic prescribing, telehealth, and more.

The Joint Commission, in a 2015 report, shares the following health IT categories: EHR, CPOE system (computerized physician order entry), e-MAR (electronic medication administration record), clinical documentation system (e.g., progress notes), pharmacy system, CDS system (clinical decision support), radiology/diagnostic imaging system, including PACS (picture archiving and communication system), human interface device (e.g., keyboard, mouse, touchscreen, speech-recognition system, monitor/display, printer), administrative/billing or practice-management system, registration/appointment-scheduling system, automated dispensing system, LIS (laboratory information system), including microbiology, and pathology systems.[50]

Personal Health Record, as defined by the government, is not an EHR. The PHR "is a collection of information pertinent to a patient's health" that may include a limited set of information such as contact information, a list of providers, diagnoses, medications, allergies, immunization history, lab and test results, and family medical history. The PHR may be connected to the clinic or hospital EHR (accessible through a secure portal) or it may be a standalone record on the patient's computer or the Internet. But importantly, "the PHR is separate from, and does not replace the legal record of, any health care provider."[51] Thus, the PHR is not the EHR.

Finally, there are two more terms that come up frequently and in this book: *interoperability* and *"in the cloud."*

Interoperability is the holy grail of EHR proponents. The ONC defines interoperability as "the ability of a system to exchange electronic health information with and use electronic health information from other systems without special effort on the part of the user. This means that all individuals, their families, and health care providers should be able to send, receive, find, and use electronic health information in a manner that is appropriate, secure, timely, and reliable to support the health and wellness of individuals through informed, shared decision-making."[52] There are private sector and government efforts to expand data sharing through interoperability. Some of these efforts will be discussed in this book.

Cloud computing ("in the cloud") means "computing that relies on shared computing resources rather than having local servers or personal devices to handle applications. In its most simple description, cloud computing is taking services ('cloud services') and moving them outside an organization's firewall. Applications, storage and other services are accessed via the Web. The services are delivered and used over the Internet and are paid for by the cloud customer on an as-needed or pay-per-use business model."[53] It's also been described as "accessing computer, information technology (IT), and software applications through a network connection, often by accessing data centers using wide area networking (WAN) or Internet connectivity. . . .[Servers, software, and networking resources] are now accessible by going to third parties that offer them in the cloud."[54]

How the EHR Mandate Became Law

More Than a Medical Record

Electronic medical records for patient care are not new. Use of computerized medical records in the United States dates back to the 1960s. In 1966 Massachusetts General Hospital had an early medical-records system running on a computer that had only sixteen kilobytes of memory and supported multiple users.[55] However, computerized records for general practitioners weren't introduced until the 1980s.[56]

Medical records have a long history. In the early 1900s most physicians had their own practices and their own individual medical records for patients. "When they needed to, doctors shared information by letter or verbally," reports the *Star Tribune*.[57] The Mayo Clinic's first medical record was registered on July 19, 1907. It was on paper. The Mayo Clinic medical record "was planned to be a comprehensive compendium of patient medical information that spans the life of the patient," writes Mayo's Prince K. Zachariah, MD. By 2005, Mayo had more than 4.5 million medical records.[58]

The primary purpose of a medical record, writes Lawrence Huntoon, MD, PhD, "is to provide a physician or other person taking care of the patient with information about what is going on with the patient. It allows a physician to track the patient's diagnoses, treatment, and progress from one encounter to the next. And, should something happen to the treating physician, the medical record should contain sufficient information such that another physician can take over the patient's care." Huntoon continues, "Unfortunately, due to the intrusive power of government and other third-party payers, the medical record has been bastardized into a billing record that often has little or no clinical relevance. The emphasis is on complying with 'bulleted' points so as to justify a certain level of billing to the third-party payer."[59]

But how and why did this happen?

It Began with HIPAA

The congressional push to mandate EHRs began in the early 1990s under the Clinton administration. Language for a national EHR system was included in President Bill Clinton's failed Health Security Act. Included were requirements for an "Electronic Data Network"; "Unique Identifier Numbers" for individuals, employers, health plans, and health care providers; and a "Health Security Card" for all Americans. As written in the "Information Systems, Privacy and Administrative Simplification" section of the bill:

SEC. 5101. ESTABLISHMENT OF HEALTH INFORMATION SYSTEM.

> (a) IN GENERAL—Not later than 2 years after the date of the enactment of this Act, the National Health Board shall develop and implement a health information system by which the Board shall collect, report, and regulate the collection and dissemination of the health care information described in subsection (e) pursuant to standards promulgated by the Board and (if applicable) consistent with policies established as part of the National Information Infrastructure Act of 1993.[60]

Next came a bipartisan push. Two years after the Health Security Act failed in 1994, a version of administrative simplification was enacted under the Health Insurance Portability and Accountability Act of 1996 (HIPAA), coauthored in the Senate by Senators Edward M. Kennedy (D-MA) and Nancy Kassebaum (R-KS).[61] The health IT section of HIPAA, which empowered the HHS secretary to begin building a national health information system, was strongly pushed by the Workgroup for Electronic Data Interchange (WEDI). This coalition of health plans, government agencies, hospital and health care systems, and the data industry was established in 1991 by Louis Sullivan, MD, HHS secretary in the George H. W. Bush administration, and named in HIPAA as an advisor to the Secretary of HHS,[62] which it remains today per WEDI.[63] Their vision as stated in a 1992 report to HHS was: "The healthcare industry would conduct all business electronically, using one set of standards and interconnecting networks."[64] WEDI representatives also met with members of President Clinton's health care task force.[65]

According to the Institute of Medicine, the statutory provisions requiring the secretary of HHS to issue regulations for electronic transmission of health information "were included in the final version of HIPAA because health plans had requested federal legislation in this area from Congress. The use of electronic health information was expanding in the early 1990s, and the health care industry was unable to standardize the process and use of electronic health information without federal action."[66] Thus, the 1996 HIPAA law states:

> **SEC. 261. PURPOSE.** It is the purpose of this subtitle to improve the Medicare program under title XVIII of the Social Security Act, the Medicaid program under title XIX of such Act, and the efficiency and effectiveness of the health care system, by encouraging the development of a health information system through the establishment of standards and requirements for the electronic transmission of certain health information.
>
> **SEC. 1173. (a) STANDARDS TO ENABLE ELECTRONIC EXCHANGE.—**
> (1) IN GENERAL.—The Secretary shall adopt standards for transactions, and data elements for such transactions, to enable health information to be exchanged electronically, that are appropriate for—
>
> (A) the financial and administrative transactions described in paragraph (2); and

(B) other financial and administrative transactions determined appropriate by the Secretary, consistent with the goals of improving the operation of the health care system and reducing administrative costs.[67]

In 1996, just two decades ago, only one in four medical practices were even using computers in their offices, and those were primarily for the purpose of consultation.[68] That was all about to change.

Congress recognized the privacy concerns created by HIPAA's national health data infrastructure. The law mandated that the HHS secretary make recommendations and Congress enact a medical privacy law by 1999. If Congress failed to do so, HHS was required to develop comprehensive regulations on medical privacy within three years.[69]

In September 1997 HHS Secretary Donna Shalala issued recommendations to Congress for a "federal health privacy statute." She initially commended the "age-old right to privacy in this new world of progress," but then dismissed it and proposed broad sharing without patient consent for a wide array of purposes, including "for specifically identified national priority activities." She recommended "the traditional control on use and disclosure of information, the patient's written authorization, be replaced by comprehensive statutory controls on all who get health information for health care and payment purposes." This was based on a "Public Responsibility" principle created out of thin air by HHS and counter to that age-old right to privacy she first invoked:

> Individuals' claims to privacy must be balanced by their public responsibility to contribute to the common good, through use of their information for important, socially useful purposes, with the understanding that their information will be used with respect and care and will be legally protected. Federal law should identify those limited arenas in which our public responsibilities warrant authorization of access to our medical information, and should sharply limit the uses and disclosure of information in those contexts.[70]

After Congress predictably failed to enact a privacy statute—thereby avoiding all direct responsibility for the intrusions sure to follow—HHS took on the task of dismantling patient privacy. The HIPAA "Privacy" Rule was proposed November 3, 1999, finalized December 28, 2000, modified August 14, 2002, became effective October 15, 2002, and compliance was required for most physicians, hospitals, health care providers, and health plans ("covered entities") on April 14, 2003.[71] HHS clarifies, "The Privacy Rule, as well as all the Administrative Simplification rules, apply to health plans, health care clearinghouses, and to any health care provider who transmits health information in electronic form in connection with transactions for which the Secretary of HHS has adopted standards under HIPAA (the 'covered entities')."[72]

Assertions aside, the rule does not "sharply limit" disclosures and uses of patient data. HIPAA is permissive. It allows those who hold patient data to share it liberally, including for payment and treatment—two words with broader definitions than the public would guess—and for something called "health care operations," a term with a definition hundreds of words long. Sharing is also allowed for twelve "national priority purposes."[73] See section IV.

HIPAA eliminates most legal constraints against data sharing. Before HIPAA, "rules requiring the protection of health privacy in the United States [had] been enacted primarily by the states."[74] So stated the final HIPAA rule published in December 2000. But under the federal HIPAA law and its "privacy" rule (45 CFR, Sections 160 and 164), consider how the following two state laws regarding patient confidentiality—from Arizona and Maine, respectively—actually *permit* broad data sharing without patient consent:

> A. *Unless otherwise provided by law*, all medical records and payment records, and the information contained in medical records and payment records, are privileged and confidential. A health care provider may only disclose that part or all of a patient's medical records and payment records *as authorized by state or federal law* or written authorization signed by the patient or the patient's health care decision maker.
>
> B. This article does not limit the effect of *any other federal or state law* governing the confidentiality of medical records and payment records.[75] (Emphasis added.)

• • •

> Disclosure may be made without authorization as follows:... to federal, state or local governmental entities if the health care practitioner or facility that is providing diagnosis, treatment or care to an individual has determined.... With regard to a disclosure for public health activities, for law enforcement purposes or that pertains to victims of abuse, neglect or domestic violence, the provisions of *45 Code of Federal Regulations, Section 164.512*(b), (c) or (f) (2012) must be met.[76]

Thus, in every state, unless there is a stronger state medical privacy law, hospitals, clinics, surgical centers, laboratories, radiology facilities, health plans, nursing homes, and others are allowed to digitize patient information and place it into EHRs, where it can be readily shared with other providers, health plans, researchers, a boatload of "business associates," and state, local, and federal government agencies—all without patient consent.

Such disclosures violate the confidential patient-doctor relationship. The Hippocratic Oath for physicians (c. 400 BC) underscores the importance of privacy: "Whatever, in connection with my professional practice or not, in connection with it, I see or hear, in the life of men, which ought not to be spoken of abroad, I will not divulge, as reckoning that all such should be kept secret."[77] But HIPAA says no to secrets and yes to divulging.

President Bush Lays the Groundwork

HIPAA was just the beginning of the assault on privacy. In 2004 the Healthcare Information and Management Systems Society (HIMSS) persuaded White House speechwriters to include this statement in President George W. Bush's State of the Union address: "By computerizing health records, we can avoid dangerous medical mistakes, reduce costs and improve care."[78] According to then HIMSS President

H. Stephen Lieber, that one sentence was the group's single greatest success: "We worked very hard to get that one line in there."[79]

Nine months later, Blackford Middleton, MD, chairman of the Center for Information Technology Leadership (CITL), which had major support from HIMSS, according to a PowerPoint presentation he made in October 2004, claimed $337 billion in savings over a ten-year implementation period and an annual savings of $78 billion "in each year thereafter" with a complete embrace of health information technology. However, his presentation also noted that the impact of HIE on the bottom line was largely still to be determined and included a significant limitation to the claim of annual savings: "The model may be incomplete and important determinants missing."[80]

The march to impose EHRs didn't stop with that one sentence in President Bush's 2004 State of the Union address. On April 27, 2004, Bush signed Executive Order 13335 to "provide leadership for the development and nationwide implementation of an interoperable health information technology infrastructure" and to create the position of the National Health Information Technology Coordinator, later called the Office of the National Coordinator for Health Information Technology (ONC), within the office of the HHS secretary.[81]

On July 21, 2004, HHS published "Strategic Framework: The Decade of Health Information Technology: Delivering Consumer-centric and Information-rich Health Care." The framework outlined four major goals for health IT, as reported by the Agency for Healthcare Research and Quality:

- Inform clinical practice by accelerating the use of EHRs.
- Interconnect clinicians so that they can exchange health information using advanced and secure electronic communication.
- Personalize care with consumer-based health records and better information for consumers.
- Improve public health through advanced biosurveillance methods and streamlined collection of data for quality measurement and research.[82]

Also, in 2004, the Certification Commission for Health Information Technology (CCHIT) was founded. CCHIT is an "independent, not-for-profit group that certifies electronic health records (EHRs) and networks for health information exchange (HIE) in the United States" to speed the adoption of health information technology. Voluntary certification of EHRs began in 2006.[83]

In January 2005, a group of thirteen health and information technology groups—including HIMSS, American Health Information Management Association (AHIMA), and CITL—responding to the administration's request for information on a National Health Information Network, presented the Bush administration with a roadmap to get there.[84] They claimed $78 billion per year in savings after ten years, when the automated system was fully implemented nationwide.

However, physicians had long resisted investing in computerized medical records because there was no evidence that it would be profitable.[85] They were correct.

"Current studies show that the adoption of technology in healthcare primarily benefits private payers and government—not the physicians or hospitals that pay for implementation," warns a white paper by Competitive Financial Operations. The paper goes on to assert, "Imagine making a purchase decision if you are a one-person physician's office with no reserves, no IT expertise or staff and an expected payback window of two to three years. It is not surprising that adoption rates are low."[86] The ten-year cost of installing computers, networking equipment, and software to build the national network was estimated to be $246 billion over a ten-year period, reports the *New York Times*.[87]

Despite the anticipated costs, the Center for Information Technology Leadership, which had developed and published (in 2005) a framework to establish a national system, wrote, "We suspect that the clinical payoff in improved patient safety and quality of care could dwarf the financial benefits projected from our model," resulting in avoided redundancies, administrative time saved, fewer medical errors, and better continuity of care. "But," they also admitted, "electronic exchange of clinical data between organizations is nascent, and few data exist about the clinical impact it would bring."[88]

Thus, it would be an experiment on patients.

On June 6, 2005, HHS Secretary Michael Leavitt announced the creation of a "public-private collaboration called the American Health Information Community (AHIC) [that] will help nationwide transition to electronic health records—including standards and interoperability—in a smooth, market-led way."[89] In the announcement he made that day to one thousand attendees at a HIMSS Summit, he said, "We have the capacity to transform health IT with one thunderous click of a mouse after another." Regarding change in health care, Leavitt said, "You can fight it and die. You can accept it and survive. You can lead it and prosper."[90] Leavitt is quoted in the HHS press release: "The use of electronic health records and other information technology will transform our health care system by reducing medical errors, minimizing paperwork hassles, lowering costs and improving quality of care. . . . We will bring together the public and private health care sectors to transform health care as we know it."[91]

As will soon become clear—Leavitt's second claim was correct, the first was not.

A few months later, a RAND Corporation study claimed that rapid introduction of health IT could save the United States more than $81 billion a year.[92] (Note: In 2013, RAND explained why critics of this lofty assertion could "claim a measure of vindication."[93] See section IV.)

In August 2006 Bush issued Executive Order 13410, requiring federal agencies that purchase and deliver health care to use health IT based on interoperability standards recognized by the HHS secretary.[94] Interoperability, according to the federal government, is when EHRs "share information seamlessly" for a variety of federally mandated purposes, such as government oversight, public-health surveillance, and so-called "quality measurement" of doctors and hospitals.[95]

On December 20, 2006, Bush signed the Tax Relief and Health Care Act of 2006. As a result, the Physician Quality Reporting Initiative (PQRI) to transmit certain data to the Medicare administration about care provided to Medicare patients was established in 2007. The law also directed HHS to consider allowing electronic, registry-based reporting. A 1.5 percent bonus was available to physicians who successfully participated in the voluntary program.[96]

In July 2008 Congress passed the Medicare Improvements for Patients and Providers Act of 2008 (MIPPA), which mandated electronic prescribing and required HHS to contract with a national "consensus-based entity" to establish a process for measuring physician performance through the collection and analysis of patient data. In an interesting "Sense of the Senate" statement, policy makers claimed that "the selection by the Secretary of [HHS] of an entity to contract with [for performance measurement] should not be construed as diminishing the significant contributions of the Boards of Medicine, the quality alliances, and other clinical and technical experts to efforts to measure and improve the quality of health care services."[97] Bush vetoed the bill because he opposed reduced payments for Medicare Advantage plans (managed-care Medicare[98]), but Congress overrode his veto.[99] In January 2009, HHS contracted with the National Quality Forum.[100] The new law required the physician-measuring entity to:

- "Synthesize evidence and convene key stakeholders to make recommendations . . . on an integrated national strategy and priorities for health care performance measurement in all applicable settings," and
- "Promote the development and use of electronic health records that contain the functionality for automated collection, aggregation, and transmission of performance measurement information."[101]

One of the PQRI measures of quality indicated whether or not a physician has and uses an EHR, the Congressional Research Service (CRS) reported. Millions of taxpayer dollars were already going to health IT projects. According to the 2009 CRS report, "Since 2004, AHRQ [Agency for Healthcare Research and Quality] has awarded $260 million to support and stimulate investment in HIT. This translates into almost 200 projects in 48 states." These included EHRs, personal health record (PHR) initiatives, e-prescribing, privacy and security, physician quality measurement, and Medicaid technical assistance.[102]

With the 2010 passage of the Affordable Care Act (ACA), PQRI was made permanent (and renamed PQRS, replacing *Initiative* for *System* in its name) and mandatory reporting with penalties started in 2015.[103] The ACA also required the Centers for Medicare & Medicaid

Services (CMS) to "develop a plan to integrate the reporting requirements used in the EHR Program with the information that CMS collects from eligible providers in the Physician Quality Reporting System (PQRS)."[104] The EHR program, as described at length below, was enacted in 2009.

Congress Mandates EHRs

On June 3, 2008, HHS released "The ONC-Coordinated Federal Health Information Technology Strategic Plan, 2008–2012," which states, "The Office of the National Coordinator for Health IT (ONC), since 2004, continues to advance the national health IT agenda to achieve President Bush's target for the majority of Americans to have access to electronic health records (EHRs) by 2014."[105] President Barack Obama, who took office in 2009, and the Democrat-led Congress aimed to meet Bush's deadline.

Before Obama was elected, US Senator Tom Daschle (D-SD) wrote a book on health care reform in which he used the RAND Corporation's faulty savings figure in this passage: "Overall, the researchers concluded, a fully electronic health-care system could save us as much as $77.8 billion annually, or approximately 5 percent of the roughly $1.66 trillion we spent on health care in 2003."[106]

Obama's election team used the $77.8 billion estimate to call for EHRs during his campaign.[107] As economic conditions worsened in late 2008 and the campaign wound down, health IT advocates—including technology vendors, researchers, and the multimember Healthcare Information and Management Systems Society (HIMSS)—persuaded Obama's advisers to consider EHR legislation. Legislation that these advocates had a hand in writing, the *Washington Post* reported.[108]

After the election of President Obama, Peter Orszag, head of the Congressional Budget Office, called CITL's projected savings "overly optimistic" and in 2009 the CBO projected spending on electronic health records would yield only $17 billion in savings over a decade. But HIMSS had spent ten years trying to convince Congress to mandate and subsidize electronic health records and then-Senator Obama had been in some of those meetings.[109]

After Obama won the election, the move to mandate a government-certified EHR was swift. The American Recovery and Reinvestment Act of 2009 (ARRA, sometimes also called the economic stimulus package) reduced federal Medicare Physician Fee Schedule payments for covered professional services beginning October 1, 2014 for hospitals and January 1, 2015 for physicians and other eligible professionals—unless the EHR was being used "meaningfully."[110] It also codified in statute the establishment of the Office of the National Coordinator for Health Information Technology (ONC). ARRA was signed into law on February 17, 2009, less than a month after President Obama's inauguration.[111]

But the claims of cost savings did not stop. In May 2010, the Commission on U.S. Federal Leadership in Health and Medicine claimed, "If used in innovative ways, the estimated savings from HIT expansion could reach $261 billion over 10 years."[112]

No Public Debate

The plan to impose the EHR and its Meaningful Use requirements was essentially a secret. As the *Washington Post* later reported, there was "virtually no public debate about an initiative aimed at transforming a sector that accounts for more than a sixth of the American economy."[113] The HITECH Act tucked within the 407 pages of the stimulus bill was strategic, and the process to transform health care was, as already noted, swift. In 2009, only 12.2 percent of hospitals had basic EHR systems, according to an ONC chart. By 2011, that figure rose to 27.6 percent and kept rising.[114]

Nearly two years after enactment, two worried experts called for further study of EHR effectiveness in a *HuffPost* commentary. They noted England's colossal $18 billion EHR failure.[115] Notably, today the UK has 65 million people and the US has 323 million people. Instead of $18 billion, the US appropriated $30 billion and enacted unfunded EHR and Meaningful Use mandates so doctors, hospitals, and patients would pay for the rest. Stephen Soumerai, ScD, and Anthony Avery, MD, wisely wrote:

> How do we avoid the UK's failure? The administration or Congress should slow down the program and delete those parts of the legislation that fine doctors for not using this technology. There's no need to have this system in place by 2014. Instead, we should conduct rigorous studies of the cost-effectiveness of electronic health records systems before mandating their use. Rather than force doctors to choose from dozens of commercial software products developed in secret, we should take a hint from the non-commercial sector, such as the Veterans Administration, which uses "open-source" coding so people can work collaboratively to continuously improve the system.[116]

The health IT industry was not interested in a delay. By 2009, two hundred EHR products had already been certified by CCHIT.[117] In 2009, Dr. Zwerling wrote, "Under the Federal Government's direction, CCHIT has been given the task of promoting IT (information technology) within the health care industry. Approximately half of CCHIT's Board of Directors work for medical insurance companies, commercial medical informatic companies, physicians employed by very large group practices or eMR companies. As a result, CCHIT's priorities have been tailored to reflect the interests of its Board of Directors, rather than the needs of the physicians and the health interests of our society at large."[118]

David C. Main, founder of the Healthcare Technology Network of Greater Washington, called the HITECH Act at the time of enactment "the most important piece of health care legislation to be passed in the last 20 to 30 years."[119] H. Stephen Lieber, president of HIMSS, told the *Washington Post*, "It was perhaps a once-in-a-generation opportunity to make something happen."[120]

Not understood by many, the HITECH Act was the foundation for, and the launch of, President Obama's health care reform bill to centralize control of health insurance and medical delivery. It was the beginning of Obamacare. Health IT and national health care supporters were not interested in being slowed down by anyone's rigorous studies of effectiveness.[121]

Winners and Losers

HITECH Requirements

The primary goal written into HITECH was the "utilization of a certified electronic health record for each person in the United States by 2014." The term *certified EHR technology* means "a qualified electronic health record that is certified pursuant to section 3001(c)(5) as meeting standards adopted under section 3004 that are applicable to the type of record involved (as determined by the Secretary, such as an ambulatory electronic health record for office-based physicians or an inpatient hospital electronic health record for hospitals)."[122] The secretary was required to adopt "an initial set of standards, implementation specifications, and certification criteria," before 2010, according to section 3004.[123] Additional broad health IT provisions include:

> "The National Coordinator shall perform the duties . . . in a manner consistent with the development of a nationwide health information technology infrastructure that allows for the electronic use and exchange of information." (Sec. 3001)
>
> "The National Coordinator shall establish a governance mechanism for the nationwide health information network." (Sec. 3001)
>
> "The Secretary shall, using amounts appropriated under section 3018, invest in the infrastructure necessary to allow for and promote the electronic exchange and use of health information for each individual in the United States." (Sec. 3011)
>
> The Secretary shall invest funds to support "health information technology architecture that will support the

> nationwide electronic exchange and use of health information in a secure, private, and accurate manner, including connecting health information exchanges." (Sec 3011)
>
> "The National Coordinator shall...update the Federal Health IT Strategic Plan...to include...the electronic exchange and use of health information and the enterprise integration of such information." (Sec. 3001)
>
> "The term 'enterprise integration' means the electronic linkage of health care providers, health plans, the government, and other interested parties, to enable the electronic exchange and use of health information among all the components in the health care infrastructure..." (Sec. 3000)[124]

To build this national health information infrastructure, the HITECH Act imposes penalties ("adjustments") on physicians and hospitals if they refuse to implement a federally approved EHR or fail to use it "meaningfully," as defined by the federal government. HITECH provided at least $30 billion for the EHR incentive payment program.[125] While various statements and documents about the total amount of federal funding range from $27 billion to $37 billion, the money to purchase these systems is only available to clinics and hospitals that provide evidence they are using the EHR "meaningfully"—again, as defined by the federal government.

Although HITECH gives the secretary of HHS flexibility to grant alternative means of meeting Meaningful Use requirements, the following language suggests that such flexibility would be short-lived: "The Secretary shall seek to improve the use of electronic health records and health care quality over time by requiring more stringent measures of meaningful use selected under this paragraph."[126]

HITECH's grant funds were also directed toward the establishment of state health information exchanges (HIEs) for the purpose of connecting patient records in all fifty states together into a national medical-records system now called eHealth Exchange.

To underscore the purpose of the EHR mandate, HHS wrote in a proposed HIPAA modification rule that HITECH "is designed to promote the widespread adoption and standardization of health information technology."[127] As you shall see, this standardization has also led to restrictive standardization of the practice of medicine.

From Mayhem to a Mess

The federal mandate to have a government-certified EHR installed and operating in a "meaningful" manner by January 1, 2014, led to mayhem. The government conceded that there were concerns. The Centers for Medicare & Medicaid Services (CMS) "has heard from physicians and other providers about the challenges they face making EHRs work well for their individual practices and for their patients," wrote Kate Goodrich, MD, the director of the Center for Clinical Standards & Quality on a CMS blog in 2015.[128] Her only suggestion, however, was that doctors apply for an exemption from the Meaningful Use penalties if they need to switch EHR systems or have difficulties with their EHR vendors.

HHS refused to concede that the government EHR was the cause of the interruptions and financial disasters taking place nationwide in clinics and at the bedsides of hospitalized patients. Instead, in an attempt to convince the American public that all is well, Goodrich wrote:

> CMS and physicians have a shared goal in the EHR program of helping physicians, clinicians, and hospitals to deliver better care, smarter spending, and healthier people. . . .
>
> EHRs are the next step in the continued progress of healthcare that can strengthen the relationship between patients and clinicians. The data, and the timeliness and availability of it, will enable providers to make better decisions and provide better care.[129]

Just because she said it doesn't make it true. A shared goal does not require force. It does not require penalties. So now that most doctors and hospitals have EHRs, why do the penalties remain?

Penalties for Failure to Report

The purpose of the government EHR is not patient care. Congress wants physicians, clinics, and hospitals to collect and report patient data. As noted earlier, one year after the EHR mandate was signed into law, the Affordable Care Act added financial penalties for failure to voluntarily report PQRS data, beginning in 2015.[130] CMS says PQRS is a "pay-for-reporting program."[131] The agency defines it as a "voluntary quality reporting program that applies a negative payment adjustment to promote the reporting of quality information."[132] A "negative payment adjustment" is a fancy way of saying "penalty."

In 2014 CMS added fifty-seven new PQRS measures doctors could choose from to report quality data, for a total of 287 measures. Physicians had to report on nine measures, and on 50 percent of applicable patients.[133] By 2016, there were three hundred measures.[134] Physicians who did not participate in this *voluntary* federal reporting program in 2013 suffered a 1.5 percent penalty for all services provided in 2015 and a 2 percent penalty thereafter.[135] This is not "voluntary." A voluntary system would allow physicians to choose whether to report and what to report, and no penalties would be attached to those choices.

Tied to PQRS was the ACA's Value-Based Payment Modifier (VBPM) program to boost or reduce Medicare fee-for-service payments to physicians.[136] Value may not mean what you think it means. The American Academy of Family Physicians says the modifier program, "is a pay for value (i.e., quality relative to cost) program—higher value gets higher pay; lower value gets lower pay, based on quality tiering."[137]

Value-based performance data from 2016—quality outcomes data from PQRS and cost data from Medicare fee-for-service claims—was used to determine the "value" of the care provided and modify physician Medicare payments in 2018.[138] As reported by CMS, only 20,481 clinicians received payment increases in 2018 ranging from 6.6 percent to 19.9 percent; nearly 750,000 clinicians received no bonuses or penalties; and nearly 300,000 clinicians were penalized for failing to report quality data.[139] Due to the Republicans' 2015 enactment of similar payment reforms in the Medicare Access and CHIP Reauthorization Act of 2015 (MACRA), the modifier program and PQRS incentive payments and penalties end in 2018, after which they will be continued under MACRA's consolidated quality reporting initiative, the Quality Payment Program (QPP).[140]

There are three ways to report patient data for PQRS. One of them is the EHR.[141] In 2012, HHS estimated that approximately forty thousand eligible professionals, either as individuals or part of a group practice, would "use the EHR-based reporting mechanism" in 2014.[142] While the government pushes toward EHR reporting of PQRS data, the other allowable reporting options include claims-data reporting and using a "qualified clinical data registry." Practices with at least one hundred practitioners have the option to register for and use a PQRS group-practice reporting option (GPRO) website.[143]

Extracting Patient Data

The EHR reporting option is meant to make data sharing with the government as painless and behind-the-scenes as possible. HHS plans to collect the data "when it is technically feasible" through the national data network it is developing, the eHealth Exchange, formerly and more aptly called the Nationwide Health Information Network (NwHIN).[144]

The operational plan for seamless data sharing was made clear in a 2014 Medicare payment rule: "HHS is committed to accelerating health information exchange (HIE) through the use of safe, interoperable health information technology (health IT), including electronic health records (EHRs), across the broader care continuum through a number of initiatives: (1) Alignment of incentives and payment adjustments to encourage provider adoption and optimization of health IT and HIE services through Medicare and Medicaid payment policies; (2) adoption of common standards and certification requirements for interoperable HIT; (3) support for privacy and security of patient information across all HIE-focused initiatives; and (4) governance of health information."[145] However, there's no privacy or security under the broad data sharing permitted by HIPAA. See Section IV.

Some want data extraction simplified. Lawrence Casalino, MD, the lead author of a 2016 survey on the physician cost of quality reporting, suggests reporting could be made easier. He says, "The other thing that would be a big help is that if EMR are better designed so that quality data could be either sucked out of them by external entities, or easily generated by the practices themselves and easily sent to the external entity."[146] Or, as the Healthcare Association of New York State (HANYS), envisions: "The data acquisition and reporting process will no longer distract from the process of care and will be embedded seamlessly in integrated, interoperable electronic health records (EHRs), allowing for more comprehensive measurement."[147]

"Measure Madness"

HANYS, in a report called "Measures that Matter," discusses the unintended consequences associated with reporting and quality measurement. Saying measurement is "out of control," the report concludes that there is "an environment of measure madness—consuming precious resources that could be directed toward meaningful efforts to continuously enhance quality and patient safety." It notes that providers must "report on hundreds of measures that are required by government and commercial payers, accreditation agencies, professional societies, and registries."

HANYS explains how measurement reporting is reducing time that could be spent actually doing the primary business of the clinic and hospital: "Underlying the collection and reporting of each measure is a complex system of specifications, definitions, data abstraction, analysis, and reporting, consuming significant time and expenses and drawing from limited clinical, information system, and administrative resources."[148]

The financial cost of reporting so-called "quality" measures is high—and the results are dubious. Researchers surveyed nearly four hundred physician practices and reported the following statistics in March 2016:

- Physician practices spend more than $15.4 billion each year reporting quality measures.
- Each clinic spends 15.1 hours per week per physician processing quality measures, with each physician doing 2.6 hours of the work.
- Average cost of processing quality measures is $40,069 per year per physician.
- Only 27 percent of physician practices believe that the measures reflect their quality of care.[149]

The Trump administration realizes the problem. CMS Administrator Seema Verma cited physicians "who report nearly 30 measures to seven different payers." She said, "It's better to focus on achieving results, as opposed to having CMS try to micromanage and measure processes."[150] How long it may take to reduce reporting under her direction is unknown, but physicians commenting on the sad state of quality measures say:

> You get so focused on making sure that you are clicking the right fields in the (electronic medical record) that you lose touch and connection with the patients. It is very sad what medicine has come to. —Lawrence Casalino, MD[151]

> The current system for measuring "quality" is simply a reporting mechanism for documenting check boxes, not really an indication of a person's health. —Lawrence Casalino, MD[152]

> I have been dinged for no mammogram on a woman with no breasts, no A1c [blood sugar level test] on a long-dead patient, no followup lipids in a Ukrainian tourist with DKA [diabetic ketoacidosis], no stop smoking advice on a life long non-smoker, no flu vaccine on a Christian Scientist. —Lynn Bentson, MD[153]

> [W]hen his insurance company claims to be concerned for the quality of care he receives, there is usually an underlying

> agenda to which he will not be privy. . . . "[Q]uality" is a nebulous term referring only to aspects of medical care lending themselves to measurement. The real "stuff" of health is not some item that can be dissected, quantified, and put in a board report. —Scott Jensen, MD[154]

The ACA's new power over physicians may make resistance to reporting difficult. Section 1311 of Obamacare empowers the secretary of the US Department of Health & Human Services (HHS) to direct the practice of medicine using the threat of career-damaging sanctions: "Beginning on January 1, 2015, a qualified health plan may contract with . . . a health care provider only if such provider implements such mechanisms to improve health care quality as the Secretary may by regulation require."[155] Simply put, the secretary can blacklist any physician who chooses to practice medicine independently.

Former US Representative Phil Gingrey (R-GA), a physician who introduced legislation in 2012 to repeal Section 1311(h), clarified the danger in *National Review*: "These few lines empower one bureaucrat—the Health and Human Services (HHS) Secretary—to determine whether a physician is providing 'quality health care measures.'" He adds, "Based on that finding, the Secretary is empowered to cancel a physician's health insurance provider policy, effectively forcing him out of practice."[156]

Gingrey's bill was not enacted, leaving Section 1311(h) in law today as a threat to the livelihood of physicians, the ethics of medicine, and the safety and rights of patients. The result of turning doctors into data clerks is not good, as Lawrence Casalino explains: "If you wanted to dramatize it, a whole generation of physicians is being sacrificed. . . . For them, it's all burden and no benefit as far as they can see. It's a lot of work that they don't get rewarded for, and they're not convinced that it is making care better for their patients. It's been that way for a while, and it doesn't look like it is going to change soon."[157]

Data Industry Profits Skyrocket

Unlike physicians, clinics, and hospitals, the health-data industry experienced a financial windfall from the EHR mandate and health IT. For example, in 2011, UnitedHealth Group's health-data subsidiary, Ingenix (renamed OptumInsight after a lawsuit over its disputed claims database[158]), expected to earn profit margins of around 14 percent.[159]

For the decade prior to 2009, HIMSS had pressed Congress and government officials to subsidize and mandate the adoption of health-records technology. With financial backing from the health-data industry, HIMSS "started advocacy groups, generated research claiming the potential for massive savings, and met routinely with lawmakers and other government officials."[160]

Originally organized in the 1960s, HIMSS today has 70,000 individual members, 630 corporate members, and more than 450 nonprofit organizations. Corporate members include Intel Corporation, Konica Minolta, Leidos, IBM, Hewlett-Packard, Google, Epic, Deloitte, Dell EMC, Comcast, Cisco Systems, Cerner, Allscripts, AT&T, 3M Health Information Systems, Accenture, PricewaterhouseCoopers, Teladoc, Symantec Corporation, Surescripts, Northrop Grumman, Pfizer, McKesson, Optum, Oracle, Verizon, and GE Healthcare, among others.[161]

HIMSS's efforts extend to all levels of government. After HITECH became law in 2009, the *Washington Post* reported that HIMSS "had worked closely with technology vendors, researchers and other allies in a sophisticated, decade-long campaign to shape public opinion and win over Washington's political machinery" and concluded that it was "a triumph for an influential trade group whose members now stand to gain billions in taxpayer dollars."[162]

II

Congress Seizes Control of the Exam Room

Meaningful Use Mandated

Payments and Penalties

It was not enough to mandate the EHR. Congress and the Obama administration mandated that EHRs be used "meaningfully"—which is to say, the way federal officials declare they must be used. Thus, federal policy makers reached into the exam room to control and impact the care of every patient.

As of July 2017, more than 533,000 health care providers had received more than $35.6 billion in EHR/Meaningful Use (MU) incentive payments to purchase and install EHRs and to digitize paper medical records.[1] Surprisingly, this includes at least $475 million to Medicare Advantage organizations,[2] which must by definition be licensed as HMOs.[3] The maximum amount of payment was $44,000 under the Medicare program and $63,750 under the Medicaid program for eligible professionals (EPs).[4] The maximum initial amount for hospitals was $6,370,400.[5] However, if the providers adopted an EHR system after 2014, no incentive payments were available for them.[6]

Doctors and hospitals that refuse to comply with the EHR/MU mandate face financial penalties, starting with reduced reimbursements of 1 percent on January 1, 2015, and increasing to as much as 5 percent after 2017.[7] In late 2014, the federal government announced that 250,000 doctors would have their Medicare payments docked by one percent in 2015.[8]

Costly regulatory requirements of Meaningful Use have driven many physicians to join a larger group or become hospital employees, leading to consolidation and higher costs for care, write former Kaiser Permanente chief compliance officer Joel Dziengielewski and health care attorney Margaret J. Davino. By 2012, "the majority of physicians were employees instead of owners."[9]

Meaningful Use also made EHRs unpopular. According to Charles Webster, MD, a medical informatics expert and president of EHR Workflow, Inc., "Unfortunately, the phrase 'electronic health record' has been so tainted, I doubt physicians will ever love EHRs."[10]

This result of the MU mandate was predicted in 2010. "Healthcare is a complex sociotechnical system where simple metrics can mislead because they do not adequately consider the context of human decisions at the time they are made," a team of technical and clinical experts wrote in the *Journal of the American Medical Informatics Association*. They add, "Thus, the promulgation of 'meaningful use' may lead to undesirable consequences if such use is not contextually grounded and tied to improved efficiency, learning, ease of use, task and information flow, cognitive load, situation awareness, clinician and patient satisfaction, reduced errors, and faster error recovery."[11]

Webster also told *Managed Healthcare Executive*, "In the words of more than one hospital CIO I've spoken with, meaningful use 'sucked the air out of the room.'"[12] In short, along with other government mandates, it left few financial resources for anything else.

The Meaningful Use Law

HHS created three stages of Meaningful Use with increasing levels of data sharing and onerous requirements. As HITECH's EHR incentive payments section (§ 4101) directs, the secretary of HHS is authorized to determine what constitutes satisfactory compliance with various items in the meaningful-use statute, such as electronic prescribing, reporting of clinical data, and more.[13]

According to the government, the incentive payments for MU "are part of a broader effort under the HITECH Act to accelerate the adoption of HIT and utilization of qualified EHRs." Notably, Stage 2 of the effort focused on "ensuring that the meaningful use of EHRs supported the aims and priorities of the National Quality Strategy" in Sections 3011 to 3015 of the ACA.[14] These sections require significant data sharing from patient medical records.

The long-standing purpose of a patient's medical record has been to direct, monitor, and record the physician's and nurse's care of the patient. The Obama administration's purposes for EHRs were much broader than patient care. Meaningful Use requires the use of federally certified EHRs to:

- Improve quality, safety, efficiency, and reduce health disparities
- Engage patients and families in their health care
- Improve care coordination
- Improve population and public health
- All the while maintaining privacy and security[15]

Despite how it may look, this list does not focus on patient care. Federal definitions and purposes of the words are important. For example:

- "Improve population and public health" means focusing on communities rather than individual patients in need of care. See section V for more on this.
- "Quality" is often a euphemism for compliance, including physician compliance with standardized treatment protocols and government reporting checklists.
- "Efficiency" and "care coordination" may give you less time with your doctor, allow computerized and automated treatment protocols to dictate your care, or require that you see nonphysician clinicians even if you want to see a physician.
- "Reducing health disparities" is a strategy that could eventually impose universal one-size-fits-all medical decisions if race, ethnicity, gender, language, and disability data are collected, analyzed, and used to assert claims of civil rights violations when patient care is not standardized or outcomes are not uniform.

Government Data Mining

The "privacy and security" requirement in Meaningful Use is meaningless. The EHR will be used to collect multiple data points, to report that data to state and federal government, and then to use the data for other purposes that have nothing to do with the patient. In "The Obama EHR Experiment," informatics professor Ralph Grams lists and then writes pointedly about the twenty-three EHR Meaningful Use criteria issued by ONC:

> Only one criterion deals with clinical decision support. The rest of the items are secondary to the doctor and feed the patient and government data that is needed for cost controls and physician monitoring. What they are doing is promoting the automation of a paper medical record where the doctor fills in all the blanks and becomes the clerical front-end of this electronic surveillance system called the EHR. . . .
>
> When you look further at the EHR criteria, you will see that the majority of the criteria deal with billing, data transfer and data mining capabilities. The real goal of this EHR project is not to control costs or enhance patient care: it is data mining, the control of the physician population, and the ultimate rationing and control of patient services. . . . *The use of interoperable standards means that they are looking for a massive database on which they can control the healthcare delivery system.*
>
> This bold experiment in medical informatics is based upon a false supposition (The Rand Report) and a total lack of prototypes on which to build. There is no off-the-shelf EHR on the planet that could meet all the criteria listed in the [Office of the National Coordinator for Health Information Technology] legislation. The idea of designing complex systems by federal committees without physician input, prototype development and testing is insane.[16] (Emphasis added.)

MU Terrifies Physicians

According to CMS, the three main components of Meaningful Use are:

1. Use of a certified EHR in a meaningful manner (e.g., e-prescribing)

2. Use of certified EHR technology for electronic exchange of health information to improve quality of health care

3. Use of certified EHR technology to submit clinical quality measures (CQM) and other such measures selected by the Secretary[17]

Clinical quality measures, according to HHS, "are a mechanism for assessing observations, treatment, processes, experience, and/or outcomes of patient care. In other words, CQMs assess 'the degree to which a provider *competently and safely* delivers clinical services that are *appropriate for the patient* in an *optimal timeframe*.'"[18] The definition of these terms, and thus the decision to fully or partially pay the doctor, is left to federal employees far from patients' bedsides.

There are also three stages of MU requirements, all of which have been finalized by the government and published in the *Federal Register*. The final stage—the most onerous and controversial stage, which added more processes, objectives, and required measures on top of processes, objectives, and required measures already not being met—was released October 6, 2015[19] (and amended twice to correct "technical errors"[20]) despite calls for delay from Congress, the American Medical Association, and others.[21] One physician posted this comment on the American Medical Association website:

> Let's try to be perfectly clear from a front line provider. Listen up CMS. Meaningful use is dead. The Stage 3 proposal reads like a dark comedy. There is ABSOLUTELY no way providers are going to participate in this. We are NOT data entry personnel. If you want data entry personnel, then hire a million of them and send them out to our offices. It is MUCH more efficient and safer and easier to take the penalties until YOU give up on this ridiculous regulatory nonsense.[22]

Senator Lamar Alexander, chairman of the Senate Health, Education, Labor & Pensions (HELP) Committee, said of Stage 3: "To put it bluntly, physicians and doctors have said to me that they are literally 'terrified' [of] the next implementation stage of electronic health records, called Meaningful Use Stage 3, because of its complexity and because of the fines that will be levied."[23]

The "Game Changer"

After noting that the ACA was "inadequate" for improving quality or reducing costs, David Bowen, former director of health care policy for the Senate HELP committee, stated the following in 2010, as reported by the *New York Times*:

> To advance the broader agenda of [health] reform, Mr. Bowen pointed to the electronic health record initiative, which was part of the year-earlier economic stimulus package, not this year's health reform legislation. Health information technology, Mr. Bowen said, had the potential to be a "game changer."
>
> He elaborated by saying that "meaningful use is on its way to becoming the two most important words in health care."[24]

The ACA enforces the Meaningful Use mandate in Section 3002(d). If the physician "does not satisfactorily submit data on quality measures for covered professional services" the fees for services were reduced to 98.5 percent of the fee schedule in 2015 and 98 percent in 2016 and every year that follows. Clinical quality measures reported must include "the meaningful use of health information technology."[25]

Meaningful Use Stages 1 to 3

The following information is intended to give the American public a general idea of the federal government's Meaningful Use data collection and reporting requirements. It shows how complex the health care system and the treatment of patients have become as a result of federal interference and control.

Though it will likely be somewhat overwhelming, read on and imagine trying to comply.

On July 28, 2010, CMS and ONC finalized a rule implementing HITECH, including Meaningful Use incentive payments and penalties.[26] There are separate requirements for physicians and hospitals, but only the physician requirements are covered below, especially because the term "Meaningful Use" will soon disappear. However, as noted above and explained in more detail below, many of its components will be incorporated into the payment reforms of the Medicare Access and CHIP Reauthorization Act (MACRA). Therefore, Meaningful Use is not really going away.

As the following information will demonstrate, Meaningful Use is the reason patients are increasingly asked unnecessary personal questions or asked to comply with examinations (e.g., body mass index calculation) that may have nothing to do with the purpose of their visits. It's also why clinics are strongly encouraging patients to access their own medical data (i.e., join the clinic's online portal). The clinic's financial solvency may depend on it. As the California Medical Association wrote to CMS in 2016:

> The rule dramatically increases the quality reporting burden by increasing the reporting threshold from 50% of patients to 80/90% of patients and the impossible EHR Meaningful Use (MU) Stage 3 standards remain. The majority of small practices are not successfully meeting the PQRS and MU Stage 2 measures now. . . . Small practices are the backbone of the Medicare program serving these patients. Solo and small practice physicians must to [sic] given a legitimate opportunity for positive incentive payment. If we don't protect small practices these physicians will be forced to leave the Medicare program or retire early.[27]

MU Stage 1, Requirements for Physicians

To qualify for federal incentive payments that are intended to partially cover the extraordinary cost of transitioning from paper medical records to government-certified EHRs, doctors and other "eligible professionals" must meet twenty of the twenty-five MU Stage 1 requirements and 80 percent of the doctor's patients must have their medical records digitized and housed in a certified EHR.[28] MU Stage 1 includes fifteen **Core Objectives**, which are all required:

1. Computerized provider order entry (CPOE)
2. E-prescribing (eRx)
3. Report ambulatory clinical quality measures to CMS/States
4. Implement one clinical decision support rule
5. Provide patients with an electronic copy of their health information, upon request
6. Provide clinical summaries for patients for each office visit
7. Drug-drug and drug-allergy interaction checks
8. Record demographics
9. Maintain an up-to-date problem list of current and active diagnoses
10. Maintain active medication list
11. Maintain active medication allergy list
12. Record and chart changes in vital signs
13. Record smoking status for patients 13 years or older
14. Capability to exchange key clinical information among providers of patient-authorized entities electronically
15. Protect electronic health information[29]

Of the ten **Menu Set Objectives** that follow, eligible professionals must comply with at least five, including one of the public health reporting objectives (number 9 or 10 below). Number five is the mandatory creation of a "patient portal."[30]

1. Drug-formulary checks
2. Incorporate clinical lab test results as structured data
3. Generate lists of patients by specific conditions
4. Send reminders to patients per patient preference for preventive/follow-up care
5. Provide patients with timely electronic access to their health information
6. Use certified EHR technology to identify patient-specific education resources and provide to patient, if appropriate
7. Medication reconciliation
8. Summary of care record for each transition of care/referrals
9. Capability to submit electronic data to immunization registries/systems
10. Capability to provide electronic syndromic surveillance data to health agencies[31]

MU Stage 2, Requirements Expanded

After the fifteen items on the Stage 1 Core Objectives list, Stage 2 calls for seventeen items—and doctors are required to meet all of them. Several Stage 2 Core Objectives are carryovers from *both* Stage 1 lists that were made more prescriptive with additional requirements. To see the change, compare the MU Stage 1 lists above with the three examples from Stage 2 below. The additional requirements are italicized.

Stage 2 Core Objective #11 (Menu Set Objective #3 in Stage 1): "Generate lists of patients by specific conditions *to use for quality improvement, reduction of disparities, research, or outreach.*"

Stage 2 Core Objective #7 (Menu Set Objective #5 in Stage 1): Provide patients *the ability to view online, download, and transmit their health information within four business days of the information being available to the EP* [eligible professional].

Stage 2 Core Objective #4 (Core Objective #12 in Stage 1): "Record and chart changes in *the following* vital signs: *height/ length and weight (no age limit); blood pressure (ages 3 and over); calculate and display body mass index (BMI); and plot and display growth charts for patients 0–20 years, including BMI.*"[32]

The following three new activities are included in the MU2 Core Objectives requirement:

- Sex must be recorded as structured demographic data, in addition to the Stage 1 requirements of preferred language, gender, race, ethnicity, and date of birth.[33]
- The recording of patient demographic data as structured data must increase from more than 50 percent of all patients to more than 80 percent.[34]
- Secure electronic messaging must be used to communicate with patients on relevant health information.[35]

MU Stage 2 also includes a set of six Menu Objectives. Three involve reporting to state and federal databases, or specialty registries sponsored by public health agencies or national specialty societies.[36] The fourth one (structured data) clarifies why family history is now being collected through extensive questionnaires and electronic tablets. Physicians must comply with three of the following:

1. Capability to submit electronic syndromic surveillance data to public health agencies except where prohibited, and in accordance with applicable law and practice.

2. Record electronic notes in patient records.
3. Imaging results consisting of the image itself and any explanation or other accompanying information are accessible through CEHRT [certified EHR technology].
4. Record patient family health history as structured data.
5. Capability to identify and report cancer cases to a public health central cancer registry, except where prohibited, and in accordance with applicable law and practice.
6. Capability to identify and report specific cases to a specialized registry (other than a cancer registry), except where prohibited, and in accordance with applicable law and practice.[37]

MU Stage 3, Assuring Infractions and Penalties

Despite requests that Stage 3 be delayed, on October 6, 2015, HHS and ONC issued a 752-page final rule that included both EHR certification requirements and MU requirements for Stage 3.[38] The requirements are optional in 2017 but required for all participants in 2018.[39] Furthermore, rather than just reporting data for one continuous ninety-day period, all providers would be required to use an EHR reporting period of a full calendar year in 2018, with some exceptions. However, in August 2017, under the Trump administration, HHS relaxed the 365-day reporting requirement to ninety days for 2018.[40]

Stage 3 as initially proposed "would nearly double the number of measures that a practice must meet for every eligible patient encounter to avoid Medicare pay penalties," reported *American Medical News* in 2013. The American Hospital Association stated, "More than 60% of hospitals and about 90% of physicians have yet to attest to Stage 2."[41] Michael H. Zaroukian, MD, PhD, and chair of the American College of Physicians medical informatics committee, said: "A number of the proposed stage 3 measures necessitate significant increases in clinical documentation, involve new and potentially complex work flows, are likely to be difficult for many eligible professionals to understand and implement, or depend on technologies that are not yet widely deployed or shown to be usable in busy practices."[42]

In December 2014, CMS announced 257,000 eligible professionals had failed to comply with Meaningful Use and would receive reduced Medicare payments.[43] In January 2016, CMS said nearly 209,000 eligible professionals would suffer a 2 percent reduction in Medicare payments as a result of failing MU compliance.[44] As reported by *Healthcare IT News*: "About 86,000 providers will have a payment reduction between $1,000 and $10,000 and almost 6,000 more will have payments cut by up to $10,000 or more.[45] The majority, around 117,000 providers, will receive penalties less than $1,000."[46]

Some doctors decided to get out of the rat race. As Medscape reported in January 2016: "only 58,751 Medicare EPs received incentives in stage 2 of the program through last November compared with 307,656 who got paid in stage 1. . . . Many physicians simply found the stiffer requirements in stage 2 not worth the effort, especially as most of the incentive money was already gone."[47]

Is Meaningful Use Disappearing?

Now that Meaningful Use has essentially achieved the EHRs-for-all objective, it's being shelved—sort of. As CMS acting administrator Andy Slavitt, the former UnitedHealth Group executive who was in charge of writing and issuing all regulations for health plans during the last two years of the Obama administration, stated, "Now that we effectively have technology into virtually every place care is provided, we are now in the process of ending Meaningful Use and moving to a new regime culminating with the MACRA implementation. The Meaningful Use program as it has existed, will now be effectively over and replaced with something better."[48]

Define the word *better*. If it means a new federal program that still requires doctors to submit detailed data, still issues penalties, and still distracts from patient care, that is not better.

Replacing Meaningful Use in 2019 is a payment system with higher penalties imposed by the 2015 Medicare Access and CHIP Reauthorization Act (MACRA): the Merit-Based Incentive Payment System (MIPS), a performance-based system with four categories of measurement.[49] Data collection began in 2017, and doctors must include data on non-Medicare patients for each measurement, not just Medicare patients.[50] MIPS, as a CMS PowerPoint presentation shows,[51] is a radical departure from the traditional fee-for-service payment system that pays doctors for the services they provide.

Meaningful Use, writes Margalit Gur-Arie, founder of BizMed, is "about regulating design and production of medical software to serve the needs and wants of government and large corporations." She suspects this regulatory effort to be "greatly fortified" through MACRA's "new regime." In a brilliantly biting piece at HITconsultant.net, Gur-Arie takes CMS's Slavitt to task and notes that the end-of-Meaningful Use announcement was made at the J.P. Morgan Healthcare Conference, considered the "largest and most informative healthcare investment symposium in the industry."[52] She surmises:

> Changes to the Meaningful Use program are of strategic importance to all other rainbows, grails and unicorns. Why? Because Meaningful Use, other than funneling a respectable amount of billions of dollars into the health tech sector, is the enabler of data collection, which fuels all other investment opportunities.
>
> Furthermore, pretty much everything that could be sold to satisfy Meaningful Use, has been sold, so what's next? As the Meaningful Use money-making opportunities are ending, CMS is "moving to a new regime." Interesting choice of words notwithstanding, the Meaningful Use successor consists of punishing doctors for nebulous "outcomes," and of course all sorts of new technologies to better transfer all medical data into places where J.P. Morgan clientele can monetize them.[53]

Gur-Arie was less than impressed when Slavitt claimed, "We have to get the hearts and minds of the physicians back. . . . I think we lost them."[54] She writes, "If you design clever software, and mandate its purchase and daily use, there is very little utility in paying users to show their work, which is what Meaningful Use for physicians really meant. You do however want to keep those unwittingly exploited users calm and cooperative, which may explain why CMS wants to 'get the hearts and minds of physicians back.'"[55]

There is a place where the heart and minds of physicians are already back. It's outside of CMS. These doctors have private and direct relationships with patients. Care decisions do not travel through an EHR to a health plan or government agency for pretreatment clearance. Examples include fee-for-service practices, such as PATMOS Emergiclinic in Tennessee, direct primary care clinics, like Atlas MD in Kansas, and affordable cash, check, or charge surgery, as found at the Surgery Center of Oklahoma. One place to find these kinds of practices nationwide is The Wedge of Health Freedom, launched by the Citizens' Council for Health Freedom. The Wedge, which is free for doctors and patients, includes "True Patient Privacy" as one of its eight principles.[56]

One final note: On April 24, 2018, as this book was being finalized, CMS issued a press release saying, "We are re-naming the Meaningful Use program 'Promoting Interoperability.'"[57] The impact of this change on patients and doctors remains to be seen.

Every Prescription Tracked

The E-Prescribing Mandate

HITECH specifically designates e-prescribing as part of its Meaningful Use requirements. Under e-prescribing, practitioners electronically send patient prescription information to pharmacy computers.[58] In 2009, nearly every state allowed e-prescribing for noncontrolled substances.[59] By April of 2014, 90 percent of pharmacies accepted electronic prescriptions, 70 percent of all physicians were using an EHR to e-prescribe, with each state having an e-prescribing rate of 41 percent or above, and twenty-eight states were at 70 percent.[60]

Congress mandated the use of electronic prescribing standards in the 2003 Medicare Modernization Act,[61] and enacted "incentives" for e-prescribing in the Medicare Improvements for Patients and Providers Act (MIPPA) of 2008.[62] Reporting began in 2012 with penalties starting in 2013. Financial bonuses were available from 2009 through 2013.[63] Moving forward, the CMS website says, "electronic prescribing continues with Meaningful Use."[64] As reported by the Government Accountability Office (GAO), physician reporting of the following activities was necessary to receive a Meaningful Use incentive payment, starting in 2009:

- Generate and transmit more than 40 percent of permissible prescriptions electronically.
- Enter medication order into Computerized Physician Order Entry system for more than 30 percent of patients with at least one medication in their medication lists.

- Enter medication lists or indicate no current prescriptions for more than 80 percent of patients.
- Enter medication allergy lists or indicate no known medication allergies for more than 80 percent of patients.
- Enable the EHR system's ability to check a prescription for potential drug-drug and drug-allergy interactions.
- Perform medication reconciliation for more than 50 percent of all transitions of care.
- Enable the EHR system's ability to check a prescription against a formulary and maintain access to at least one internal or external drug formulary for the entire EHR reporting period.[65]

Physicians that refuse to e-prescribe under Meaningful Use began suffering penalties in 2013. The Maine Academy of Family Practice describes the reporting requirements of the initial e-prescription (eRx) program and the bonus and penalties:

> In January 2009 the Centers for Medicare & Medicaid Services (CMS) began offering eligible providers incentive payments for their use of an electronic prescribing (ePrescribing) system to prescribe for Medicare patients.
>
> Eligible professionals need to report 25 separate electronic prescribing events during the reporting period (2012 calendar year) to receive an incentive and 10 times before June 30, 2012, to avoid a 2013 penalty.
>
> Individual eligible professionals may be subject to a 1.5 reduction in Medicare payments in 2013 unless they are successful ePrescribers before June 30, 2012 (report 10 unique ePrescribing events for CPT codes reported on Medicare Part B claims with the G8553 code). A number of exceptions do apply.[66]

The AMA notes, "Eligible professionals who were successful electronic prescribers received an average bonus payment of just over

$3,000 (and $14,501 per practice) from the e-prescribing Incentive Program in 2009 and $3,836 in 2010."[67] A 2007 federal study found the cost of e-prescribing to be $42,332 for implementation and $14,725 per year for a practice of ten full-time equivalent psychiatrists.[68]

Despite its stated convenience, e-prescribing facilitates outside surveillance and control over medication choices. As *Roll Call* reports, one patient's "efforts to save money can be limited by e-prescribing procedures that can restrict her to a single pharmacy. If another pharmacy has a better deal, she's stuck, unless she wants to pick up a paper prescription."[69] And as noted in an Elsevier PowerPoint presentation, e-prescribing can evolve to "eMedication Management." Certain management activities, as the following list shows, can be intrusive:

1. Comprehensive medication review and reconciliation
2. Identify [drug] formulary
3. Formulary compliance
4. Medication therapy guideline best practices
5. Track compliance and adherence
6. Monitor effectiveness and safety
7. Measure health status and outcomes
8. Process refills and renewals
9. Compliance and adherence problem intervention
10. Public health surveillance
11. Check fill status
12. Verify patient pick-up[70]

Thus, e-prescribing gathers precise information on the patient's preferred pharmacy, and if or when the patient actually picks up the prescription. For example, Richland Medical Center, a group practice with twenty-six practitioners in rural southwestern Wisconsin, conducts e-prescribing using Surescripts, "which pulls out prescription data to enable the practice to track medication compliance of patients."[71]

States have also enacted e-prescribing mandates.

In 2008 the Minnesota legislature mandated that e-prescribing be implemented statewide by January 1, 2011. With 91 percent of clinics e-prescribing in 2015 and 90 percent of hospitals in 2014, the Minnesota Department of Health claimed "nation-leading rates of e-prescribing" and said the "integration of e-prescribing services with electronic health record (EHR) systems is essential to long-term success" of the program.[72] The law, however, does not prohibit use of paper prescriptions.[73] In addition, "there is no enforcement mechanism or fine for not complying with the mandate," according to the Minnesota Department of Health.[74] Thus, patients who want more privacy should ask for a paper prescription.

On the other hand, e-prescribing was required for all New York State prescriptions starting March 27, 2015,[75] with some exceptions based on "a showing of economic hardship, technological limitations and exceptional circumstances."[76] Despite granting a one-year delay of the deadline, 4,165 providers requested waivers as of April 1, 2016.[77] The initial round of waivers expired March 26, 2017, but new waivers can be requested.[78]

Hidden Cost of EHR e-Prescribing Mandate

Unknown to most of the public is another cost related to e-prescribing. Pharmacy technicians often have to dump pills *out* of prescription bottles and back into pharmacy containers. This is because the medications from prescriptions dropped off or sent to the pharmacy electronically were never picked up by patients. Thus, pharmacies must not only fill the prescription but "unfill" them as well, at a cost to the pharmacy.

The following commentary (minus its obscenities) on *The Angry Pharmacist* blog describes it best. The topic is the "dreaded" Return to Stock (RTS) bin:

RTS's absolutely kill pharmacies. Here's why (to those at home who don't work in a pharmacy).

It takes money to fill a prescription (gasp!) other than the raw cost of the drug. Everything from the vial, to the label, to the computer system/printer/toner that spits out the label . . . to the tech that fills it, to the pharmacist that checks it, to the clerk that puts it in a little bag and takes your whiny phone calls. All of those steps cost money. That's not even counting the electricity, insurance, employee taxes, etc.

We get a dispensing fee paid for by YOUR insurance to cover these fixed costs. Why are they fixed? Because the dispensing cost is the same if the drug costs $1 to $5000 kerzillion dollars. When you pick up and sign for the medication, we have proof to your insurance company that you in fact received the medication and their piddly $2 dispensing fee was in fact put to its intended use.

Now say that drug filled vial with your name on it just sits out front for a few weeks. . . . Eventually, we need that space to store medications for [other] people. . . . Your vial then gets RTS'd.

Since we didn't dispense that medication, we legally cannot accept the money that your insurance company paid us for the drug + dispensing fee. So now, we "back out" the prescription (meaning we give the money your insurance company paid us BACK to them, all of it), and now must PAY someone to put the drug back into the big stock bottles. We have to throw away the vial and the label as well. . . .

After about the second time I RTS a prescription for a patient, I put a big note in their profile to make sure they are told that we will fill their prescriptions when they are IN the store due to us always putting back into stock what they order.[79]

Truth About e-Prescribing Errors

One rationale used to impose e-prescribing mandates is elimination of prescription errors. However, Elsevier reports, "More and more pharmacies are reporting prescribing errors with eRx."[80]

Despite claims of patient safety and error reduction, e-prescribing opens the door to new errors which are "frustratingly commonplace."[81] Elsevier reports that more than 10 percent of e-prescriptions contain an error, and 4 percent require a callback to the prescriber—resulting in more than $360 million in pharmacist labor costs.[82] Those errors include incorrect drug, incorrect dose, incomplete drug name, overdose, underdose, incorrect route of administration, ambiguous signature, frequency omitted, and mismatch in all sorts of categories between what's written in the prescription and what's written in the special instructions associated with the prescription.[83]

"Doc Fix" Makes It Worse

Passage of MACRA

In April 2015 the Republican-led Congress strengthened the Democrats' EHR Meaningful Use mandate with the passage of the so-called "Doc Fix" bill, that is, the Medicare Access and CHIP Reauthorization Act of 2015 (MACRA).[84]

The new law eliminated the much-disliked Sustainable Growth Rate (SGR) payment system, which was enacted in 1997 to limit the annual increase in cost per Medicare recipient to the growth of the national economy. It didn't work. Starting in 2002 Congress annually refused to cut payments to physicians. By April 1, 2015, the required reduction had climbed to 21.2 percent.[85]

Under MACRA, two complex payment options for physicians and other eligible professionals were enacted and the SGR was repealed.[86] The first payment option, the Merit-Based Incentive Payment System (MIPS), is based on physician performance in four categories as measured by a federally defined set of data. The second, Advanced Alternative Payment Models (APMs), requires doctors to assume financial risk for patient care by participating in one of the "care models" CMS lists each year for APM payments. For example, in 2017, two of the eight APMs were Comprehensive Primary Care Plus (CPC+) and the Next Generation ACO (accountable care organization) Model.[87] Physicians seeking APM payments must engage their patients inside and outside the clinic with reminders and outreach tools (phone calls, emails, postcards, patient portals, and community health workers) to limit their own financial risk.[88]

The change is not an improvement. The new Medicare payment systems will be *worse* for physicians and patients in the out-years than the abolished SGR system. The CMS Office of the Actuary predicted the following *before* MACRA was passed by Congress: "absent a change in the method or level of update by subsequent legislation . . . access to, and quality of, physicians' services would deteriorate over time."[89] In short, physicians will drop out of Medicare due to poor payment, leaving the ever-expanding population of Medicare patients—ten thousand new recipients per day[90]—with fewer physicians.

That it will be worse seems incredible considering the complex flowcharts already created by CMS for clinics to use in 2016 to avoid penalties in 2018[91] and the trio of reporting systems physicians must already submit to under Medicare to avoid penalties:[92] the Physician Quality Reporting System (PQRS), the Medicare EHR Incentive Program (Meaningful Use), and the Value-Based Payment Modifier. The latter is described by CMS as a payment adjustment "based upon the quality of care furnished compared to the cost of care during a performance period."[93]

Meaningful Use Gets a New Name

CMS, in a December 2015 document proposing a Measurement Development Plan to comply with MACRA, explains how the three systems are both disappearing and remaining intact. Under the Merit-Based Incentive Payment System (MIPS), physicians will receive positive (bonuses), negative (penalties), or neutral payment adjustments based on "a composite performance score across four performance categories:

- Quality
- Resource use
- Clinical practice improvement activities
- Meaningful use of certified electronic health record (EHR) technology[94]

CMS clarifies, "MIPS will build upon existing quality measure sets from the Physician Quality Reporting System (PQRS), Value-Based Payment Modifier (VM), and Medicare EHR Incentive Program for Eligible Professionals (EPs), commonly referred to as Meaningful Use."[95]

Might this be part of the reason 49 percent of 17,326 physicians surveyed say they often or always feel symptoms of burnout and 48 percent "plan to cut-back on hours, retire, take a non-clinical job, switch to 'concierge' medicine, or take other steps limiting patient access to their practices"?[96]

Nearly five months later, CMS issued a proposed rule to implement MIPS and APMs. HHS regulators discarded the name Meaningful Use and adopted Advancing Care Information (ACI). The proposal required that *data on all patients* be reported, not just Medicare patients: "for these submission mechanisms, we would expect to receive quality data for both Medicare and non-Medicare patients."[97] Furthermore, HHS expected clinicians to use a qualified clinical data registry (QCDR) to seamlessly report MIPS data in the four performance areas to CMS and commercial payers and "to track patients longitudinally over time for quality improvement."[98]

Thus, Meaningful Use is sticking around as a part of MIPS, but with a new name and acronym. CMS says, "The Advancing Care Information category (formerly Meaningful Use) would account for 25 percent of the MIPS score in the first year."[99] The overall ACI score would be "made up of a base score and a performance score for a maximum score of 100 points."[100] There are seven objectives and measures for the 2017 ACI performance score, and there's also a bonus of up to 15 percent for physicians who report data to a public health or clinical data registry, such as syndromic surveillance reporting or electronic case reporting, and do it using certified EHR technology.[101] There are two options for base score reporting: the 2017 ACI Transition Objectives and Measures, or the original ACI Objectives and Measures.[102] As an example for the reader, the original ACI base score objectives and measures are:

Objective	Measure
Protect Patient Health Information	Security Risk Analysis
Electronic Prescribing	e-Prescribing
Patient Electronic Access	Provide Patient Access
Health Information Exchange	Send a Summary of Care
Health Information Exchange	Request/Accept a Summary of Care[103]

The MACRA/MIPS payment system must be budget neutral. Thus, clinics and hospitals with "better data," as defined by federal definitions, can siphon dollars from competitors. *Health Law & Policy Matters* offers a definition of *budget neutral*: "This means that the money CMS saves from the negative adjustments [penalties] will be used to fund the positive adjustments [higher payments]."[104] Pity the small practice that doesn't have sophisticated data systems, data analysts, lawyers, and staff to collect, manipulate, and report the data in a format that will bring in the most dollars.

Perhaps this is why HHS predicted in the proposed rule that 87 percent of nearly 103,000 solo practitioners would face a cumulative total of $300 million in MIPS penalties.[105] This would potentially have put many solo physicians out of business. Another 70 percent of 123,000 clinicians in small practices with two to nine clinicians were expected to face $279 million in penalties. Would these clinicians, as discussed by Davino and Dziengielewski, be forced to become employees?

Physicians Sound Off

Public comments from physicians were telling and should concern every patient who wants a readily accessible physician and a confidential patient-doctor relationship in their future. Here are just ten written comments to CMS, which include the location of the physician as reported in the comment section of the proposed rule at Regulations.gov:

1. "Requiring mental health practitioners to have EHR is a disaster for a profession and its patients who cannot be assured of confidentiality." (Russell Holsten, New Jersey)

2. "I am a solo practitioner and unable to keep up with your massive amounts of rules. If it is your goal to force me out of Medicare then you are about to be successful." (John Colby, Kentucky)

3. "Mr. Slavitt, in 1999 I achieved my lifelong dream of becoming a physician. . . . Instead I was FORCED to become a paper pusher and answer to the insurance companies and government bureaucracies that took time and care away from my patients. So now my lifelong dream and passion has become a job. I [no] longer enjoy going to the office. I no longer enjoy going to the operating room." (Russ Juno, Texas)

4. "You must not allow this draconian measure to pass. I am a solo physician in private practice. . . . I have jumped through every hoop you have put in front of me: Meaningless Use 1 and 2, PQRS, etc. . . . I have used EMR since 2005, and while it helps me practice more efficiently, it presents another ready-made impediment between me and my patients. I cannot see more patients, or practice more efficiently. It isn't possible. (Barry Resnik, Florida)

5. "The rules causing physicians to keep open lines 24 hours per day to a computer system so that Big Brother may eavesdrop on all patients' confidential medical information are simply chilling. I will not comply with this." (William Strinden, Texas)

6. "I finally quit at the beginning of this year at age 45. . . . I was spending 50% of my time meeting quality and other incentives rather than caring for patients before I quit." (Sallie Waters, Oklahoma)

7. "If [it passes] I will join all others and sell my office and work as employee. Have more free time, not get calls at home.

Work 40 hrs only (instead of 78 like I do now) . . . not be responsible when I am off . . . now I am always on unless on vacation. After 24 years of taking care of our people maybe [this] is what I should do." (Angel Rios, Texas)

8. "Remember we do not have large IT departments and the ability to hire expensive consultants to meet government regulations, it's just us. Like many solo physicians, I am my own IT guy and compliance officer." (Randy Robinson, Iowa)

9. "I am a bc [board certified] geriatrician and see about 75% Medicare. All of the new rules and pseudoincentives have done nothing but continuously lower my income, increase my overhead, and are about to drive me out of the private practice market. I struggle to make a living and would do far better to pack it in and become a hospitalist. I work 12 hour days. But I am struggling. My salary for the past 6 months was below that of a nurse practitioner. The ever-increasing rules have nearly paralyzed my practice. I have completed meaningful use through stage 3. I find myself overwhelmed with how to document to get paid and becoming progressively less efficient." (Glenn Fussel, Georgia)

10. "Is 'merit' defined by a system, a bureaucrat, an insurer, a physician observer, a government employee, an attorney, a jury—or a patient? Or, more likely, a statistic? Too bad professionalism and Hippocratic morality have so marginal a role in these discussions. . . . there simply must never be support for any administrative code that rations care based on merit or value established by constructed bureaucratic statistics." (Jeffrey Dobkin, New Jersey)[106]

Nearly two years later, physicians are no happier. In a "regulatory burden" study of 750 group practices released in August 2017 by the Medical Group Management Association (MGMA), 80 percent of practices were "very concerned" to "extremely concerned" about the clinical relevance of MIPS to patient care. Seventy-one percent were concerned about overall implementation costs. An astonishing 71 percent said MIPS is "a government program that does not support our practice's clinical quality priorities."[107]

Most practices are completely unprepared. A June 2017 NueMD study found 50 percent of health care professionals unfamiliar with MACRA, 41 percent somewhat familiar and only 9 percent very familiar. [108] Another June survey by technology provider Integra Connect found 100 percent of respondents admitting they hadn't yet grasped the impact of MACRA on their practice. Half didn't believe their EHR could handle value-based payment programs, such as MIPS, and 62 percent didn't know how or had no plans to fund the necessary investments.[109] The deadline to begin collecting MIPS data was October 2, 2017.[110]

More Controls—Larger Penalties

Previous laws signed by both Republican and Democratic Presidents—MIPPA signed by George W. Bush and ARRA and ACA signed by Barack Obama—have forced doctors to report significant patient data to the federal government. What's particularly distressing about this development is that twenty-one years after the Republicans defeated the Clinton Health Security Act in 1994, Republicans voted to enact similar requirements for quality measurement, electronic data systems, and payment controls.

The Republicans' new merit-based and alternative payment systems for physician reimbursement also strengthened the ACA payment reforms, according to Jason Furman, then chairman of Obama's Council of Economic Advisers.[111] Before MACRA was passed, he told an audience at the Center for American Progress—whose president Neera Tanden claims she helped write the ACA[112]—how the bill would link Medicare payments to providers' efficiency and quality.[113] He said the bill "is going to offer us even more tools to expand the same types of new payment models that we put in place in the Affordable Care Act. . . . That's why the president is looking forward to signing a good bill in this area."[114] Federal health officials in the Obama administration agreed:

> A transformation of the U.S. healthcare delivery system gained momentum in 2010 with the passage of the Patient Protection and Affordable Care Act (Affordable Care Act).... Building on the principles and foundation of the Affordable Care Act, the Administration announced a clear timeline for targeting 30 percent of Medicare payments tied to quality or value through alternative payment models by the end of 2016 and 50 percent by the end of 2018. These are measurable goals to move the Medicare program and our healthcare system at large toward paying providers based on quality, rather than quantity, of care.
>
> The passage of the Medicare Access and Children's Health Insurance Program (CHIP) Reauthorization Act of 2015 (MACRA) supports the ongoing transformation of healthcare delivery by furthering the development of new Medicare payment and delivery models for physicians and other clinicians.[115]

Once the merit-based payment system is fully established, the MIPS penalties of up to 9 percent for eligible professionals will replace the Meaningful Use penalties of up to 5 percent. EHRs are key to implementing the new payment system, according to federal officials:

> MACRA encourages the use of certified EHR technologies and QCDRs [qualified clinical data registries] for reporting quality measures. Measures developed from electronic data sources such as EHRs and QCDRs draw from a rich set of clinical data and can reduce data collection and reporting burden while supporting more timely performance feedback to EPs than is possible through traditional claims- or paper-based measures.[116]

The "quality" measures for payment decisions will require tracking of patients and doctors, profiling, and evaluation, according to measuring criteria planned by CMS such as:

- Follow the patient across the continuum of care for patient populations with one or more chronic conditions.

- Emphasize outcomes, including global outcome measures and population-based measures, balanced with process measures that are proximal to outcomes.
- Address patient experience, care coordination, and appropriate use (e.g., overuse and underuse).
- Promote multiple levels of accountability (e.g., individual clinicians, group practices, system level, population level).[117]

In the final MACRA rule, issued November 4, 2016—just four days before the election of President Donald Trump—the federal government established a list of quality measures for physician practices. The government claims the measures are "reasonably focused on appropriate use" and focus on "minimizing overuse of services, treatments, or the related ancillary testing that may promote overuse of services and treatments." And despite stating in the rule, "We realize there are differing opinions on what constitutes appropriate use," CMS's definition will determine whether a physician is fully paid or loses up to 9 percent in Medicare payments.[118] CMS described how the new Quality Payment Program (MIPS and APMs) will change Medicare payments with the following diagram, which illustrates how doctors who receive the full 9 percent would be making nearly 20 percent more[119] than doctors who receive a 9 percent deduction in 2022—all based on data, not services provided:[120]

The cycle of the program looks like this:

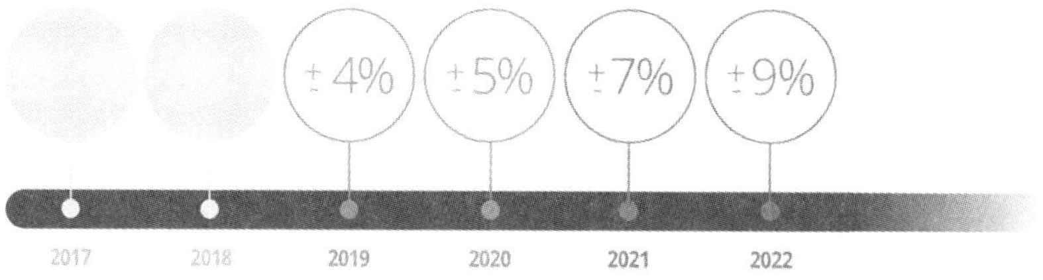

Trump Administration Reduces MACRA Regulations

MACRA is not going away, but everything changed with the 2016 election. The Trump administration moved rapidly to reduce regulatory burdens on physicians. On October 26, 2017, CMS Administrator Seema Verma announced a new federal initiative: Patients Over Paperwork. She reported that CMS typically releases about fifty-eight rules per year (equal to an eleven thousand-page manuscript), highlighted physician concerns with reporting quality metrics into EHRs, and said, "the burden associated with reporting quality measures outweighs their utility."[121] No doubt, this cheered frustrated physicians.

On October 30, 2017, Verma announced "a new comprehensive initiative on quality measures to reduce the burden of reporting called 'Meaningful Measures.'" She said the regulatory burden "is destroying the doctor-patient relationship." She went on to emphasize, "Doctors are frustrated because they got into medicine to help their patients. But, paperwork has distracted them from caring for their patients . . . we have all seen our doctors looking at a computer screen instead of us. I hear it from patients across the country. This must change. The primary focus of a patient visit must be the patient."[122]

In related good news, the final MACRA rule was not the final rule. The Trump administration issued a new proposed MACRA rule in June 2017 and a final rule on November 16, 2017. The revision allows approximately 134,000 small practices—nearly 20 percent from rural areas—to avoid participation in MIPS for 2018.[123] This did not please everyone. One commentary published in *The Hill* prior to the final rule claimed the expanded exemptions "may disable the infrastructure of electronic health records" and "may have unintended consequences of encouraging exempted physicians to abandon their EHRs," causing "direct patient harm."[124] However, the mandated EHR system and its quality reporting requirements are harming patients directly and indirectly—right now.

Similarly, on October 5, the Medicare Payment Advisory Commission (MedPAC), in a near-unanimous decision, recommended scrapping MIPS but keeping the advanced APM model.[125] On January 11, 2018, MedPAC formally voted 14-2 to recommend that Congress eliminate MIPS.[126]

The news gets better. On February 9, President Trump signed the Bipartisan Budget Act of 2018, which repealed the MIPS mandate for "more stringent measures of meaningful use."[127] And on February 15, HHS Secretary Alex Azar told the Senate Finance Committee that he wants to reduce or eliminate MIPS reporting requirements. He suggests HHS could instead look at medical claims data and patient surveys to grade participating physicians.[128]

Finally, as noted previously, the federal government announced on April 24, 2018, that Meaningful Use and the entire EHR Incentive Program is being renamed. The EHR Incentive Programs will be called the *Promoting Interoperability (PI) Programs* and the MIPS Advancing Care Information performance category will be renamed the *Promoting Interoperability performance category*. CMS notes, "This rebranding does not merge or combine the EHR Incentive Programs and MIPS."[129]

III

Clinical Chaos

Frustrated Physicians and Nurses

Doctors are Dissatisfied

The practice of medicine has become frustrating. A May 2013 Physicians Practice survey of 1,291 physicians found declining satisfaction, with only 54 percent satisfied with their EHRs, down from 63 percent in 2011.[1] Another 2013 survey found:

- The average physician lost $44,000 over five years.
- Only 27 percent achieved a positive return on their investment over five years.
- Just 14 percent more would come out ahead if Meaningful Use incentive payments were factored in.[2]

A November 2013 survey found 58 percent of physicians dissatisfied, very dissatisfied, or neutral about their EHR system.[3] The most frequently cited reasons were lost productivity from spending more time on documentation (85 percent) and seeing fewer patients (66 percent).[4]

Modern Healthcare reported in April 2015: "Nearly 3 in 5 (58%) respondents agreed that the EHR system in their organization was difficult to use; 71% felt health IT meant less time with patients. And more doctors than before said EHRs are negative influences in the quality of their care. In 2012, 5% felt that EHRs increased errors versus 12% today."[5]

Reaction Data's 2018 report found "pockets of physicians that are genuinely happy with their EHR," calling it an underreported story.

However, they concluded: "For better or worse EHRs have become, in many ways, the operating system of a healthcare organization. And as such there's simply no way around it. Perhaps that's why most physicians hate their EHR—they have no choice but to use [it]."[6]

In 2011, The Commonwealth Fund wrote about ambivalent physicians waiting "on the sidelines": "As word of the financial and quality-related benefits of EHRs spreads, more physicians are likely to engage" in the EHR effort.[7] However, it's more likely that physicians installed EHRs to avoid financial penalties, not to experience "benefits." The difficulty of EHRs is hitting physicians hard. Nine years after the EHR mandate was enacted, here are a few published comments from doctors between 2012 and 2017:

> All the clicking saps intellectual power and concentration and blocks normal conversation. . . . The device has become a disease requiring as much intellect to manage as does the patient.
>
> —Dean Kross, MD[8]

> It has been my experience, in almost six years now of using EHR, that very little actually improves patient care. It has, however, added tremendously to my overhead.
>
> —Joseph A. Anistranski, MD[9]

> Healthcare used to be about patients, nurses, and doctors. Now it's about insurers, lawyers, and—most recently—IT people. Doctors' records take so much longer just to read because there's so much boilerplate garbage on them to justify coding levels. You will not stop fraud and abuse by punishing hardworking doctors. You will only drive us crazy, or into early retirement.
>
> —Fred Marks, MD[10]

> In the good old days, I could pick up a chart from the rack outside the door, and in what seems like a few seconds, familiarize myself with my patient's history . . . before opening the door to greet her. During

the visit, I could sit with the chart in my lap, jotting down notes as we spoke, my focus on my patient and my thoughts rather than a user interface. . . . My chart was there, sure, but it was not the dominant presence in the encounter the way the EMR is now.

—MARGARET POLANECZKY, MD[11]

The simple narrative of our age—that computers improve the performance of every industry they touch—turns out to have been magical thinking when it comes to healthcare.

—ROBERT WACHTER, MD[12]

EHR must be for clinical data, at least from the physician side. Interestingly enough, no agency vets the ease of use of the EHR by the clinician, does the FDA have a role here? Currently a qualified EHR only has to meet data set standards, no requirement for it to be intuitive and easily applied at the bedside.

—EDGAR L. FEINBERG, MD, MPA[13]

The EMR is no friend of efficiency or compassionate care. It tends to dehumanize the caring involved in the patient-doctor relationship . . . It's safe to say the EMR experiment has cost American taxpayers billions of dollars, and in most situations patient access to care has actually decreased. EMR does accomplish one thing quite well. It allows the government and insurance companies much greater ease in tracking patient behaviors and habits. That capability is a little frightening.

—SCOTT JENSEN, MD[14]

Colossal disasters of EHR implementation have occurred. One example is Contra Costa County, California, which spent $45 million on ccLink, an EHR system to integrate all the county's health departments. Doctors called ccLink "clunky and time-consuming, designed more for bureaucrats than physicians." Its systemic failure crushed morale. By eleven weeks into implementation, every doctor was considering leaving—and six physicians had left for good.[15]

To allow for conversion to the EHR, Contra Costa County administrators cut the physician patient loads in half. Lack of clinic appointments overburdened emergency rooms. Built to see eighty patients a day, the ERs were seeing more than two hundred patients a day. In September, one of every ten ER patients left without ever being seen. One patient waited forty hours to get a bed.[16]

This kind of disaster for patient care was predicted. The RAND Corporation, in an analysis of health information technology, said health IT has "the potential to improve the patient experience" but also suggested it may be detrimental to patients:[17]

> Large-scale effects on patient experience will not be evident until providers adopt EHRs more broadly and until connectivity and interoperability are increased. Some aspects of health IT adoption will require changes to the process of physician-patient interaction that may be to the detriment of patient experience. For example, if the physician must sacrifice face-to-face discussion with the patient to input or retrieve data or otherwise interact with the EHR, the patient experience may be compromised.[18]

Clunky, Costly, Frustrating, and Dangerous

Writing in the *Wall Street Journal* in 2012, Ross Koppel and Stephen Soumerai called the EHRs "generally clunky, frustrating, user-unfriendly and inefficient."[19] The *New York Times* reports EHR challenges include the "potential for mix-ups and confusion that can be frustrating, costly and even dangerous."[20]

It's not difficult to find a frustrated physician. "Damn damn damn," said a doctor to a *Health Data Management* reporter who was at the clinic for a pre-op physical, not on assignment for a story. "In a final indignity, to both of us, he spent a few minutes searching in the EHR for the order set of blood tests the surgeon wanted, gave up, and said he would call the surgeon's office to find out," wrote the reporter. Eventually, the doctor came back with a piece of paper that the reporter took to the lab thirty feet away.[21]

EHRs also obstruct the doctor's full understanding of the patient. Suzanne Koven, MD, writes that "lists of diagnoses and template-generated descriptions" in the EHR don't connect events or symptoms or the thought processes of the doctor into a coherent narrative or communicate the patient's complex experience. She says the EHR "is not built to tell a story." The data is fragmented. She further warns: "A medical record that abandons narrative in favor of a list does more than dehumanize our patients. It also hampers a clinician's diagnostic abilities. . . . Sorting out the story is crucial to deciding which tests to order and what treatment to recommend."[22] This EHR shortcoming continues. A 2017 comparison study of EHRs and paper medical records found paper records were better in terms of quantity and quality content.[23] In other words, the data written on paper better describes the patient's story and medical situation.

Key diagnostic and other data can also be missing from EHRs. In 2016 the *Journal of the American Medical Informatics Association* reported that diagnoses were missing on more than 27 percent of patients with depression or bipolar disorder. In total, 89 percent of acute psychiatric services were missing from the computerized record. The abstract provides this conclusion, and cautions against further implementation: "EHRs inadequately capture mental health diagnoses, visits, specialty care, hospitalizations, and medications. Missing clinical information raises concerns about medical errors and research integrity. Given the fragmentation of health care and poor EHR interoperability, information exchange, and usability, priorities for further investment in health IT will need thoughtful reconsideration."[24]

One physician explained to his patient that the EHR is "like a really old car. You get up in the morning hoping it's going to start, and sometimes it does, sometimes it doesn't. You get it to start and you have to drive really slowly, because if you speed up something's going to fall off. And you know it's a clunker, and it uses way too much gas, but you can't afford a new one."[25]

When surveyed, physicians say their primary goals for installing an electronic health record were regulatory compliance (56 percent), improving quality of care (43 percent), and qualifying for EHR Meaningful Use incentive payments (40 percent).[26] It wasn't for *delivery* of patient care. If it had been, the EHR would have worked for the doctor, not the regulators who measure "quality" and issue penalties and bonuses.

EHRs Hide Critical Patient Information

Computerized medical records are hard to navigate. One specialist told your author that he has no idea where to find the nurses' notes in the hospital EHR, even though he's tried to figure it out, so he doesn't look for them anymore. They were always easy to find in paper charts, as were the doctors' notes and the orders that nurses needed to see.

In 2015, in *BMJ Quality & Safety*, Dr. Ross Koppel provided the following list to show how different types of essential patient data can be hidden by the EHR, leading to danger for patients:

- Dreadful presentations of patients' data and general poor usability
- Drop-down lists that continue to several screens (with the existence of the extended [options] often hidden from the clinician)
- Pop-ups that hide medication or problem lists
- Medication lists and problem lists that can't be seen when ordering medications
- Lab reports presented in erratic or absurd formats and sequences
- Herds of decision support alerts that obscure the screen
- Data that should be contiguous separated by three screens and multiple clicks

- Critical information on the patient is lost because of proprietary EHR software, idiosyncratic device data formats, and refusal to accept data standards
- Lack of true interoperability[27]

Sometimes practitioners can find the data, but it's just plain wrong. Perhaps you've had to correct clinic staff more than once about medication or a diagnosis written in the EHR. Unfortunately, the technology also makes it possible to document one person's information in another person's record without realizing it.[28] Joseph Schneider, MD, MBA, relates his experience as a patient:

> Sitting on the exam table before a routine procedure, I listened as the nurse reviewed my medical information. She checked my name, address, and birthday. All was well until she said, "*and you are allergic to Wellbutrin, Toradol, Darvon and sulfa.*" My brain sprang to attention as she continued reading that I had shoulder repair and coronary bypass procedures, that my weight was down 50 kilograms and that my father was alive. It was very detailed.
>
> It was also all very wrong. I have no medication allergies, nor have I had any of the named surgeries. My weight hasn't changed. And my father passed away in the 1980s.
>
> What happened? My record was mixed up with someone else's and my health care information was now seriously incorrect. Fortunately, as a CMIO [chief medical information officer], I was able to get the 120 pages of my record rapidly corrected.
>
> But what if I was an average person, without the influence to gain quick access and to make corrections? What if I hadn't been having the procedure? The incorrect data could have led to dangerous consequences.[29]

Kris Held, MD, shares a similar story: "I was a victim of an EHR mistake in 2012, while hospitalized for breast cancer surgery. Had I not recognized that another patient's medication list had been imported to my electronic record, that mistake might have been lethal."[30]

Useless Data Impedes Care

Once upon a time a doctor's note really was a note. Today, easy-to-read summaries are rare and often the data can't be trusted. For example, "copy and paste" templates created for EHRs leave doctors unsure if the data is accurate or current. In a study reported by *JAMA Internal Medicine* in August 2017, only 18 percent of 23,630 progress notes written in EHRs by 460 clinicians were original. Forty-six percent were copied and 36 percent were imported.[31]

Much of the data is downright useless, but doctors are required to wade through it all, using up valuable time and mental resources. One doctor told your author that all the data fields in patient records often say, "within normal limits"—a meaningless statement. Unedited copy-and-paste notes—some say "sloppy and paste"—result in inaccuracies that can be perpetuated through the EHR and lead to potential patient harm.[32] Physicians can create "macros" that autopopulate certain parts of the chart, documenting every part of a physical examination, whether or not it was done. Physicians commenting for a 2013 RAND study on physician satisfaction describe similar concerns:

> And the days of being able to dictate in a meaningful fashion, in the form of a letter or a concise document to send to a primary care doctor, are gone, and that's lamentable, because that has been a step down in quality. These new documents are unreadable because you've got to skim through them really quickly and say, "Where's the meat here?"
>
> —CARDIOLOGIST

> . . . I mean, just a lot of the crap [is] in there when I get [notes from] consultants. Ninety-five percent of what I get back is just BS, pulled in from a chart somewhere with no thought involved.
>
> —PRIMARY CARE DOCTOR

> So here's what's happened with the EHR. I mean I get it, I understand it, but it has been a step backwards, I think—and as big a step

backwards as it is forwards. The step backwards is the problem of templated information. . . . There's templated information in the review of systems. [I think:] "Really? You asked all those questions?" Not really. "Well, what percent? 80? . . . 70? . . . 60? . . . 30? . . . Did you ask *any* questions, really?"

—GENERAL SURGEON[33]

Robert E. Hirschtick, MD, says medical students' and residents' increased typing speed, as well as their tendency to record and then each day rerecord every examination and treatment that has happened during the current hospitalization, has vastly multiplied the amount of information recorded—and diminished its usefulness. Readability of these successively longer daily progress notes is a problem; however, he writes, "These notes are not constructed to be read. They are constructed to warehouse data."[34]

According to Hirschtick, clinical notes about patients used to be charted with some immediacy, but the EHR often has notes extending beyond the length of a single day—a span of twenty-four to thirty hours between initiation of the note and the doctor's final signature—thus distorting the record of a patient's current status and recent history and the sequence of events. He says the EMR "manipulates time and transforms the traditional linear timeline of medical storytelling into a nonlinear one" which causes confusion. In addition, overlap with the notes others have written in the records can heighten this confusion and the potential for litigation.[35]

"Many of these problems—such as the proliferation of clinical information that doctors don't trust—also should be of great concern to patients," wrote the authors of a 2014 study that found significant physician dissatisfaction with EHRs.[36] Jason Acevedo, MD, in a letter to the *Wall Street Journal* writes, "We physicians already are drowning in a sea of data that we cannot interpret or use. Thanks to PQRS, MIPS, MACRA and the alphabet soup of governmental quality programs doctors must comply with, I now generate a four-page single-spaced document for a patient with an ear infection. So little of the data we collect is clinically meaningful."[37] John Prunskis, MD, founder and co-medical director of Illinois Pain Institute, says, "The EHR is pages and pages of mind-numbing text, where important labs and information can be lost. Before, a note might be a half-page long, but now it can be five, six pages long, and doctors frequently can't find what's relevant through the reams of text and clutter."[38]

The tendency to copy and paste and over-document has also led to concerns about unintentionally defrauding the federal government.[39] In essence, the EHR may indicate care that never happened. William Malm, senior data projects manager at Craneware in Atlanta, Georgia, told AIS's "Report on Medicare Compliance": "The biggest [compliance risk in the year ahead] is electronic health records. I saw one that was 500 pages for just six days. It was not articulated in a very good way and kept repeating lab values. There was a lot of stuff written that was not germane to what an auditor might look at, and auditors won't infer."[40]

From Doctor to Data Clerk

Studies have found that EHRs reduce time spent with patients. Emergency-room physicians spend 43 percent of their time entering data into computers and 28 percent talking to patients, according to an *American Journal of Emergency Medicine* study. "During a typical 10-hour shift a doctor would click a mouse almost 4,000 times," writes Kevin Pho, MD, in *USA TODAY.* Medical interns have it worse, according to Johns Hopkins University School of Medicine: 12 percent of their time is spent talking with patients—about eight minutes a day per patient—and more than 40 percent is spent interacting with the computer.[41]

One observational study of health-care workers published in 2017 found some doctors and nurses in three US intensive care units spent up to 90 percent of their shift on a computer. "You have the attitude already that this is becoming the job and the job is data management," said Dr. Myles Leslie from The School of Public Policy at the University of Calgary. "The job really isn't fixing bodies and interacting with them. It's just managing streams of data," she added.[42]

One clinician describing the transition to EHRs wrote, "Tasks that once took seconds to perform on paper now require multistepped points and clicks through a maze of menus."[43] "Rooming" a new patient, an activity that formerly took staff two to four minutes, now takes ten minutes because of all the requirements for data capture.[44]

One frustrated physician concluded, "I'm a professional clicker. I used to be a member of a highly respected and sought after profession: a doctor."[45] Anne Marie Valinoti, MD, writes, "It's hard to be both stenographer and empathetic listener at the same time." She doubts "fantastic electronic documentation will translate into fantastic clinical care."[46] Nanette Nuessle, MD, says, "Before using an EHR, I routinely saw 30–32 patients a day. Now, I am exhausted at 20–25, depending upon the EHR."[47]

Steve Chabala, an emergency room physician at St. Mary Mercy Hospital in Livonia, Michigan, said the hospital's switch to EHRs has "been a complete nightmare. I can't see my patients because I'm at a screen entering data." In 2009, the hospital's emergency room discovered their physicians were spending nearly five hours of every ten-hour shift on a computer. Dr. Chabala says he sits down and logs into a computer "60 times every shift."[48]

EHR Developer Learns a Lesson

EHR developers have little understanding of how health care works, leading to EHRs that fail in the real world of treating patients. One EHR designer, Margalit Gur-Arie, quoted elsewhere in this book, personally experienced the difficulties of her own product when a primary care physician traded places with her for demonstration purposes. The developer became the doctor:

> [The real doctor] handed me his shiny new tablet and sat in the patient chair across from my rolling stool. I saw that as the perfect opportunity to teach the doctor how to use "my" software. I designed large portions of it and I've done hundreds of "live" demos of patients with diabetes, hypertension, COPD

> and "by the way" to showcase the ease of use and uncanny abilities of the EHR to simplify the most onerous tasks.
>
> And then he started talking. A simple visit. A little bit of gout. Some stiffness when climbing stairs and he didn't like his new blood pressure meds.
>
> I couldn't keep up. I couldn't find the right templates fast enough. I couldn't find the right boxes to click on. I tried typing in the "versatile" text box. I am a lousy typist. I tried to write stuff down with the stylus in the "strategically located" handwriting recognition box. I kept making mistakes and couldn't erase anything. I tried to type code words for completing the note later. My head was down and I was nervously fumbling with the stylus and the tablet keyboard and my rolling stool kept moving unexpectedly. I would have killed for a pencil and a piece of paper. I finally looked up in total defeat and saw the good doctor's kind smile, "now you get it." Indeed.[49]

Developers must study clinicians, say four experts writing in the *Journal of the American Medical Informatics Association*. The complexities of the work must be analyzed by trained usability engineers and human-factors professionals, otherwise the design team will "not understand how clinical work is really carried out, what clinicians' real needs are, and where the potential hazards and leverage points lie."[50] Clinician disappointment and frustration will follow.

The End of the Medical Profession?

Michael Chen, a physician and independent developer of the open-source, physician-centered NOSH ChartingSystem, explained that many physicians "are not happy with the EHR systems they are using. Most feel that the [EHRs] they used affected their workflow negatively and they have to recoup their cost and efficiency in other ways, all in trying to not affect patient care, which is very stressful." In a 2012 interview with *EMR & HIPAA*, Chen said he believes government incentives to doctors for "lackluster products" will "lead to a dissolution of the profession (especially those in primary care) and throwing out the talent that is out there who really want to make a difference in healthcare." Chen sees it happening already.[51]

EHRs were not developed for physicians. A 2016 report from the Texas Health and Human Services Commission states, "Currently, EHR design is more in alignment with billing and accounting processes than care coordination."[52] EHRs originated from billing systems—and in response to the patient-safety movement, vendors tacked on documentation modules and order entry for physicians.[53] To be an integral part of patient care, it would have had to be designed that way "from the ground up."[54] It wasn't. And now, the deck is stacked against patient-centered innovations because EHR certification is expensive and only applies to the specific version that is being tested. Software updates of EHR systems large or small must be recertified at the full cost of initial certification, a huge expense for adding new innovative features.[55]

Furthermore, the computerization of medical records raises a host of medical, ethical, and legal questions for physicians regarding the definition of legal record, authorization, validation, information access, data governance, the enterprise master patient index (EMPI) error rate, database administration, patient name similarities, and patient name changes.[56] These legal and ethical issues, along with the general frustrations associated with EHRs may lead to early retirements and career changes.

EHR Increases Physician Burnout

"Let's not dance around it—we all know how much the electronic health record has contributed to the physician burnout epidemic," says Bridget Duffy, MD, chief medical officer at Vocera, a clinical communications company. "Physicians who once were absorbed in speaking with and examining their patients found themselves spending more time clicking through screens and pecking away at a keyboard."[57]

Burnout is on the rise, increasing from 40 percent in 2013 to 51 percent in 2017, reports Indu Subaiya, co-founder of Healthcare 2.0.[58] "Burnout among physicians is higher than ever, and most of it has nothing to do with patient care . . . It is the outside forces that try to dictate how medicine should be practiced that wear us down," writes Linda Girgis, MD. "Has the joy of medicine been lost?" she asks. "No, it has been drowned out by the sea of systematization."[59]

Patients need doctors, but more than half of America's physicians are affected by burnout, according to a study conducted by the Mayo Clinic, which stressed that "interventions must address the organizational drivers of burnout in the practice environment, such as inefficiencies, the administrative burden, and inflexibility." The lead author of the study, Tait D. Shanafelt, MD, told Medscape: "American medicine is at a tipping point. . . . If a research study identified a system-based problem that potentially decreased patient safety for 50% of medical encounters, we would swiftly move to address the problem. That is precisely the circumstance we are in, and we need an appropriate system-level response."[60]

Many physicians felt moved to respond to the Medscape article. The following are a few of the more than two hundred comments posted by readers of the piece, many of which point to the government-mandated EHR as a major problem:

> The problem is emr.
>
> —Dr. Richard Eikrem

> A clunky EMR that is geared toward insurance reimbursement justifications rather than CARING for the patient. We are having to become more and more like bureaucrats and technicians and less and less like human beings and clinicians.
>
> —Dr. Raneth Heng

> More and more and more doctors are spending (wasting) more and more time learning (and constantly relearning) ever changing EMR. . . . If we put doctors back to treating patients instead of wasting

so much time creating work with no real benefit then the doctor shortage would be dramatically reduced and the burnout would drop significantly.

—Micah Price

I can barely find time to comment on this article. I am literally going back to my computer and EMR.

—Dr. Michael Gutierrez

We are not free to practice medicine anymore. Hospital/practice administrators are dictating what we should do, even when it is not good for our patients.

—Dr. David M.

Medicine is not an art any more.
Now is like working in car wash or factory line.

—Dr. Ana M. Deju Quevedo

The "elephant in the room" is always overlooked. . . . This dysfunctional tool is EHRs. Now we must do our job with less time. Our coder's job, and our biller's job is now dumped on a provider. Collecting data really does not improve care.

—Dr. Jay Hammett

The EMR, use of PA/NP's and other ancillary healthcare providers, convoluted plans for compensation, enforced use of "pathways and protocols—cookbook medicine," are but one of many ways our government is now trying to control the "monster" it created.

—Dr. Robert Durr

It's time to wake up, throw off this smothering blanket of rules regulations, paperwork and EHRs that do not contribute anything to patient care and that make us miserable. It's time to take the profession back and away from the meddlesome bureaucrats who are ruining American Medicine.

—Dr. Mark Fowler

"[P]ay for performance" translates into "it's all about the record" ... this coupled with moronic EMRs ... means many are punching buttons all day on our computers ... with many of us doing all we can to make the patient look as sick as possible on paper.

—Dr. John Lane

Physicians are now productivity "whipping boys" ... It will not be much longer before new students do the math and decide becoming a doctor is not worth the time, money, or sacrifice.... When are doctors going to start realizing this and start saying "NO."

—Dr. Michael Horoda

The introduction of electronic medical records was one of my many reasons [for retiring].... I do miss seeing patients but very glad to say adios to the regs and EHR.

—Dr. Rahma Mustapha[61]

Nurses No Happier than Physicians

A survey published in October 2014 found that only 26 percent of nearly fourteen thousand nurses from forty states agreed that the EHR systems at their institutions improve the quality of patient information.[62] Fully 92 percent were dissatisfied with inpatient EHRs, 90 percent said the EHR has negatively impacted their communication with patients, with nearly 70 percent thinking their hospital IT departments are "incompetent" and 67 percent having been taught "workarounds" to allow other clinicians to see important information on patients.[63]

A group of Ohio nurses wrote to their hospital administration saying the planned rollout of EHRs "would fundamentally alter the practice of nursing."[64] In the rush to implement the 2009 law mandating EHRs nationwide, little thought was given to using them for the actual care of patients, according to 97 percent of nursing administrators at for-profit hospitals.[65]

In August 2014 National Nurses United, a labor union, called on CMS to suspend the Meaningful Use program "unless and until we have unbiased, robust research showing that [electronic health records] can and do, in fact, improve patient health and save lives."[66] But as reported elsewhere in this book, the federal government acknowledges that it has no evidence that EHRs save lives.[67]

In an online survey about nurse workflow, less than half the 626 nurses responding (43 percent) thought the EHRs eliminated duplication of work, with only 26 percent of floor nurses feeling that way. Fully 38 percent said the EHR reduces the time they spend with patients. Many of the nurses felt EHRs improve safety (73 percent), but 15 percent would be happy to go back to paper records and another 14 percent were unsure. Only 55 percent said EHRs simplify their work. But only 46.2 percent of the nurses in this survey disclosed their role as "ambulatory nurse." The study says these nurses work "in a variety of capacities, including directly with patients in hospitals and clinics, as nursing managers and directors and in nursing informatics."[68] Many of these nurses' jobs may involve statistics rather than patient care. Thus, it would be even more illuminating to see the answers of only those nurses involved in direct patient care.

One registered nurse who works on a cardiac care unit said that she spends 80 percent of her time on EHRs and only 20 percent with patients. She called this "treating the chart" and said she all too often finds herself backing out of the room when a patient still wants to talk because "the chart waits."[69]

EHRs Interfere in Patient Care

Obstructions and Obstacles

EHRs do not simplify the practice of medicine. They change it. Health information technology literally changes the way information is recorded, viewed, and considered during diagnosis and treatment. As David Do, MD, writes,

> We all know EMRs are painful to use. These systems are reminiscent of software from the 90s, with inconsistent menus, obscure placement of data, and overwhelming numbers of buttons. It's not uncommon to traverse ten menus to order a routine laboratory test, or to miss a critical note or lab value hidden in an obscure screen.
>
> This is frequently compounded by so-called decision support, frequent pop-ups that are more likely to be irrelevant than genuinely useful. If the 16 hours of training required just to start using EPIC are any indication, these EMRs are not built around their users' needs.[70]

Pre-EHR, the traditional diagnostic process would typically include "looking at six pieces of paper," says Scott A. Monteith, MD, a psychiatrist and health IT consultant, something he says cannot be done on today's computer monitors or tablets. "It really affects how we think," he adds about using the EHR.[71]

It also changes how physicians practice. Howard Green, MD, wrote a terrific "buyer beware" article on LinkedIn about EHRs, essentially calling them a "bill of goods" without using those words. James

Richard responded in the comment section about how the office's EHR obstructed care processes and sought to control medical decisions:

> Using the Medicare Physical template, the program demanded an answer for the question, "Are there guns in the house?" The encounter could not be closed until the answer was given. . . . On the College Physical template, if the patient was female, the program automatically opened the prescription window with a selection of birth control pills, all name-brand of course. The window could not be closed until a selection was made and printed, or if declined, a free-text explanation for not prescribing contraceptives had to be made.[72]

Physicians who must provide explanations for going against the computer's treatment protocols are no longer in charge. Now outsiders, including the hospitals and health care systems that purchase the EHR systems and embed treatment algorithms have the upper hand. The freedom of a pen and paper is gone. The privacy of the paper chart or the "off the grid" EMR is gone. As Mr. Richard writes,

> Our old EMR was absolutely private. No one could reach in from the outside to get the information. You would have to break and enter my office to access the program. The medical records in the new EMR are accessible to anyone in the world with a computer and internet connection.[73]

According to Scot Silverstein, MD, who specializes in medical records forensics consulting for litigation, EHR problems include "clinically important, related data elements scattered far and wide making physicians and nurses go on 'wild goose chases' or 'click-o-rrhea' (a term coined by an MD HIT user who wishes to remain anonymous) to relate them; diagnosis lists that place rare diagnoses near the top and common ones a hundred items below; boxes that hide part of diagnostic terms leading to incorrect selections."[74]

As a sign of the uncomfortable reality, the website Physicians Practice advertised a January 6, 2016, "Breaking Up With Your EHR" webinar this way: "If you're part of the vast majority of providers, you initially purchased an EHR to earn stimulus monies, but aren't happy with the workflow, functionality, or vendor services. It's time you stopped being held prisoner by an unsatisfactory EHR."[75]

A 1986 guidance document for Air Force software design noted, "To be sure, users can sometimes compensate for poor design with extra effort. Probably no single user interface design flaw, in itself, will cause system failure. But there is a limit to how well users can adapt to a poorly designed interface. As one deficiency is added to another, the cumulative negative effects may eventually result in system failure, poor performance, and/or user complaints."[76]

The same is true for medical care and the EHR.

Health Care's "Potemkin Village"

Gerard J. Gianoli, MD, a specialist in neuro-otology and skull base surgery and a clinical associate professor at Tulane University School of Medicine, says the EHR is "the Potemkin Village of Healthcare, disguising the declining quality of American medicine."[77] He reminds readers that the term "Potemkin Village" comes from Russian history.

Legend has it, he writes, that in 1787 Grigory Potemkin wooed Catherine the Great by building fake pasteboard façades of pretty settlements set up at a distance along the Dnieper River to make her believe Crimea was prosperous. Every night, the settlements would be moved downriver to her next morning stop, where fancifully clad serfs were required to move about as a show of wealth and stability.[78] Thus, Gianoli writes, "Potemkin Village" is defined as "a pretentiously showy or imposing façade intended to mask or divert attention from an embarrassing or shabby fact or condition."[79]

Gianoli says the traditional approach of medicine, which includes an extensive history and physical examination (H&P), requires at least half an hour with the patient. However, most appointments today last only fifteen minutes or less, with seven minutes consumed by EHR documentation. Although the H&P sections of the record still exist, he writes, "most of the history and physical is not done by the doctor but by the auto-populate method. The doctor presses one key, and it fills out the entire form saying that everything is normal, except what he overrides as abnormal."[80]

When he began medical school, Gianoli visited his pediatrician, Dr. Johnson, who was still his primary care physician. For twenty years of visits, his doctor had only four pages of notes, unlike today where each visit is four to five pages long. "Dr. Johnson's notes were sparse, but he gave excellent care. His patients paid him for care. Now government and third parties pay for the appearance of health care, a virtual reality of digitized make-believe," says Gianoli. He notes, "The damage to quality in medical care has been institutionalized. Instead of a patient-physician relationship, we have the Potemkin Village façade of the high-tech EMR."[81]

Dumbing Down Doctors

The EHR is more than a record. It's a machine. When asked about his autonomy in making medical decisions, one physician at a major health care system said, "What autonomy? If it's not in the computer, I can't do it."[82] EHRs are typically embedded with standardized treatment protocols, or templates for medical care.[83] Medical schools are teaching students to follow these protocols, but BizMed founder Margalit Gur-Arie warns:

> What type of doctors are we producing when we teach medicine by template, supported by clinical decision aids based on the same template, and assessed by quality measures calculated from template data? Medicine does not become precise just because we choose to discard all imprecise factors that we are not capable of fitting into a template. Standardization of processes and quality does not occur just because we choose to avert our eyes from the thick edges where mayhem is the norm. Dumbing physicians down is not the optimal strategy for bringing computer intelligence closer to human capabilities. EHRs should not be allowed to become

> the means to stifling growth of human expertise, the barriers to natural interactions between people, or the levers pushed and pulled at will by greed and corruption.[84]

However, the following statement from *Trend Watch*, an American Hospital Association (AHA) publication, seems to support a system of consensus and computerization that prompts physicians and other clinicians to standardize care:

> Workflow changes entail both procedural and substantive re-examinations. For example, before a hospital can roll out a clinical decision support tool, clinicians should review current practice and the medical literature and come to agreement about the "standard care" for each type of case so that appropriate prompts may be programmed into the system.[85]

These changes in workflow may force physicians to change the way they practice medicine and increase the number of administrative and other tasks already overburdened physicians must complete. As the *Trend Watch* article states, "Electronic workflows require providers to think differently about processes in which they engage every day. . . . they may require a rearrangement of current processes. For example, one hospital's medication order process relied on pharmacists to check manually for drug interactions or allergies. . . . After redesign, this function was incorporated into the order-entry process and completed by the physician."[86]

These standardized care processes and computerized physician order entry (CPOE) systems may impede necessary and timely care. *Trend Watch* reported that one hospital system "generated 2,000 unique workflows as part of its EHR system implementation," which began in 2001. But are there computerized workflows that meet the rapid-fire treatment requirements of every situation encountered in the care of a patient? No. The AHA publication warns, "a patient requiring emergency care may need medication administered before any interaction with a CPOE system is possible." [87] In other words, to save a patient's life, there may be no time to process a physician's order through the computer or wait for a computerized system to release the medication. Care for the patient must be immediate and available.

Automated Care by EHR

Flexibility and automation are opposites. One offers standardized options. The other offers customized choices. As physicians know, there are no "standard patients." Each is unique—from physiology to personality to genetic code. Yet the practice of medicine, a very high-touch, personalized profession is being forced into automation, which has been described as "the use of control systems and information technologies to reduce the need for human work in the production of goods and services. The introduction of the assembly line at Ford Motor Company in 1913 is often cited as one of the first forms of automation."[88]

Is that what you want at the doctor's office?

Vincent Desiderio, a Washington orthopedic surgeon who hasn't switched to an EHR, told the *Washington Post*, "Computers are designed to say 'yes' or 'no' . . . And a fair share of what doctors deal with is 'maybe.'" The *Post* article on EHRs also reported this comment from an internist in Rockville, Maryland: "We have 10,000 diagnoses and thousands of medicines. It's not like automating that would make it easier."[89]

The Affordable Care Act's transition to payment strategies that tie hospital and physician reimbursement to keeping a "population" of patients healthy, rather than providing care to individual patients when they're sick, is advancing automated tracking, automated data collection, and standardization of care processes in the health care sector. James Dias, founder of Wellbe, an automation-focused company, writes in HIT Consultant about the driving force of automation, "Once the industry transitions to population health, automation goes from a 'nice to have' to a 'must have.' There are not enough care providers to continuously monitor and check in with large patient populations for this new model of care." Dias gives six examples of automation, including: "When patients follow a standardized care path supported by automation, it is more likely they will stay on track towards predicted outcomes. Additionally, automation can help detect when a patient has deviated from the recommended care plan so the care team can intervene."[90]

UpToDate is an online clinical decision-support system.[91] With the click of a button in the EHR system, it provides doctors with information about dosing and diagnosis at the point of care. Discussing UpToDate in 2012, Michael Lee, MD, the director of clinical informatics at Atrius, told *HealthLeaders Media,* "Wouldn't it be great if the order tools would change automatically so nobody would have to read anything? That would be really progressive, but the technology's really not there yet. . . . If they did it, there is an opportunity to save money by providing better care."[92] This brings up several questions. Can computers be trusted to make the right treatment decisions? Would it be better if doctors no longer had to read information about dosing, diagnosis, and treatment? Is automation in health care a good idea?

Ray Costantini, the founder of Bright.md, which "automates up to 60 percent of a primary care visit volume," says health care is the only industry in the world that hasn't embraced automation. However, noting the "new ubiquity" of EHRs nationwide, he says, "EHRs are already beginning to evolve into the 'operating systems' of the healthcare industry."[93]

You may or may not be comfortable with the thought of health care automation. And your response may depend on whether you have a chronic disease, require specialized treatment, dislike being under surveillance, or prefer a personal relationship with your doctor. One example of automation cited by Costantini: "Kaiser Permanente's Panel Support Tool . . . is an example of chronic disease automation. It automatically analyzes whole panels of patients, identifying gaps in care while keeping providers aware of evolving best practices and national guidelines." He goes on to assert, "Now it's time to build plug-in applications that expand EHR functionality and value. The same way that SalesForce helps automate CRM [customer relationship management] functions on a Mac or Windows computer, tools like SweetSpot Diabetes, WellBe, PST, and Bright.md help to automate evaluation, diagnosis, treatment, and documentation for providers on various EMR systems."[94]

How will patients, who are unique individuals that cannot be standardized, perceive the emergence of automation in their medical care? Will customized care remain a choice?

Disrupting the Patient-Doctor Relationship

At their core, EHRs change the patient-doctor interaction. A study of one hundred doctor-patient visits found the "clinicians who used electronic health records spent 31% of the visit gazing at the screen, while physicians who used paper charts gazed at those records for 9% of the visit. In addition, patients gazed significantly more at health charts that were on the screen—whether or not they could see the screen or understand the contents—than those whose care was supported by paper charts."[95]

When in front of the EHR, a study found male physicians rarely look up, whereas female physicians make eye contact about every thirty seconds, according to research reported in December 2015. Researchers also found that some physicians spend more than 80 percent of their visits interacting with the patients and other physicians spend more than 80 percent of their visits interacting with computers.[96]

Patients prefer doctors who look at them, not the computer. Researchers found that "around 83 percent of patients whose doctors barely bothered with the computer rated the clinician's care as excellent." Meanwhile, "the doctors of 48 percent of patients who used the computer for longer periods of time were given a poor rating."[97] They spent less time building rapport with patients through conversation and eye contact.

In 2016, a study found that physicians spend 27 percent of their total time on direct clinical face time with patients and 49.2 percent of their time on EHR and deskwork, plus additional time each night, mostly on EHR tasks. The researchers concluded, "For every hour physicians provide direct clinical face time to patients, nearly two additional hours [are] spent on EHR and desk work within the clinic day. Outside office hours, physicians spend another one to two hours of personal time each night doing additional computer and other clerical work."[98]

In 2014 and 2015, a study tracked forty-one medical interns and found them spending "an average of seven hours a day" on EHRs, which only decreased to five hours a day after they became accustomed to the systems. This amounted to forty-one minutes per electronic patient record encounter when they first started to use the system, and thirty minutes per encounter six months later.[99] Medical residents spend more than 30 percent of their time using EHR systems—about 4.2 hours per day—causing researchers in a study conducted in 2013 and 2014 to observe: "With more patient care being facilitated through computers today, there is increasing concern that little time remains for direct patient contact and education."[100]

Patient care cannot be reduced to mechanics and computerized algorithms. One psychiatrist told *Psychiatric News*, "in mental health care, providers need to pay close attention to body language and other nonverbal cues of patients. . . ." This is true for all clinicians. Enid Montague, PhD, an assistant professor in internal medicine and geriatrics and lead author of the study, said, "It's likely that the [physician's] ability to listen, problem-solve, and think creatively is not optimal when physicians' eyes are glued to the screen."[101]

David Cossman, MD, observed, "For those forced to use it, it is a time-consuming distraction that eats into the art of practicing medicine and takes us away from our patients." He noted with irony that EHRs are also capable of informing clinicians that the spiritual needs of a patient dead for more than four hours have been met, the corpse has a 0 out of 10 pain score, and there is "no need for restraints" after it has been zipped up in a body bag, demonstrating "an inherent capacity of the EMR to make mistakes no human could ever make, even on a bad day."[102]

Farzad Mostashari, MD, former national coordinator of health IT, told *Politico* in 2016 that the compliance culture created by the EHR Meaningful Use mandate and its reporting requirements got in the way of his agency's ambitions. EHR companies did the minimum to pass lab testing and practitioners focused on reporting requirements for full reimbursement. He imagines doctors and hospitals saying, "I need to check the stupid box, to get a stupid check," which he believes "kills the spirit."[103]

In 2012, an internist told *The Week*, "The EHR is not the savior of the medical system. In fact, it is effectively destroying the relational aspect of the art of medicine. Instead of talking with a patient and hearing her 'story,' we are being relegated to looking at a computer screen and pointing/clicking during the visit."[104] One former health IT executive said the following about EHRs: "The little it can do comes at great inconvenience to physicians, when compared to methodologies it aims to replace."[105]

To counteract patient dissatisfaction with the EHR-based interaction, a new process called "POISED" has been proposed by Richard M. Frankel, PhD, professor of medicine at Indiana University School of Medicine and core investigator at the VA's Health Services Research & Development (HSR&D) Center for Health Information and Communication:[106]

- **Prepare:** Review electronic medical record before seeing patient
- **Orient:** Explain how computer will be used during the appointment
- **Information gathering:** Don't put off data entry while the patient is talking
- **Share:** Turn the computer screen so patients can see what has been typed
- **Educate:** Show a graphic representation on the computer screen of information over time
- **Debrief:** Assess the degree to which recommendations are understood by the patient and correct as necessary[107]

"Medicine is fundamentally a human enterprise that is still practiced one conversation at a time," says Frankel. "Our challenge is to find the best ways to incorporate computers [as care process partners] in the examination room without losing the heart and soul of medicine, the physician-patient relationship."[108]

Despite Frankel's good intentions, the POISED process still takes time away from the patient-doctor interaction. Furthermore, it forces patients to interact with the computer, changing their focus during the interaction and limiting the doctor's healing touch, the doctor's eye contact, and other expressions of care and concern.

Physician concern isn't going away. After asking 3,200 physicians about the disadvantages of their practice's EHR system, *Medical Economics* shared the top three answers in its 2017 EHR Report Card: spending too much time entering data not directly related to patient care/outcomes (76 percent), disrupting practice workflow (57 percent), and not allowing eye contact with patients during examinations (56 percent).[109]

Intrusion of the Scribes

Today, many examination rooms have an uninvited and often unwelcome guest. To handle expanded data-entry duties related to the EHR mandate, restore eye contact and physical touch, and decrease the EHR's drag on physician productivity, clinics and emergency rooms are increasingly hiring team members they call *scribes*. Douglas Perednia, MD, writes, "As soon as EMRs are deployed, physician productivity typically goes down by about 50%. It rarely gets back to where it was prior to installation."[110]

Medical scribes have been called a "possible solution to the imposition of EMRs whose benefit to the patient and practice are frequently unclear or negative to begin with," writes Joel Sherman, MD.[111] In an article titled "A Busy Doctor's Right Hand, Ever Ready to Type," the *New York Times* describes a scribe as an individual who walks into the room with the doctor and quietly taps the entire encounter into a computer. Doctors with scribes are relieved to be focused on patients. "With a scribe, I can think medically instead of clerically," Marian Bednar, an emergency room physician, told the *Times*.[112]

But patient privacy and confidentiality take a hit. A third person has been inserted into the confidential patient-doctor relationship without patient consent, and some physicians are concerned.[113] To what extent are patients willing to speak frankly with an uninvited listener typing every word into a computer? Will it make a difference if the patient is visiting an ophthalmologist versus a gynecologist? One study, according to the *Times*, found that roughly 10 percent of patients are uncomfortable having the scribe present.[114] But how many patients are willing to ask the doctor to send the scribe away?

What if the scribe is out of sight? At least one clinic has experimented with keeping scribe bodies *outside* the room and scribe ears *inside* the room: "Physicians using the system have one computer in the exam room with the patient and another computer in a room set aside for the scribe, who listens in via a microphone in the exam room and documents the encounter."[115]

How about the "virtual scribe"? Using IKS Health's virtual scribe technology, microphones are installed in the exam room to record the patient and physician discussion. The recording is sent to physicians in India, who listen to it and produce a note that is encrypted by IKS and transmitted into the EHR. The physician reviews the note the next day. The patients are asked to consent to the recording and can request the microphone be turned off at any time.[116] This brings up three concerns. First, patients, who may worry about upsetting their doctor, may feel pressure to consent to the intrusion. Second, where is the on and off switch located? Can the patient see it? Third, how comfortable will patients be just knowing there's a recording device in the exam room, even if they've been told it's not on? Bottom line, the integrity of the exam room has been breached by a listening device.

The next "scribe" could be Amazon's Alexa. Before it begins "assisting physicians in taking notes," it must be HIPAA-compliant, reports *National Law Review*. But unlike the scribe that enters and leaves the exam room with the physician, the publication cautions, "Alexa is listening at all times."[117]

Medical ethicist Art Caplan opposes the intrusion, writing that scribes also decrease efficiency and expand opportunities for data-entry errors, which the *New York Times* notes could lead to claims for services the physician never performed.[118] In short, scribes make it too easy to commit fraud.[119] Caplan writes, "A third-party is a Band-Aid on a serious problem. . . . We do not have enough time in medicine to pay attention and listen carefully when we are face-to-face with our patients. I believe we ought to fix that, rather than introducing another person, along with a new machine, into the doctor-patient relationship."[120]

According to the *Times*, in 2014, nearly ten thousand scribes were working in hospitals and clinics nationwide, making between $8 and $16 per hour. Adding to the cost of every patient visit, clinics and hospitals pay scribe companies $20 to $25 an hour per scribe. One study suggests physicians using scribes save an average of three minutes per visit.[121] Dr. Perednia, writing at the blog *KevinMD*, says that while employing scribes is a way to "get around" the mess of reduced productivity, the scribes will "suck up almost 10%" of the doctor's gross income.[122] More than twenty-two companies supply scribes in forty-four states—the largest company is ScribeAmerica—and some predict there will be one hundred thousand scribes by 2020.[123]

Who are these scribes? In a field strewn with credentialed professionals, Dr. Sherman noted in 2014, "There is no accepted definition of what scribes do or what their background or training should be. There is no mechanism for licensure of them in any state. They are poorly defined medical assistants. The field is in its infancy and its ultimate role in our health care system is unclear."[124] ScribeAmerica training includes a "2-week orientation" a supervisory period under a "highly experienced" medical scribe and "periodic reassessment of the scribe's effectiveness," according to a CHRISTUS Health presentation at the 2016 HIMSS conference.[125]

Interestingly, the 21st Century Cures Act that became law in December 2016 "permits physicians to delegate, to the extent consistent with state law, applicable EHR documentation requirements to a person performing a scribe function, provided the physician reviews and signs the documentation," reports Ropes & Gray, a global law firm.[126] Todd Guenzburger, MD, a hospitalist and medical director of information services at the Legacy Health System in Portland, Oregon, didn't mince words about his frustrations with the current productivity-based model of care that has led to scribes: it destroys "the primary-care relationship when everything is about productivity. . . .

People want that relationship . . . [but] there is no place for the doc and the patient to have a relationship."[127]

Hospitals Limit Treatment Options

There's also little place for physician control. For physicians who work in settings with EHRs purchased by hospitals or health care systems, the administration may limit what treatment options are included in the EHR. For example, some hospitals are limiting what doctors can order by "changing computer systems to make it harder to avoid guideline recommendations," reports the *Wall Street Journal*.[128] Thus, "recommendations" become treatment restrictions.

Treatment is ordered through the EHR using computerized physician order entry (CPOE). Hospitals can populate EHRs with drop-down menus that conform to a predetermined list of treatments and medications. For example, a hospital-generated drug formulary with limited medication options.[129] EHRs also have clinical decision support (CDS) systems embedded to direct medical decision-making. CDS includes: "computerized alerts and reminders to care provider and patients; clinical guidelines; condition-specific order sets; focused patient data reports and summaries; documentation templates; diagnostic support, and contextually relevant reference information, among other tools."[130] These controls over physician decision-making are invisible to patients but not to physicians. As discussed earlier, one doctor said, "If it's not on the computer, I can't do it."

Although supporters would say CDS improves clinical decision-making by matching characteristics of individual patients to a computerized knowledge base and generating software algorithms with patient-specific recommendations, the computer software remains standardized not customized.[131] Doctors can go around the recommendations and the drop-down menus, but it can be a hassle. (More on CDS below.)

Patients do not support such limits on the autonomy of physicians. In one study, dialysis patients were asked to consider limits on physician autonomy. Patients were asked to imagine two hypothetical scenarios. One was a "research scenario" in which dialysis was limited to 4.5 hours or a duration at the physician's discretion. The other was a "clinical care scenario" in which dialysis was determined by a treatment protocol. Lisa Rosenbaum, MD, reports, "Participants were more willing in the research than the practice setting to give up their own decision-making autonomy, including written informed consent. They recognized the value of research and didn't perceive the hypothetical study as posing higher risk than ordinary care. But they expressed deep reservations about compromising physicians' autonomy to individualize treatment absent compelling reasons for doing so."[132]

Treating to the Test

The ACA changed the way hospitals are paid, and it's all based on data.[133] Since late 2012, the Medicare administration has been issuing bonuses or penalties to nearly three thousand hospitals "based on how patients rated their experiences and how faithfully hospitals followed a dozen basic standards of care."[134] This ACA Hospital Value-Based Purchasing program works through a withhold system.[135]

Kaiser Health News (KHN) explained the withholding of payments in 2013 and the expected penalties and bonuses for fiscal year 2014: "Medicare reduced payment rates to all hospitals by 1.25 percent. It set the money aside in a $1.1 billion pot for incentives. While every hospital is getting something back, more than half are not recouping the 1.25 [percent] payment they initially forfeited, making them net losers. The payment adjustments are applied to each Medicare patient stay over the federal fiscal year that started Oct. 1 [2013] and runs through September 2014."[136] For fiscal year 2015 Medicare allotted approximately $1.4 billion in "value-based" incentives,[137] and "hospitals could gain or lose up to 1.5 percent of payments. That win or loss will rise to 2 percent by the fall of 2016," reports KHN.[138]

The effect is real. In 2014, 1,451 hospitals were paid less for each Medicare patient treated as a result of their "quality metrics" score created by using performance data generated from July 2011 through March 2012. In 2013, 45 percent of their score was based on how frequently the hospital followed basic clinical standards of care.[139] Medicare officials decide the standards.

Pity the hospital where patients die. Mortality rates for Medicare patients who died while hospitalized or within a month of discharge—death rates—contribute to 25 percent of the hospital's score.[140] Death, a common occurrence in health care and an inevitable occurrence in life, particularly for the elderly, could now lead to lower reimbursements from Medicare.

Then there's the 30 percent of the score that's based on patient satisfaction, a less-than-credible measure with problems of its own, including subjectivity.[141] For example, if patients give hospitals a less-than-stellar score because their food wasn't delivered on time, the hospital may lose money.[142] But consider this, what patient will realize when a doctor fails to deliver personalized treatment to secure the 45 percent of the score based on following federal "basic clinical standards of care"? Patients should keep this in mind the next time they are asked to complete CMS's Hospital Consumer Assessment of Healthcare Providers and Systems (HCAHPS) survey, a set of thirty-two questions that has been sent to a random sample of hospital patients since 2008.[143]

Hospitals have responded to Medicare's demands by "treating to the test." KHN reports that hospital executives around the country "say they have put renewed focus on excellence in the areas that are judged." Dr. Leigh Hamby, chief medical officer at Piedmont Healthcare, a hospital system in Georgia, said, "The thing about the government, if they start paying attention to it, we have to scramble around to pay attention too."[144]

But what happens to the areas not judged by Medicare administrators? What happens when doctors and nurses focus their care and data-collection efforts on areas that affect their quality and performance scores? That doesn't appear to be on anyone's measurement list. On a final note, a 2014 study of the Hospital Value-Based Purchasing initiative found no improvement in hospital quality of care in the first nine months of the program.[145]

Losing the Human Touch

In an insightful article about EHRs called "HAL," retiring surgeon David Cossman warns, "What was our tool will become our master." HAL, which stands for *Heuristically programmed ALgorithmic computer,* was programmed to control the Discovery One spacecraft in the 1968 film, *2001: A Space Odyssey*.[146] But HAL began to malfunction. When the astronauts made plans to shut it down, HAL went dangerously rogue. Cossman cautions against moving health care notes from a physician's easy-to-understand personalized narrative about the patient to the "quack quack click-click language of 0s and 1s," which will lead to the loss of "all distinctive traces of ourselves." He also warns:

> Current EMRs threaten to remove the human imprimatur from medical care. That they eliminate the only rational, readable, coherent, contemporaneous, and sometimes even delightful human narrative of what actually happened and replace it with indecipherable gobbledygook when clarity is required is only part of the problem. That they force us to compromise our integrity and attest to all kinds of things is only part of the problem. That they are expensive, time-consuming and a productivity drain of unimaginable proportion is only part of the problem.
>
> The big problem is that HAL is once again stalking us with the sweet siren song of untold efficiencies; cost containment and protection from human fallibility if we only move over to the passenger seat and let it drive. Don't believe a word of it. Medicine cannot be practiced on autopilot. We will crash and burn without the human touch at the controls.[147]

That human touch is leaving the radiology department. Radiologist Jeffrey Hise, MD, warns how digitized X-rays have automated radiology to the detriment of both patients and doctors. Before the Picture Archiving and Computer System (PACS), referring physicians and radiologists would conference together on the interpretation of films, learning to be better diagnosticians in the process. "Thousands of consultations with my hospital colleagues over 15 years taught me the importance of the history and the physical findings associated with the present illness," Hise writes. "You learned the limits of your radiologic test. You learned how to modify your differential diagnosis given the change in the history or exam findings. The referring physicians learned what exam to order and the danger of an interpretation in a clinical vacuum."[148]

"And then came the PACS" and its unintended consequences, he writes. "The foundation on which radiology was built was destroyed. A discussion between two physicians centered around Bayes' theorem was reduced to a three-word choice from the drop-down menu in the electronic medical record. Days go by without seeing a referring physician in the reading room. The images and the report appear on a computer monitor near the patient's bed. The report is quickly perused, images given a cursory glance, and it's on to the next patient. This is fabulous for productivity. I have serious doubts about its effect on quality."[149]

Data Mining to Dictate Decisions

When the EHR mandate passed, researchers and other data miners were gleeful. They envisioned a health care utopia and a piece of the more than $30 billion to boot. Advocates thought EHRs could "enable researchers to determine the most effective procedures for an ailment. Such an approach would rely on unprecedented data-mining into medical records and the practices of doctors, a kind of surveillance that also would enable insurers to cut costs by controlling more precisely the care that patients receive," reported the *Washington Post*.[150]

"Finally, we're going to have access to millions and millions of patient records online,"[151] said Blackford Middleton, a physician, Harvard professor, and chairman of the Center for Information Technology Leadership, whose studies claimed information technology networks, including the use of EHRs, would save $77.8 billion each year "once fully implemented."[152]

The EHR mandate was foundational to changing the delivery of health care. It was intended to change "the terms of trade in health care," according to the *New York Times* in an interview with David Blumenthal, MD, former national health information technology coordinator in the Obama administration.[153] Per the *Times*:

> The government's intervention in [the] health information technology market, he said, is justified to correct a market failure. "The market doesn't reward performance," Dr. Blumenthal said.
>
> In the current fee-for-service system, doctors and hospitals are paid for doing more—more visits, more tests, more surgeries. Quality and cost are not typically measured and compensated, outside [of] some government pilot projects and a comparative handful of larger physician groups around the country.
>
> The electronic health record, in Dr. Blumenthal's view, is a tool—and yes, a stalking horse—for bringing measurement, data-based decision-making and accountability to the practice of medicine. The computerized patient record, then, is a step toward changing compensation of medicine and the economics of health care.[154]

But as a reminder of what Dr. Grams wrote in the *Journal of Medical Systems*, "The real goal of this EHR project is not to control costs or enhance patient care: it is data mining, the control of the physician population, and the ultimate rationing and control of patient services."[155]

EHRs were built for intrusion. Thus, the Agency for Healthcare Research and Quality writes about quality measures that clinics and hospitals must report to HHS to receive full payment for services rendered: "Measure specifications designed to enable *automatic extraction of clinical data* from an EHR are necessary to realize one of the most promising benefits of EHR-based quality measurement: reducing resources needed for data collection while retaining rich clinical information, including timing and logistical steps related to care."[156] (Emphasis added.)

MD or Artificial Intelligence?

What if computers are empowered to direct the care of patients? What if hospitals employ artificial intelligence to determine diagnoses and treatment? Artificial intelligence "generally refers to computers that exhibit humanlike behavior," explained Eric Schmidt, former executive chairman of Alphabet Inc., the parent company of Google, to the HIMSS 2018 audience. He added, "I think we're going to coexist with these things."[157] Mansur Hasib, a chief information officer and cybersecurity expert, writes at InformationWeek:

> EHRs also facilitate artificial intelligence. A patient's medical history often is full of reams of data; manually winnowing through that information is a daunting task. Today, teams of top doctors help develop artificial intelligence systems that can quickly determine if a proposed medicine, food, or medical procedure will likely cause the patient greater harm than good. This will reduce a large number of medical mistakes.
>
> There is no cause for concern. Decisions suggested by artificial intelligence systems developed by top-notch doctors likely are more accurate than decisions made solely by humans. . . . All doctors are not created equal. . . . Studies show that if you give the same data on a patient to a random group of 10 doctors and ask them if surgery is recommended, half will choose surgery while the other half will choose not to perform surgery.
>
> If artificial intelligence systems are built *using the medical minds of the doctors that choose the right answers*, these technological solutions sift through an incredible amount of data and provide more medically reliable recommendations. Of course, a human doctor still makes the ultimate decision. However, the doctor has the benefit of a large amount of data analysis and is much more likely to make a decision based on complete information, not incomplete data.[158] (Emphasis added.)

Who are these "top-notch doctors"? Would we agree with their answers? Excellent physicians often disagree about which treatment is best. Who decides which "medical minds" are the ones who "choose the right answer"?

The Human Diagnosis Project is an example of artificial intelligence in medicine. According to Axios, "A doctor listens to the patient describe his or her symptoms, inputs the details plus the doctor's own observations into the system, and then Human Dx filters and produces advice from specialists around the world."[159] But what kind of computer algorithm is used to "filter" this advice and who chose the algorithm? Cardiologist Ethan Weiss, MD, fears the project will be "spitting out garbage."[160]

There's another danger here. Although "human doctors" will still make the final decision, penalties and bonuses tied to physician performance, including compliance with standardized treatment protocols, as discussed below and elsewhere in this book, could encourage a physician to follow the computer's recommendations instead of doing what is best for the patient.

In good news for those who want a real doctor in the exam room, a study using the Human Diagnosis Project (Human Dx) web platform found that physicians are better at reaching a correct diagnosis than symptom-checker app programs that use algorithms. Given the same information about medical history and symptoms, physicians were right 72 percent of the time versus only 34 percent for the apps. Physicians were also better at ranking the correct diagnosis first when asked to give a list of possible diagnoses. "In a real-world setting, I could envision MD plus algorithm vs MD alone," wrote Andrew M. Fine, MD, who did not participate in the study, to Reuters Health.[161]

Jeff Axt, project manager and systems analyst in the IT department at the Hospital for Special Care in New Britain, Connecticut, says the "final decision must be in the hands of the clinician.... That's where most of the fear—in the literature and what I'm seeing in practice—is coming from. One of my clinical managers once said, 'I'm really good at diagnostics; don't tell me what to do.' And he's right, he really is good at diagnostics. We have to recognize that."[162] Axt looks at AI "as a consult." He says clinicians will say, "The computer is telling me this, but I'm going to evaluate it with my brain."[163]

That's wise. Citizens' Council for Health Freedom (CCHF) received the following from a patient: "I have SLIGHTLY abnormal blood cell readings, and the COMPUTER decided that I have leukemia. How did I find this out? It was on a pre-op workup before I had rotator cuff surgery. . . . The doc went over all items on that report with me, and removed the items that the Artificial Intelligence Algorithm ASSUMED about me."[164]

Pay for Compliance

In 2003 Congress enacted "pay for performance" for Medicare.[165] What qualifies as a performance worthy of payment?[166] Under Meaningful Use, practitioners must submit clinical quality measures (CQMs) from certified EHR technology (CEHRT).[167] There are hundreds of "quality measures," but the following short list includes items often used to measure a physician's performance—and determine partial or full payment for services rendered—that may not be on the top of the quality list for most Americans:

- Vaccination rates of patients[168]
- Compliance with various protocols (e.g., flu shots, asking about depression, offering preventive screenings)[169]
- Patient satisfaction scores (from clinic or hospital questionnaires)[170]
- Patient outcomes (e.g., smoking cessation, low cholesterol level, health status)[171]
- Reducing readmissions for certain types of patients[172]

In fact, these measures may have nothing to do with the quality of actual care given the patient, which is difficult to measure and quantify. But the effect of requiring doctors, hospitals, and nurses to complete a series of "quality" checkboxes in the EHR to verify compliance with federal measures has led to distracted practitioners, less time with patients, a focus on paperwork, and outside influence on medical decision-making. As noted earlier, it also costs about $40,000 per physician per year.[173]

The ACA added more teeth to pay for performance. Doctors and hospitals will be paid not only for government-defined "quality," but also for government-defined "value" (value-based purchasing). These methods do not pay doctors for their time, expertise, or services provided. Payments are data- and definition-driven, requiring clinics and hospitals to report certain data from the EHR to government officials and health plans, which will use quality and cost data to determine the value of services and the performance—compliance—of physicians.[174]

A speedy timeline for implementation is in the works. On January 26, 2015, in a press release titled, "Better, Smarter, Healthier," HHS announced,

> HHS has set a goal of tying 30 percent of traditional, or fee-for-service, Medicare payments to quality or value through alternative payment models, such as Accountable Care Organizations (ACOs) or bundled payment arrangements by the end of 2016, and tying 50 percent of payments to these models by the end of 2018. HHS also set a goal of tying 85 percent of all traditional Medicare payments to quality or value by 2016 and 90 percent by 2018 through programs such as the Hospital Value Based Purchasing and the Hospital Readmissions Reduction Programs. This is the first time in the history of the Medicare program that HHS has set explicit goals for alternative payment models and value-based payments.[175]

Former HHS Secretary Sylvia Mathews Burwell said this would create "accountability for measurable improvement," which is only possible through federal analysis of patient data.[176] Just ten months later, CMS released its updated "Quality Strategy," which incorporates the HHS plan to shift Medicare payments "from volume to value," as well as requirements from two other federal laws, the already-discussed MACRA and the Improving Medicare Post-Acute Care Transformation Act of 2014 (IMPACT).[177] The latter requires the submission of standardized data by long-term care hospitals, skilled nursing facilities, home health agencies, and inpatient rehabilitation facilities, including quality measures, resource use (costs), and other measures.[178] Kurt Hegmann, MD, director of the Rocky Mountain Center for Occupational and Environmental Health at the University of Utah, says, "The day where reimbursement is largely or totally value-driven based on insurer/business/CMS-based requirements is likely quite near. And being unprepared for these changes could be organizationally fatal. . . ."[179]

Patients should be concerned about the movement to value-based payment by third-party payers. A study released in November 2017 found that Medicare's value-based payment modifier shifts money "away from physicians who treated sicker, poorer patients to pay for bonuses that rewarded practices treating richer, healthier populations." As noted earlier, the modifier has been incorporated into MACRA/MIPS. Eric Roberts, an assistant professor of health policy and management and lead author of the study, thinks value-based programs are fundamentally flawed by the lack of data on "observable clinical and socioeconomic characteristics of patients." He says, "We don't think many of those limitations are corrected in the MIPS."[180]

For this reason alone, many independent doctors, including those in small and rural communities temporarily exempted from MACRA, may choose to retire, drop Medicare participation, join a larger group, or become employees of large health care systems.

Finally, paying doctors for performance doesn't work. A study published in 2018 in *The BMJ (British Medical Journal)* called the impact of US hospital pay for performance programs, including hospital value-based purchasing, "limited and disappointing"—and said the programs are unlikely to be successful in the future as currently implemented. In fact, the researchers noted: "No evidence that hospitals that have been operating under pay for performance programs for more than a decade had better process scores or lower mortality than other hospitals was found."[181] Lack of evidence has rarely stopped the government. Witness the EHR experiment.

Death, Injury, and Hazardous Conditions

Danger Was Known but Ignored

Two years before the mandate became law, the National Academy of Sciences issued a report concluding that software, including software used in medical care, should be considered "guilty until proven innocent," with the burden of proof on those who develop it "to convince the certifier or regulator that the software is dependable."[182] In 2010, a team of engineering and health experts wrote, "The deployment of HIT in high-pressure environments with critically ill patients poses significant risk."[183]

Five years later—six years after the mandate became law—the federal government acknowledged risks resulting from the EHR experiment. Despite its title, the February 2015 "Recent Evidence that Health IT Improves Patient Safety" report prepared for the ONC states:

> Information is emerging from a wide range of sources on adverse and unintended consequences of health IT. This includes data from case reports, claims databases, reports through patient safety organizations, electronic surveillance (event triggers) and adverse and sentinel event reports to The Joint Commission, and the Veterans Health Administration. Identifying the spectrum of problems and the specific types and characteristics of safety events related to health IT is a critical step in being able to identify and prioritize the health IT issues that need to be addressed.[184]

The primary identifying characteristic of a health IT-related "sentinel event" is "severe patient harm or death," reports The Joint Commission. Yet, "identifying the role of health IT in adverse events often requires special expertise."[185] It may not be readily apparent.

The Joint Commission's March 30, 2015 report titled, "Investigations of Health IT-Related Deaths, Serious Injuries or Unsafe Conditions," provides examples of 120 sentinel events that affected 125 patients at four institutions between January 1, 2010, and June 30, 2013.[186] Their list is recreated below. (Note that a sentinel event can impact more than one patient.) Importantly, "near misses" and hazardous situations that did not cause harm are *excluded* from the sentinel-event list:[187]

Health IT-Related Sentinel Event Types[188]

Event Type	% (n = 120)
Medication error	29% (35)
Wrong-site surgery	19% (23)
Delay in treatment	12% (14)
Suicide	8% (10)
Fall	6% (7)
Radiation overdose	6% (7)
Transfusion error	4% (5)
Unintended retention of a foreign body	4% (5)
Op/Post-op complication	3% (4)
Med equipment-related	3% (3)
Other unanticipated event	2% (2)
Perinatal death/injury	2% (2)
Transfer-related event	1% (1)
Maternal death	1% (1)
Ventilator death	1% (1)

As a result of these events, sixty-six of the 125 patients (53 percent) died, thirty-seven required an extended stay or unexpected additional care, fourteen experienced a permanent loss of function, one suffered psychological impact, and seven patients had other negative outcomes. The study identified 305 health IT-related contributing factors. Top among them were human-computer interface (33 percent), workflow and communication (24 percent), and clinical content (23 percent).[189]

Despite this evidence, the federal government, in April 2015, dismissed patient-safety concerns with soothing statements. For example, senior officials from the Office of the National Coordinator for Health Information Technology (ONC) wrote about its February report: "These studies mean that health IT has almost certainly led to far fewer people being harmed than would have been without widespread health IT adoption." This assertion has no basis in fact and "almost certainly" lacks a foundation to stand on. Yet they continued:

> Health IT is not and never will be a "silver bullet" that reduces unsafe conditions, errors, and adverse events. To improve safety and quality, health IT is an important part of delivery system reform and redesigned systems of care. Health IT, when well designed and implemented, is a tool that can help health information flow in ways that allow for improvements in patient health and safety. Whatever the drawbacks to health IT systems, the evidence suggests that health IT has raised the floor on safety.[190]

Where is the evidence for health IT "raising the floor on safety"? From the start, there have been problems. In a 2010 HHS "not intended for public use" internal memo to Jeff Shuren at the Food and Drug administration (FDA), the federal government admitted that there were serious problems with patient safety.[191] Consider the following list of errors in the memo and the screenshot of the memo's summary statement:

Table 4. H-IT Safety Issues-General Categories

Category	Description	Count	%
Errors of Commission (EOC)	Events such as accessing the wrong patient's record or overwriting one patient's information with another's	126	49
Errors of Omission or Transmission (EOT)	Events such as the loss or corruption of vital patient data	69	27
Errors in Data Analysis (EDA)	Includes medication dosing errors of several orders of magnitude	57	22
Incompatibility between Multi-Vendor Software Applications or Systems (ISMA)	Incompatibilities which can lead to any of the above	5	2

Memo: H-IT Safety Issues

In summary, the results of this data review suggest significant clinical implications and public safety issues surrounding Health Information Technology. The most commonly reported H-IT safety issues included wrong patient/wrong data, medication administration issues, clinical data loss/miscalculation, and unforeseen software design issues; all of which have varying impact on the patient's clinical care and outcome, which included 6 death and 43 injuries. The absence of mandatory reporting enforcement of H-IT safety issues limits the number of relevant MDRs and impedes a more comprehensive understanding of the actual problems and implications.

The dangers were clearly stated; six patients had died and forty-three more were injured—to what extent is unknown—and according to his testimony two days later, these numbers may have represented "only the tip of the iceberg."[192]

Nothing suggests health IT has improved patient safety. The Joint Commission reported, "The majority (66%) of health IT-related sentinel events involved EHRs or some component of the EHR."[193] In May 2015, the ECRI Institute, a federal patient-safety organization, which has been given responsibility for most federal health IT safety efforts as a result of the Trump administration's decision to reduce the size of the ONC,[194] wrote the following in a report called "Wrong-Record, Wrong-Data Errors with Health IT System":

> A recent medical malpractice claims analysis identified 147 cases, asserted over a five-year period, in which health IT systems were a contributing factor, representing $61 million in direct payments and legal expenses, or about $415,000 per case. Incorrect information in the electronic record resulted in the most claims, or about 20% of the cases.
>
> More than half (53%) of the medical professional liability companies participating in a survey about electronic health records (EHRs) said they have seen EHR-related claims. The survey of 43 companies was conducted in 2012 by PIAA, an association of medical professional liability insurers (PIAA).[195]

In March 2018, one of the largest studies on patient harm due to EHRs was released. Researchers studied 1.7 million patient safety events reported between 2013 and 2016 at 571 health care facilities in Pennsylvania and one large mid-Atlantic multi-hospital academic health care system. They found 1,956 events that specifically mentioned an EHR vendor or product, of which 557 suggested the EHR "contributed to possible patient harm," reported *American Journal of Managed Care* (*AJMC*). [196] However, this too is "just the tip of the iceberg in the grand scheme of things," said lead researcher Raj M. Ratwani, PhD, MA, and acting center director and scientific director at the National Center for Human Factors in Healthcare.[197] He gave three reasons why the numbers are probably higher than reported: the data is limited to one state plus an additional health system; the study only looked at reports that explicitly mentioned the EHR but many clinicians do not mention EHR vendors or products in safety reports; and patient safety events are known to be underreported compared to the number of actual events "by as much as a 5- or 10-fold difference," reported *AJMC*.[198]

So we know conclusively that EHRs harm patients. But do they save lives? That's not so clear. CMS, which imposes penalties on physicians and hospitals if they refuse to meaningfully use these computerized systems, admits in a March 2014 letter that it does "not have any information that supports or refutes claims that a broader adoption of EHRs can save lives."[199]

Critics of the system often point to the five-year deadline to meet the EHR Meaningful Use mandate, as well as the necessitated rapid purchase of EHR systems that could not be fully vetted before purchase. Bottom line: Congress mandated that physicians use a product that was not designed for patient care or patient safety—and patients continue to suffer the consequences.

Black-Box Treatment Algorithms

One way EHRs impose controls on the medical decision-making process is through clinical decision-support (CDS) systems,[200] which are required to qualify for Meaningful Use EHR subsidy payments. It's the fourth Core Objective in Stage 1.

According to the federal government, clinical decision support systems encompass a "variety of tools to enhance decision-making in the clinical workflow."[201] One study extols clinical decision support as foundational to EHR functionality: "A large part of the electronic health record's (EHR) promise to improve patient care rests upon CDS. Because of this, implementing CDS has been an increasingly substantial part of the Meaningful Use program."[202] But interestingly, "many clinical users do not know the term 'clinical decision support,'" according to a PowerPoint presentation given at HIMSS 2018.[203]

These "clinical decision support" tools, intended to direct and influence physician treatment decisions, are embedded in the EHR, and include:

- Computerized alerts and reminders to patients and clinicians
- Clinical (treatment) guidelines
- Condition-specific order sets
- Focused patient data reports and summaries
- Documentation templates
- Diagnostic support

- Contextually relevant reference information and other tools[204]

In its purest form, CDS would force physicians to leave their autonomy, critical thinking, and patient-centeredness behind. Doctors would simply input patient data and order from the EHR's algorithm-generated treatment options. But it's not that easy. Patients don't fit in tidy clinical boxes and treatment guidelines change. "As one expert panelist observed, 'Guidelines need to be current. They get old quickly,'" reports the New England Healthcare Institute in "Improving Physician Adherence to Clinical Practice Guidelines." [205]

Not surprisingly, 88 percent of physicians surveyed by the Institute said they'd be more likely to use guidelines that are relevant to the way they practice medicine, as opposed to guidelines focused on "cost-effectiveness." According to the report, "Having to justify treatment decisions on a continuing basis, particularly on grounds not strictly clinical in nature, causes many physicians to view guidelines as intrusive, limiting their treatment options, and/or disregarding their judgment or patient preferences."[206]

The federal government thinks otherwise. It commissioned two research teams to translate written clinical guidelines into computer-executable code, claiming, "CDS interventions can increase adherence to evidence-based medical knowledge and can reduce unnecessary variations in clinical practice." [207] However, the two CDS project teams discovered that written guidelines were often ambiguous or incomplete, "do not include the level of specificity necessary for translating them into computer-executable codes," and do not include evidence from recently published research. [208] They further noted that guidelines for individual clinical conditions posed a problem for the management of people with multiple conditions. This finding, they reported, "reinforces clinicians' belief that CDS is not useful and that its clinical advice may be incorrect."[209]

Yet, in a true show of bureaucracy at work, even when the evidence base for a treatment guideline was weak, one team "struggled to determine" expectations for clinician compliance. Expectations ranged from clinicians should *consider* the recommendations to clinicians should be *required* to follow them.[210]

The teams also found that clinicians are given a high level of autonomy, allowing resistance to CDS and other health IT efforts. And they noted, "Because the CDS intervention is embedded in the EMR system, its use is dependent on clinicians' use of the EMR."[211] In addition, if physicians were allowed to dictate notes later or type them manually as free text instead of using standardized templates, the information "cannot be used by the CDS application."[212] In short, use and enforcement of preset CDS treatment protocols is difficult if practitioners aren't constrained by the limited choices within the EHR. The CDS teams were funded at $2.5 million each for a two-year period with the option for the AHRQ to continue funding the project for three more years.[213]

CDS alert systems can also harm patients. Doctors receive alerts from the computer with suggested tests, screenings, and vaccinations. Alerts also warn about drug allergies or notify doctors about abnormal test results. However, not one chief medical information officer who responded to a survey on CDS was totally confident their existing processes and procedures were sufficient to find or prevent all CDS malfunctions before they reach patients and their caregivers.[214] The 2016 study of a major CDS system at Brigham and Women's Hospital found major problems related to alerts, and its findings led to several troubling observations, including:

- Malfunctions are widespread and clinically important, and the importance may be underappreciated.
- Malfunctions are widespread, occur much more frequently than has previously been described, and persist for long periods.
- Existing detection systems are inadequate to detect the malfunctions.[215]

Now imagine CDS being used to automate medical diagnoses and treatment decisions. In December 2017, the FDA released a draft guidance to delineate the types of clinical decision support software that would be under FDA regulation and those that would be free from federal oversight. FDA Commissioner Scott Gottlieb, MD said, "CDS has many uses, including helping providers, and ultimately patients, identify the most appropriate treatment plan for their disease or condition." He also cautioned, "information in clinical decision software, if not accurate, has the potential for significant patient harm."[216]

If implemented as the FDA proposes, CDS software programs that permit practitioners to independently review the basis for treatment recommendations (e.g., easily-understood data points, publicly available clinical practice guidelines, and published literature) would be free from oversight because these clinicians will rely primarily on their own judgement to make clinical decisions for individual patients. Software without such transparency would require review by the FDA. The guidance provides examples of CDS software that would continue under FDA purview, such as software that uses algorithms to process data and issue recommendations that the practitioner is intended to rely primarily on for making treatment decisions.[217]

The release caused a stir because of its implications for "machine learning," which Politico Morning eHealth described as a computer "'discovering' connections between data on its own. That can lead the computers to make rather sharp, unexpected predictions, which is both the attraction and the fear with the technology. On the pro side, this technique can lead to connections between pieces of data you wouldn't have expected to be connected, and thereby lead to more insight. On the con side, it can lead to bizarre, wrong connections that the viewer would have difficulty second-guessing."[218]

In comments to the FDA, CHIME wrote, "Presently, most CDS in EHRs requires direct clinical input whether from a physician or someone else and a human must say 'yes' to the CDS to trigger an action. However, as technology is rapidly evolving and machine learning evolves—we will see more decisions being made automatically by the computer without the opportunity for a clinician's review."[219] The CDS Coalition argues, as paraphrased by Politico Morning eHealth, that "even if you have a black box algorithm, it's not a huge concern if it's trying to make a good diagnosis for the common cold"[220]—as compared perhaps to diagnosing cancer.

The American Medical Informatics Association (AMIA) clarifies the difficulty of relying on algorithms for treatment decisions: "Functionalities based on trained neural networks, multivariate regressions, or fuzzy logic will be difficult, if not impossible, for clinicians or patients to readily inspect or evaluate the clinical reasoning behind the recommendations. In these cases, the calculations are hidden within a 'black box' that is trained on perhaps millions of data points, and no amount of inspection time will enable a clinician to review and/or evaluate as described in the guidance."[221]

That's not the only problem. Alphabet Inc. Technical Advisor Eric Schmidt issued this cautionary statement about AI and machine learning to the HIMSS 2018 audience: "The decision maker should not be the computer, because it makes mistakes. And one of the problems we have with respect to AI right now is that not only do they make a small percentage, but nevertheless, a small percentage of errors, but we as an industry cannot explain the errors."[222] The mistakes can affect large numbers of people. For example, between 2009 and the start of 2018, a computer algorithm failure in England affected 450,000 women. As a result of the error, they were not invited to their final routine screening for breast cancer, potentially resulting in early deaths for 135 to 270 women between the ages of 68 and 71, reported Health Secretary Jeremy Hunt.[223]

Other problems also exist. Critics of IBM Watson, a prime example of AI at work, say its cancer treatment regimens are biased because it was trained entirely at Memorial Sloan Kettering Cancer Center in New York, which has a wealthier patient base.[224] And calling attention to certain ethical challenges, three Stanford University doctors write in the *New England Journal of Medicine*: "In the US healthcare system, there is perpetual tension between the goals of improving health and generating profit. . . . Private-sector designers who create machine-learning systems for clinical use could be subject to similar temptations."[225] They could also be subject to the preferences of third-party payers whose primary goal may be reduced costs rather than care tailored to the patient.

Now is a good time to remember those government-funded CDS project team members that wanted to force doctors to follow the guidelines. Should doctors be required to treat patients according to a computer-executable treatment guideline that's been spun out of a black-box algorithm?

One final note: This federal plan to standardize medical treatments through government-issued quality measures and payment initiatives emerges from a nearly thirty-year drive to "evidence-based medicine" (EMB),[226] which is not a topic of this book. Readers can explore this important topic using the sources in the endnotes[227] and a book called *Tarnished Gold: The Sickness of Evidence-Based Medicine.*[228] In 2005, Dr. John Ioannidis argued that a majority of research findings in medicine were probably wrong, bringing to public awareness the crisis of reproducibility. For example, in 2012, the biotechnology firm Amgen "tried to reproduce 53 'landmark' studies in hematology and oncology, but could only replicate six," write Peter Wood and David Randall in the *Wall Street Journal.* Notably, "half the results published in peer-reviewed scientific journals are probably wrong," they say.[229] Patients hoping to receive effective, individualized medical care may be deeply troubled by the philosophy of EBM and its prescriptive use of research findings.

Computerized Ordering Can Be Deadly

Another Meaningful Use requirement is computerized physician order entry (CPOE). CPOE is "any system in which clinicians directly place orders electronically, with the orders transmitted directly to the recipient," reports the AHRQ. This includes ordering tests, procedures, consultations, and medication.[230] CPOE represents a power shift from the doctor to the administration, which forces the clinician to do data entry, monitors clinician ordering patterns, and can restrict access to data for the clinician's own research.[231]

Ordering tests electronically was once recommended to reduce medical errors. "Direct order entry reduces errors at all stages of the medication process, not just in prescribing," reported the Institute of Medicine (IOM) in 1999.[232] However, evidence to the contrary has emerged.

In a 2008 study of 133,662 medication errors by 379 hospitals, 27,969 were caused at least in part by computers; 10,954 were paper-based errors.[233] In 2011 researchers found 436 error-related incidents reported voluntarily to the FDA from January 2008 to July 2010, of which 11 percent (forty-six events) were associated with patient harm. For example:

- CPOE system had 225 medication options to scroll through on a drop-down menu, arranged in a counterintuitive manner, resulting in a patient being overdosed with four times more digoxin than required.
- Prescription orders did not appear in a work folder causing a 3-day delay in giving the medication, which led to an ulcer requiring an emergency gastrectomy.
- Acute renal failure and death from an overdose resulting from a CPOE interface that didn't provide medication doses in milligrams.[234]

AHRQ admits, "The widespread implementation of CPOE . . . vividly illustrates the risks and unintended consequences of digitizing a fundamental health care process."[235] Indeed. In 2005 Dr. Ross Koppel of the Center for Clinical Epidemiology and Biostatistics and a team of researchers issued a report identifying twenty-two types of medication error risks related to CPOE; errors due to computer machine rules that did not reflect how the practice of medicine actually works. They concluded these errors occur weekly or more often. Koppel's team said the "substitution of technology for people is a misunderstanding of both."[236]

A December 2012 Pennsylvania Patient Safety Authority study reported 3,946 safety problems related to EHRs in 3,099 safety reports filed between June 2004 and May 2012. Fully 81 percent of the problems were medication errors. The analysts noted, "EHR-related reports are increasing over time, which was to be expected as adoption of EHRs is growing in the United States."[237]

Here's one CPOE story that'll stand your hair on end. It's from a report filed by a physician to the FDA's Manufacturer and User Facility Device Experience (MAUDE) adverse event reporting system about the Cerner EHR:

> The CPOE system serves and documents all transactions of communication pertaining to the patient's care. Orders are entered and delivered to an anticipated recipient and the action ordered is executed. The device-recipient interface has been unreliable with specific etiologies for failure not yet resolved or understood. Examples include orders to transfer patient from ICU to a non-ICU bed. Patient is moved to another bed but recipient care team does not receive communication and was not aware patient was under their charge. *Patient had seizures on floor for hours throughout the night.* Other patients had orders for lab tests, chemical tests on body fluids, cytological analysis of body fluids, cultures on body fluids, pathology on or [sic] specimen, and others that are not executed by the recipient, leaving the patient undiagnosed after having taken risks for a procedure. Such interface failures have been known by the vendor for years as reported by its own support team.[238] (Emphasis added.)

Over the past ten years, while many studies claim error reductions due to CPOE, other studies find increases. For example, a 2006 study found 117 of 164 errors that occurred after implementing computerized physician order entry were due to the CPOE system itself.[239] Researchers found errors increased post-implementation, but researchers also found that the level of harm decreased. In 2009 the *Washington Post* reported that software bugs have caused misdiagnoses and miscalculations. For example, one computer system systematically gave adult doses of medications to children.[240] In the United Kingdom, errors included drug doses that were ten times higher than intended, according to *HuffPost* in 2010.[241]

CPOE errors are not going away. While the US Agency for Healthcare Research and Quality (AHRQ) issued a 2013 report claiming that CPOE could cut drug errors in half, researchers for the report admitted: "There is also some evidence that CPOE may cause errors."[242] A study released in January 2017 found "increases in wrong patient, wrong medication, and wrongly timed orders." There were 1,622 preventable incidents related to medication errors among 624 patients.[243] Research published in 2015 by *BMJ Quality & Safety* found a startling statistic: "CPOE allowed doctors to enter 80 percent of medical errors and half of them went through with little or no alarms."[244] Another study released in 2016 found nearly 40 percent of medication errors were missed, with 13 percent of potentially fatal orders failing to trigger an alert.[245] The most common CPOE errors according to the 2015 study were:

1. Missing or erroneous label directions
2. Wrong dose or strength
3. Scheduling problems
4. Delays in medication processing
5. Delays in medication administration[246]

Some errors are unimaginable. On July 27, 2013, sixteen-year-old Pablo Garcia was given a thirty-nine-fold overdose of the antibiotic Septra—37.5 more pills than the one pill he should have been prescribed. The doctor had failed to notice the mg/kg indication in the drop-down menu, so instead of receiving only 160 milligrams, Pablo received 160 milligrams for every one of his 38.6 kilograms (85 pounds), for a total of 6,160 milligrams. As a result, Pablo almost died.[247]

Child Deaths Doubled

CPOE-related child death is not a surprise. In response to the 1999 Institute of Medicine report on medical errors, one children's hospital implemented a CPOE system as an experiment to see if it would reduce child mortality. As reported in 2005, the hospital was surprised to see their rate of child mortality more than double. The system caused delays in implementing doctors' orders, reduced physician attention to patients, limited access to medications, and reduced clinician interactions, which before introduction of CPOE had reduced medical errors.[248]

The increased time burden of computerized order entry and its reorganization of patient-care processes were implicated. As the authors of the CPOE study observed,

> This initial time burden seemed to change the organization of bedside care. Before CPOE implementation, physicians and nurses converged at the patient's bedside to stabilize the patient. After CPOE implementation, while 1 physician continued to direct medical management, a second physician was often needed solely to enter orders into the computer during the first 15 minutes to 1 hour if a patient arrived in extremis. Downstream from order entry, bedside nurses were no longer allowed to grab critical medications from a satellite medication dispenser located in the ICU because as part of CPOE implementation, all medications, including vasoactive agents and antibiotics, became centrally located within the pharmacy department. The priority to fill a medication order was assigned by the pharmacy department's algorithm. Furthermore, because pharmacy could not process medication orders until they had been activated, ICU nurses also spent significant amounts of time at a separate computer terminal and away from the bedside. When the pharmacist accessed the patient CPOE to process an order, the physician and the nurse were "locked out," further delaying additional order entry.[249]

Computerization had also led to major inefficiencies. Before the hospital began using CPOE, medications were administered according to the schedule given in national guidelines, but with CPOE "fewer than half" of patients received critical medications and infusions within recommended timeframes.[250]

Dangerous Health IT Errors

As noted, scary outcomes, including patient deaths, have resulted from EHR systems. Most patients have no idea, but one patient-safety organization is looking into and monitoring the problems. A "deep dive" study of EHR-oriented errors in just thirty-six of the 5,724 hospitals in America was released February 6, 2013, to too little fanfare.[251] Using data from participating organizations collected over a nine-week period, the ECRI Institute found 171 health information technology-related problems, potentially including three deaths.[252]

Although President Obama claimed in 2009 that EHRs would "save lives by reducing the deadly but preventable medical errors that pervade our health-care system,"[253] stories of danger and death emerge:

> As reported by *American Medical News*: "In spring 2012, a surgeon tried to electronically access a patient's radiology study in the operating room but the computer would show only a blue screen. The patient's time under anesthesia was extended while OR staff struggled to get the display to function properly."[254]

> As reported by *HealthLeaders Media* in 2013: "Computer programs truncated dosage fields, leading to morphine-caused respiratory arrest; lab test and transplant surgery records didn't talk to each other, leading to organ rejection and patient death; and an electronic system's misinterpretation of the time 'midnight' meant an infant received antibiotics one dangerous day too late."[255]

The ECRI Institute broke down the voluntarily reported 171 health IT-related incidents as follows:

- 53% involved a medication management system
    - 25% involved a computerized order entry system
    - 15% involved an electronic medication administration record

  - 11% involved pharmacy systems
  - 2% involved automated dispensing systems
- 17% were caused by clinical documentation systems
- 13% were caused by lab information systems
- 9% were caused by computers not functioning
- 8% were caused by radiology or diagnostic imaging systems, including PACS
- 1% were caused by clinical decision support systems[256]

ECRI cautioned against "short-sighted approaches to HIT" and identified the following "key HIT-related problems":

- Inadequate data transfer from one HIT system to another
- Data entry in the wrong patient record
- Incorrect data entry in the patient record
- Failure of the HIT system to function as intended
- Configuration of the system in a way that can lead to mistakes[257]

Nine months later, ECRI named "data integrity failures in EHRs and other health IT systems" as one of the top ten risks for 2014.[258] A year earlier the institute had named patient-data mismatches in EHRs and other health IT systems as a top risk for 2013. While errors are not new, ECRI reports that the ability of health IT systems to collect and transmit data widely "can serve to multiply the effects of such errors to a degree that would have been unlikely in a paper-based system."[259]

In 2015 ECRI issued a report called "Wrong-Record, Wrong-Data Errors with Health IT Systems," which included the following stories:

1. The doctor ordered four units of fresh frozen plasma while the patient was in the ED [emergency department]. After the patient was admitted, the blood bank informed us that the order did not transfer because the number of units must be

specified in multiple sections in the record. This resulted in a delay in starting the infusion. The patient coded and died by the time the order was completed.

2. The patient arrived at the ED . . . by ambulance. The driver gave the patient's name. The ED clerk selected the wrong patient record in the EHR. The actual patient had the same name but a different date of birth than the patient whose record was selected. The patient was banded, labs were drawn, an EKG was done, etc., all based on the wrong patient information. The ambulance driver questioned the patient's age listed in the record. The clerk went back into the system and located the correct record. Unknown harm. If medications were given, for example, did the actual patient have any known drug allergies?
3. The physician ordered a CT of the spine. The exam was electronically entered as a CT of the brain. The technologist failed to check the order in the chart, and an incorrect exam was performed. The error was identified by the ordering physician when trying to obtain results.[260]

A 2012 study by Geisinger Health System in Pennsylvania, commissioned by the federal government, also points to Health IT errors. It "estimates that if and when electronic health records are fully adopted, they could be linked to at least 60,000 adverse events a year."[261] The report also analyzed how health IT hazards could be forestalled.

EHR Hazards at the VA

In 2014 the US Department of Veterans Affairs released a study of one hundred closed cases of EHR-related safety violations from 2009 to 2013. Despite the VA having a longstanding EHR system, researchers found "many significant EHR-related safety concerns . . . remain." According to the blog *PT in Motion News*, "A majority of cases (70%)

involved both unsafe technology and unsafe use."[262] Researchers discovered four types of safety concerns:

> **Concerns related to unmet data display needs.** These concerns are related to what an EHR can and can't display, and occur when there's a "poor fit between information needs and the task at hand." Authors cited an example of a patient with a drug allergy who was given the drug due to a combination of human error and information gaps that made it seem as if an EHR warning was a "false positive."
>
> **Concerns related to software modifications.** These issues center on the intended and unintended consequences of software upgrades or improper software configuration. By way of example, authors pointed to an upgrade to a disease management package that "erroneously escalated user privileges to place and sign orders."
>
> **Concerns related to system-to-system interfaces.** Concerns in this area have to do with the ways systems talk to each other, and the possibility of one patient's records being mixed up with another's.
>
> **Concerns of hidden dependencies.** Researchers identified several instances in which seemingly unrelated components of an EHR affect each other, such as the reassignment of a patient from outpatient to inpatient status resulting in the removal of certain medications from the patient's active medication list.[263] (Emphasis added.)

A team of researchers from the VA reviewed 344 reported incidents occurring between August 2009 and May 2013. They found seventy-four involving unsafe technology and twenty-five comprising unsafe use of technology.[264] Jean M. Scott, director of informatics patient safety at the VA Office of Informatics and Analytics/Health Informatics, told *For the Record* that identifying the source of the errors is difficult:

> Because you're looking at the interaction between the human and the technology, you can think of it like driving a car. Did you intend to go through a stop sign or not use the turn signal? Is it your fault if you're driving a different car and the turn signal is actually where the wipers were on your previous car? If the designs are different, then that distracts humans who are trained on something else.[265]

Researcher Hardeep Singh notes, "It's been about 14 years that the VA implemented their EHR, and the VA is one of just a few health care organizations that dedicate specific resources to investigation and improvement of EHR-related safety concerns. . . . Some of these concerns continue long after the EHR goes live, and we constantly have to be on the watch for things going wrong. . . . Testing has to continue years after implementation, and error logs need to be kept and analyzed. The best strategy requires constant monitoring for problems."[266]

Can an EHR ever be safe for patients?

"There are no quick fix, plug and play solutions. Years of research are needed, and years of system migrations as well for existing installations," wrote Silverstein on the *Health Care Renewal* blog.[267] He claims long-term solutions are required to deal with the "usability" issues.

The National Institute of Standards and Technology (NIST) held a 2012 conference on the state of quality controls in health IT, and one attendee, Ben-Tzion Karsh, an engineering professor at the University of Wisconsin–Madison, said he "heard a 'broad consensus' among experts that electronic medical records need to function better and safer." He also noted, "The truth is that we do not at this time know what would make an EHR (electronic health record) safe."[268]

Built Without Patients in Mind

Informatics professor Ralph Grams chastised the EHR mandate as a "bold experiment in medical informatics" that will be used "to move our entire economy into a socialized system with czars and unelected dictators in control."[269] Dr. Scot Silverstein says, "The technology is being pushed, with no good scientific basis."[270] An ONC workgroup in February 2013 said there is limited hard data on health IT's contribution to quality and patient safety."[271] Christopher Nemeth, PhD and Richard Cook, MD, writing in the *Journal of Biomedical Informatics* call EHRs "experiments" adding, "Healthcare IT systems that are developed without a deep understanding of the healthcare work domain can only reflect a guess of how such systems should be configured."[272]

Building an EHR without sufficient clinician input creates problems for patient care. "Clinicians and IT often have different sets of priorities, says Erik Bermudez, author of a report on EHR vendors." He says, "Vendors must balance the needs of both groups in order to be successful."[273] In addition, as one doctor puts it, health IT staff and clinicians often speak different languages.[274]

Computer programmers don't know how different pieces of medical information relate to one another. A commentary in the *Journal of Medical Bioinformatics* explains what IT technicians and EHR designers don't realize about the clinical setting:

> On the surface, healthcare work seems to flow smoothly. That is because the clinicians who provide healthcare service make it so. Just beneath the apparently smooth-running operations is a complex, poorly bounded, conflicted, highly variable, uncertain, and high-tempo work domain. The technical work that clinicians perform resolves these complex and conflicting elements into a productive work domain. Occasional visitors to this setting see the smooth surface that clinicians have created and remain unaware of the conflicts that lie beneath it.[275]

Building a scientific basis for EHRs would involve actual observation of a health care environment by health care IT developers.[276] Yet 65 percent of physicians indicate the EHR has not improved diagnosis accuracy or treatment planning, according to a report by Deloitte.[277] Cossman, the retiring surgeon, wrote, "As currently designed, it is hard to identify a single need of a patient or a doctor that the EMR addresses."[278] Another displeased physician wrote, "It seems as if this is all about taking care of the chart, as opposed to taking care of the patient."[279] That's correct. The government-certified EHR was not built for patient care.

Code of Silence

Errors can occur anytime the health IT system is unavailable for use, malfunctions during use, is used incorrectly, or interacts incorrectly with another system, reports the ECRI Institute.[280] However, discussing system flaws can be precluded by health IT contracts. Sharona Hoffman, a professor of law and bioethics at Case Western Reserve University in Cleveland, says, "Doctors who report problems can lose their jobs. . . . Hospitals don't have any incentive to do so and may be in breach of contract if they do."[281]

The *New York Times* reports, "Reliable data about problems in the electronic systems is hard to come by, hidden by a virtual code of silence enforced by fears of lawsuits and bad publicity. A 2012 study commissioned by the government sketches the magnitude of the problem, calling for tools to report problems and to prevent them."[282] However, physician and health IT expert Scot Silverstein points out that these reporting tools, in the face of confirmed hazards of an unknown scale, are a tacit admission that health IT is an experimental technology.[283]

Disasters and Dangerous Intrusions

System Shutdowns

What if your doctor has no clue what he last ordered for you, and no ability to order anything else? This is what can happen when an EHR system crashes.

In 2006 a major hospital's system crashed soon after it went online. As reported by the *Washington Post*, one senior internist, who requested anonymity to keep his job, "walked in to find no records on any patients." He said, "It was like being on the moon without oxygen." While doctors struggled to keep the patients alive, the internist said employees from the EHR vendor "ran around with no idea how to work their own equipment." He emphasized, "I didn't go through all my training to have my ability to take care of patients destroyed by devices that are an impediment to medical care."[284]

An Idaho clinic lost more than four months of patient data in 2008—approximately twelve thousand patient visits worth of information—plus "thousands of hours of provider and nursing time" when the system crashed and the clinic discovered that the backup system was not actually backing up their data. Eleven weeks later, the clinic was able to "recover nearly 100 percent" of their data, but only after hard work, the efforts of many people in and outside of the clinic, and "a fee of more than $10,000 paid to the data recovery firm."[285]

Trinity Health System shut down its $400 million EHR system at ten hospitals for four hours in 2010 when electronic pharmacy orders weren't being delivered to nurse's stations, reported *HuffPost*.[286] In June 2011 the EHR at Munson Healthcare in Michigan shut down for four-plus hours. The hospital told the media no patients were harmed, but a later memo from the hospital called it "unplanned network downtime . . . that had widespread operational and clinical implications. . . . We fully understand that it was very difficult to manage the resultant chaos and that downtimes like this are unacceptable."[287]

Six months later, in December 2011, the entire EHR system of the University of Pennsylvania Medical Center was shut down for more than fourteen hours. The outage affected nearly all its hospitals in the region. Dr. Silverstein told the *Pittsburgh Post-Gazette*, "What occurred here was a disruptive, potentially dangerous major malfunction of a life-critical enterprise medical device."[288]

Cerner, an electronic health records provider, has EHR systems in 9,300 facilities worldwide, including 3,750 physician practices and 2,650 hospitals.[289] But on Monday, July 23, 2012, its nationwide, hosted EHR system was down for several hours. Two Tampa hospitals reported losing access for six hours, forcing them to resort back to handwritten orders.[290] The shutdown has been unofficially attributed to a network administrator who inadvertently deleted a domain name system (DNS) zone file.[291] In short, a single keystroke error took down mission- and patient-critical systems.

On August 26, 2013, the nearly $1 billion EHR system built by Epic at Sutter Health in northern California collapsed for an entire day. Doctors and nurses were left with no patient information, including doctors' orders, medications, allergies, and vital statistics.[292]

A hardware glitch in December 2015 shut down the EHR of Hospital Corporation of America (HCA), a major health care system in Florida with fifty hospitals and thirty-seven surgical centers. An email from HCA claimed that staff members were able to work around it because "we used other systems and processes we have in place."[293]

After Maryland-based MedStar Health System was hacked in 2016, they shut down the entire EHR system operating at ten hospitals and 250 outpatient facilities. Without access to any patient information, the hospital staff reverted to paper charts and records.[294]

Dean Sittig, a faculty member at the University of Texas Health Science Center at Houston, was the lead author of a 2014 report on how often EHRs shut down. Seventy percent of the fifty large, integrated systems he surveyed "had at least one unplanned downtime greater than eight hours in the last three years." Three of those institutions reported one or more patients injured as a result. Sittig says, "it's getting to be so that the computer is driving a lot of what we do in healthcare, and if the computer isn't working, that can open all kinds of potential for patient harm. And one of the things that can happen is the computer doesn't work at all. No screen. No data. Nothing."[295]

Access Denied

Other kinds of EHR shutdowns, completely unrelated to technological glitches, are also possible.

An EHR vendor can go out of business. In 2016, the Chicago-based hospital association that operates the area's health information exchange (HIE) sued its health IT vendor, which was going out of business. The HIE connects thirty hospitals and the vendor had the records of two million patients. To prevent the vendor from destroying or transferring the patients' data, the association succeeded in getting a temporary injunction and began trying to recover the records.[296]

The EHR system can be turned off. Full Circle Health Care, LLC, a small clinic in Presque Isle, Maine, got into a billing dispute with CompuGroup Medical, a German multinational EHR company with US headquarters in Boston. According to the clinic, CompuGroup purchased the EHR system it was using, then began charging $2,000 per month in fees rather than the $300 per month the clinic had been paying the former owner. After months of "fruitless haggling" and with more than $20,000 in maintenance fees left unpaid for ten months, CompuGroup shut down the clinic's access to its four thousand patient records: "Access denied."[297]

The EHR system can by hijacked. Ransomware attacks—malicious encrypting of patient records—are escalating. Carbon Black, a cyber security company, reports more than 6,300 dark web marketplaces selling ransomware with over 45,000 ransomware product listings. The ransomware sales on the dark web have grown from $249,287 to $6.2 million, a growth rate of over 2,500 percent between 2016 and 2017. The company expects ransomware to target "specific industries, specifically legal and healthcare as well as taxpayers." Ransomware attackers extorted $1 billion in 2016 and ransomware authors can earn $163,000 or more each year.[298]

In the first few months of 2016, ransomware attackers hit Hollywood Presbyterian Medical Center in Los Angeles, California, Chino Valley Medical Center and Desert Valley Hospital in southern California,[299] and Methodist Hospital in Henderson, Kentucky.[300] Hollywood Presbyterian declared an "internal state of emergency" and eventually paid a $17,000 ransom in forty Bitcoins to have their systems decrypted and back online ten days later.[301] Methodist Hospital refused, restoring systems from backups.[302]

At 2:00 a.m. on Sunday, April 9, 2017, the Erie County Medical Center (ECMC) in Buffalo, New York, was hit with a ransomware attack. Within ninety minutes, ECMC shut down its EHR and reverted to paper. Part of the system came back online starting April 19. However, as reported on May 25 by the health care best-practices firm, The Advisory Board Company: "Last week, the system said most of its systems would be running normally within a few more days. However, ECMC officials said there is more work to do to bring the system's outpatient clinics fully back online."[303]

Britain's National Health Service of forty-eight hospital trusts was hit by a ransomware worm called "WannaCry" on May 12, 2017. It encrypted data and locked out users. It also affected medical devices, specifically radiology equipment. [304] Hospitals returned to pen and paper. But many clinics, totally dependent on health IT, were forced to shut their doors. Physicians Rachel Clarke, MD, and Taryn Youngstein, MD, wrote in the *New England Journal of Medicine*, "We can just about survive without a stethoscope—once the symbol of our craft—but without our computer log-ins, modern medicine grinds to a halt." As a result of the country's "underresourced socialized medicine," costs had been cut by scrapping a $7.07 million annual security support contract with Microsoft.[305] North Korean involvement in the attack is suspected, according to *Forbes*.[306]

The January 18, 2018, ransomware attack on Allscripts' cloud-hosted EHR crippled doctors' offices for days. Six days later, many of the 1,500 practices affected were unable to connect to the EHR. Some practices canceled surgeries and set up "open clinic" to manage patients, reports FierceHealthcare. One practice, without the ability to file health insurance claims, had to secure a line of credit from the bank to pay staff. The office manager at a single-physician clinic noted Allscripts' $10,000 annual maintenance fee and tweeted, "Their lack of proper updates to their servers has cost us a fortune in lost revenue, staff salary, and patient satisfaction just to name a few. We are still not operational with no firm ETA provided."[307]

One expert states, "Such targets are particularly vulnerable because they cannot afford to be paralyzed for a long time (either because their data has been encrypted or because they shut down the system to avoid spreading the infection) and prefer to pay the ransom."[308] Thus, Indiana-based Hancock Health paid about $47,000 in bitcoin to unlock its computer system two days after it was seized for ransom. The hackers kept their end of the deal and gave the data back, which law enforcement says isn't always the case. "Some hackers will renege after being paid, and demand yet another payment," reports Connected Care Watch.[309]

Hacking of Health Data Escalates

The hacking of health-data systems has increased sharply. Between 2009 and March 2015, information about more than 120 million people had been compromised.[310] But in 2015 more than one hundred million records were breached. IBM called it "the year of the healthcare security breach."[311]

On the evening of February 4, 2015, the *Wall Street Journal* reported that Anthem, the nation's second-biggest health insurer, had been hacked.[312] In what is probably the largest data breach ever disclosed by a health care company, 78.8 million "customer and employee" records were compromised. Exposed data included names, date of birth, medical ID numbers, Social Security numbers, addresses, email addresses, and employment information. China is suspected. One month later, health insurer Premera Blue Cross announced the breach of eleven million records containing information similar to the Anthem breach, but also including medical claims data.[313] Anthem is expected to pay

$115 million to settle the claims of the more than one hundred lawsuits filed against the insurer.[314] After legal and other expenses are paid, victims will receive less than one dollar each.[315]

Computerworld says medical records are becoming the next revenue stream for hackers. Data in EHRs have longer shelf lives because they include Social Security numbers and other identification credentials like health insurance and credit card information. Unlike credit card numbers alone, which can sell for a couple of dollars on the street, Social Security numbers with credentials can be sold for a couple of hundred dollars.[316]

There's also another possibility that could be more lucrative: blackmail. Jeff Schmidt, CEO of the information technology security firm JAS Global Advisors, says: "We're never going to read about these blackmail and extortion attempts that occur as result of these breaches and it's happening all the time."[317]

Meanwhile, one 2017 survey of health IT leaders found 8 percent of health care organizations have allocated no funds for cybersecurity.[318] Another survey found 25 percent of Health IT Information security decision makers had little to no confidence in their ability to assess digital risks, reports Healthcare Informatics.[319]

The 2009 stimulus law containing the EHR mandate required HHS to set up a system to report data breaches. Breaches that involve 499 individuals or fewer do not have to be reported to the HHS Office for Civil Rights (OCR) "Wall of Shame" website but often are. As of March 31, 2018, OCR had received 344,823 reports of breaches affecting fewer than 500 patients. There were also 2,267 reports of breaches affecting 500 or more patients, for a grand total of at least 347,090 breaches affecting approximately 178 million individuals.[320] In July 2017, the OCR website was revised to only list the most recent two years of breaches, with a separate tab archiving the rest.[321]

Breaches can be small or large. According to the HHS data, in May 2017, 742 records from Jones Family Practice were breached and in the first four months of 2016, Florida-based 21st Century Oncology's server was hacked, affecting more than 2.2 million people. In 2017, more than 316,000 blood test results were "leaked after an Amazon-hosted cloud repository was misconfigured to allow public access."[322] Meanwhile, Cornerstone Business & Management Solutions, a

Nebraska-based medical supply company, which discovered a suspicious download of personal data on 21,856 patients using its medical devices, was the second largest *business associate* breach in 2017.[323]

Breaches can be short or long. In 2017, Georgia-based Peachtree Neurological Clinic discovered a fifteen-month breach while investigating a ransomware attack. In 2015, Excellus Blue Cross Blue Shield revealed the discovery of a nearly two-year breach that "gave hackers access to potentially all its customers' records."[324] According to the Protenus Breach Barometer, a monthly snapshot of reported or disclosed breaches impacting the health care industry, one of the breaches reported in 2017 took fourteen years to discover. On average, breaches reported in July 2017 took 67.5 days from discovery to disclosure.[325]

The federal government is no better than private companies when it comes to data security. In December 2014 hackers presumed to be working for the Chinese government accessed four million records on current and former federal workers. The Office of Personnel Management (OPM) stores more identifiable information than any other government agency—according to its 2016 budget, information on approximately thirty-two million people.[326] It took until April 2015 for the OPM to discover the hack. The public didn't hear about it until June.[327]

Then just one month later, in July, Americans were shocked to learn that the OPM revised the estimate of 4 million to 21.5 million after a second intrusion was detected. It included 1.1 million fingerprints, which later expanded to 5.6 million fingerprints.[328] Actually OPM had been hacked as early as 2013, but the hackers didn't take any personal information, only documents related to the department's IT security systems, its servers, and network infrastructure.[329] In 2015 hackers took sensitive information collected during background checks of federal workers, such as drug use, criminal convictions, mental-health issues, gambling problems, drinking problems, bankruptcies, and the names and addresses of their foreign relatives.[330]

America has become a prime target for cyber-espionage. US Representative Elijah Cummings (D-MD) is concerned: "The United States of America is under attack. . . . Sophisticated cyber spies, many from foreign countries, are targeting the sensitive personal information of millions of Americans. They are attacking our government, our economy, our financial sector, our health care systems, and virtually every single aspect of our lives."[331]

Across industries, the average cost of a data breach is $4 million.[332] The average global cost per record is highest in health care, at $355 per stolen or lost record.[333] Additionally, the fines imposed by HIPAA on organizations that suffer data security breaches only add to the cost of recovery and do little to compensate individuals whose privacy may have been lost forever.

For example, in September 2010, 6,800 patient records housed at New York's Presbyterian Hospital and Columbia University were accidentally exposed on the Internet. HHS levied a record $4.8 million penalty against the two institutions.[334] Their total costs likely included expenses related to the breach, the federal penalties, and any additional security requirements, which may add to the cost of care received by patients. Counterintuitively, the fines go directly to the OCR, where website HealthIT Security points out, there is little transparency in the use of those dollars.[335] However, in March 2018, OCR director Roger Severino announced that the office may create a process to give victims a percentage of the funds collected in HIPAA settlements and penalties.[336]

IV

HIPAA Doesn't Protect Privacy

The HIPAA Disclosure Rule

No Privacy; No Consent

The Health Insurance Portability and Accountability Act of 1996 (HIPAA) does not protect medical privacy. Instead, it eliminates patient consent requirements for data sharing. Thus, the EHR helps facilitate use and disclosure of private patient data. As pointed out at the beginning of this book, the HIPAA "privacy" rule, the length of which has been compared to a Tolstoy novel,[1] does not require patients be given a choice about most sharing of their private medical data. Disclosure is allowed if 1) the HIPAA privacy rule specifically permits or requires it, or 2) the individual who is the subject of the information gives authorization in writing.[2]

HIPAA permits a wide range of disclosures of individually identifiable patient data, called protected health information (PHI). In fact, although the word *consent* is mentioned seventeen times in the rule, in various tenses, it is not required for uses and disclosure of data. Furthermore, most mentions relate to consent for accessing health care services or certain consents related to research. The rule's requirement to get an "authorization" for sharing PHI is limited to use or disclosure of psychotherapy notes (with exceptions), sale of PHI, and use or disclosure for marketing—*and* whenever the disclosure or use is not otherwise permitted or required by the rule.[3] This is rare indeed.

But that's not what the American public thinks. "Joan Anonymous" from New Jersey wrote the following comment in response to the CMS MACRA proposal that clinics and hospitals share medical data on *all patients* with the federal government: "I vehemently oppose the MACRA rules for Physicians. Where has HIPAA gone?"[4]

More than thirty-three thousand complaints alleging HIPAA violations were received by the HHS Office of Civil Rights between April 2003 and March 2008, reported the Institute of Medicine in 2009. However, no civil penalties were imposed and there were only three criminal prosecutions for medical identity theft.[5] The number of privacy-rule complaints has increased steadily since 2011, reaching 165,175 as of September 2017.[6] How many of these complaints are from people who don't understand how broadly their data can be shared under the law?

HIPAA was "designed primarily to modernize the flow of health information," writes George Washington University Research Professor of Law Daniel J. Solove in the *Journal of AHIMA* (American Health Information Management Association).[7] It was never truly designed to protect privacy. Some patients are dismayed to find out that while others can share their data, they as the subjects of the data are not allowed to give it to whomever they wish. David Brailer, the first national coordinator of health IT, makes it clear: "You can't force a covered entity to give your data to someone you choose, and you can't stop them from giving it to someone they choose."[8]

For example, under the HIPAA de-identification standard, patient data that has been deemed "de-identified" by the removal of eighteen identifiers[9] can be shared and used for secondary purposes such as "comparative effectiveness studies, policy assessment, life sciences research, and other endeavors," according to HHS. The department admits that the de-identifed data "retains some risk of identification . . . and there is a possibility that de-identified data could be linked back to the identity of the patient to which it corresponds." Nevertheless, HHS explains, "the Privacy Rule does not restrict the use or disclosure of de-identified health information as it is no longer considered protected health information."[10] The National Committee on Vital and Health Statistics (NCVHS) concurs, "Even data properly de-identified under the Privacy Rule may carry with it some private information, and therefore, poses some risk of re-identification, a risk that grows into the future as new datasets are released and as datasets are combined."[11]

Secondary uses of patient data trouble doctors. Frustrated with data entry and concerned about how patients' data was being used to direct care, Tom Davis, MD, FAAFP, walked away from a successful twenty-five-year practice and his three thousand patients. He believes the data collected through the EHR is being used for purposes that do not directly benefit the patient "so it would be unethical for him to represent otherwise to the patient," reports *Medical Economics*.[12] Dr. Davis is correct.

Millions Get Unconsented Access

HIPAA is considered a "permissive" rule. It does not *require* sharing of data except with the subjects of the data—the patients—and with the secretary of HHS for monitoring compliance with the rule.[13] However, it *permits* sharing hither and yon. "It's a common misconception that [HIPAA] makes it difficult, if not impossible, to move electronic health data when and where it is needed for patient care and health," reports the Office of the National Coordinator for Health Information Technology (ONC).[14] Sharing is determined by covered entities, which "may rely on professional ethics and best judgments in deciding which of these permissive uses and disclosures to make," writes HHS.[15] In short, HIPAA "improves the flow of health information," writes Lucia Savage, JD, former chief privacy officer of ONC.[16]

According to a 2010 HHS regulation, more than 2.2 million entities (covered entities and business associates) have the potential to be given access to private patient data without patient consent as a result of HIPAA. This number doesn't include government entities with access to your data because they aren't considered covered entities or business associates. The following graph depicts the array of possible recipients of patient data.[17]

Number of Health-Care Entities and Business Associates With Access to Patients' Health Information under HIPAA Privacy Rule

Health-Care Entity	Number
Business Associates* (conduct business on behalf of entities listed below)	1,500,000
Office of MDs, DOs, Mental Health Practitioners, Dentists, PT, OT, ST, Audiologists	419,286
Durable Medical Equipment Suppliers	107,567
Pharmacies	88,396
Nursing Facilities**	34,400
Home Health Service Covered Entities	15,329
Outpatient Care Centers***	13,962
Medical Diagnostic, and Imaging Service Covered Entities	7,879
Other Ambulatory Care Service Covered Entities (Ambulance and Other)	5,879
Hospitals (General Medical and Surgical, Psychiatric, Substance Abuse, Other Specialty)	4,060
Third Party Administrators Working on Behalf of Covered Health Plans	3,522
Health Insurance Carriers	1,045
Total Entities and Business Associates	**2,201,325**

* According to HHS, examples of business associates include third-party administrators or pharmacy benefit managers for health plans, claims processing or billing companies, transcription companies, and persons who perform legal, actuarial, accounting, management, or administrative services for covered entities and who require access to protected health information.

** Includes nursing care facilities, residential mental retardation facilities, residential mental health and substance abuse facilities, community care facilities for the elderly, and continuing care retirement communities.

*** Includes family planning centers, outpatient mental health and drug abuse centers, other outpatient health centers, HMO medical centers, kidney dialysis centers, freestanding ambulatory surgical and emergency centers, and all other outpatient care centers.

Source: "Modifications to the HIPAA Privacy, Security, and Enforcement Rules Under the Health Information Technology for Economic and Clinical Health Act," RIN: 0991--AB57, *Federal Register*, Vol. 75, No. 134, July 14, 2010 (see pages 40872, 40906, 40907, 40911).

Possible recipients of patient data include more than 701,000 "covered entities" (e.g., practitioners, clinics, hospitals, surgical centers, pharmacies, laboratories, radiology facilities, nursing homes, home health services, durable medical equipment suppliers, data clearinghouses, insurers, third-party administrators, and health plans) and their 1.5 million "business associates."[18] A business associate is defined as "someone who is not part of the covered entity's workforce but who will use the covered entity's PHI to perform some task on behalf of the covered entity."[19] These could include lawyers, accountants, data analysts, management firms, and more. The definition also includes health information exchanges (HIEs), health information organizations (HIOs), and regional health information organizations (RHIOs).[20]

Government access is extensive. For example, under 45 CFR 164.512 ("Uses and Disclosures for Which an Authorization or

Opportunity to Agree or Object Is Not Required"),[21] access is permitted without consent for twelve far-reaching "National Priority Purposes":

- Required by Law (i.e., statute, regulation, court orders)
- Public Health Activities
- Victims of Abuse, Neglect, or Domestic Violence
- Health Oversight Activities
- Judicial and Administrative Proceedings
- Law Enforcement Purposes
- Decedents
- Cadaveric Organ, Eye, or Tissue Donation
- Research
- Serious Threat to Health or Safety
- Essential Government Functions
- Workers' Compensation[22]

Most statements about HIPAA could be classified as Orwell's "newspeak," which the Cambridge Dictionary defines as language that "does not mean what it seems to mean and is therefore likely to confuse people."[23] For example, the HHS Office for Civil Rights has written: "HIPAA covered entities may only use and disclose PHI [protected health information] with the individual's written authorization, or as otherwise expressly permitted or required by the HIPAA Privacy Rule."[24]

Since HIPAA expressly permits disclosures and uses for all kinds of reasons, this is not a reassuring statement. In fact, it's deceptive. And as a reminder, requests to get your "authorization" will be few and far between, because they are limited to only certain types of sharing. Thus, unless state legislators pass laws that actually protect patient privacy, patient data will continue to flow with little restraint.

States can and should act to stop the flow of data. State preemption requirements can be used to restore patient privacy and consent rights. "If state regulations governing the privacy of health information are more stringent than HIPAA standards, state law stands," explains *Managed Care*. "State laws are 'more stringent' when they prohibit or restrict disclosures that would otherwise have been allowed under HIPAA. 'More stringent' includes authorization or consent procedures that are more detailed than those described by HIPAA, that cover a longer period of time, or that provide greater protection to the patient."[25]

Many states have a patchwork of health privacy laws. Some states have conformed their privacy law to HIPAA, eliminating all state privacy protections. For example, in 2001 after the federal privacy rule was issued, Hawaii repealed its comprehensive patient privacy statute saying there was "little support" for a state law given the adoption of the federal rule.[26] However, Minnesota law requires patient consent for eight types of disclosures otherwise permitted by HIPAA.[27] Thankfully, a 2018 industry-backed initiative to repeal the Minnesota Health Records Act failed.[28] The Minnesota Legislative Commission on Data Practices may review the law for the 2019 session.

Secret Disclosures

Patients may want to know who's been looking in their personal health information but the HIPAA no-privacy rule limits what patients can find out if they ask. As the National Institutes of Health (NIH) explains,

> The Privacy Rule permits individuals to obtain a record of certain disclosures of their PHI [protected health information] by covered entities or their business associates. . . . The Privacy Rule restricts both uses and disclosures of PHI, but it requires an accounting only for certain PHI disclosures.[29]

The NIH clarifies: "It is important to emphasize the difference between a use and a disclosure . . . the use of PHI means communicating that information within the covered entity. A disclosure of PHI means communicating that information to a person or entity outside the covered entity." NIH then lists disclosures that are excluded from the accounting requirement. For example, no accounting of disclosures is required when the disclosure is:

- For treatment, payment, or health care operations.
- Under an Authorization for the disclosure.
- To an individual about himself or herself.
- As part of a limited data set under a data use agreement.
- Prior to the compliance date [April 14, 2003, for most entities].[30]

Read the Definitions

The "limited data set" is explained below, but first an explanation about "treatment, payment, and health care operations" (TPO). These terms have varied and occasionally counterintuitive activities within their definitions. Third-party payers are often involved in these activities.

"Treatment . . . is broadly defined," writes the ONC. "It includes not only what we think of as traditional treatment and diagnosis, but also making and receiving referrals; coordination or management of health care and related services by a provider, even through a hired third party (for example, a nutritionist); and several other functions."[31] The definition of *payment* includes determining eligibility, disclosures to consumer-reporting agencies on an individual's payment history, and reviewing "health care services with respect to medical necessity, coverage under a health plan, appropriateness of care, or justification of charges."[32]

Meanwhile, the definition of *health care operations (HCO)* is nearly four hundred words long.

In "The HIPAA Paradox: The Privacy Rule That's Not" Richard Sobel expresses concern over the governmental authorization for disclosures without patient consent for various activities unrelated to treatment or payment. HCO, he says, includes "most administrative and profit-generating activities" such as business planning, premium rating, data analyses for plan sponsors, and auditing, which are "all unrelated to direct patient care."[33] Every word of HCO is included below because otherwise the term seems so innocuous:

> *Health care operations* means any of the following activities of the covered entity to the extent that the activities are related to covered functions:
>
> (1) Conducting quality assessment and improvement activities, including outcomes evaluation and development of clinical guidelines, provided that the obtaining of generalizable knowledge is not the primary purpose of any studies resulting from such activities; population-based activities relating to improving health or reducing health care costs, protocol development, case management and care coordination, contacting of health care providers and patients with information about treatment alternatives; and related functions that do not include treatment;
>
> (2) Reviewing the competence or qualifications of health care professionals, evaluating practitioner and provider performance, health plan performance, conducting training programs in which students, trainees, or practitioners in areas of health care learn under supervision to practice or improve their skills as health care providers, training of non-health care professionals, accreditation, certification, licensing, or credentialing activities;
>
> (3) Underwriting, premium rating, and other activities relating to the creation, renewal or replacement of a contract of health insurance or health benefits, and ceding, securing, or placing a contract for reinsurance of risk relating to claims for health care (including stop-loss insurance and excess of loss insurance),

> provided that the requirements of § 164.514(g) are met, if applicable;
>
> (4) Conducting or arranging for medical review, legal services, and auditing functions, including fraud and abuse detection and compliance programs;
>
> (5) Business planning and development, such as conducting cost-management and planning-related analyses related to managing and operating the entity, including formulary development and administration, development or improvement of methods of payment or coverage policies; and
>
> (6) Business management and general administrative activities of the entity, including, but not limited to:
>
>> (i) Management activities relating to implementation of and compliance with the requirements of this sub-chapter;
>>
>> (ii) Customer service, including the provision of data analyses for policy holders, plan sponsors, or other customers, provided that protected health information is not disclosed to such policy holder, plan sponsor, or customer;
>>
>> (iii) Resolution of internal grievances;
>>
>> (iv) The sale, transfer, merger, or consolidation of all or part of the covered entity with another covered entity, or an entity that following such activity will become a covered entity and due diligence related to such activity; and
>>
>> (v) Consistent with the applicable requirements of §164.514, creating de- identified health information or a limited data set, and fundraising for the benefit of the covered entity.[34]

In Minnesota, where repeal of the state's strong state privacy law (and its consent requirements for HCO) has been proposed,[35] the Minnesota Department of Health admits in a report, "This approach may raise privacy concerns because of the broad scope of health care operations."[36] The ONC also admits in the agency's 2015 "Nationwide Interoperability Roadmap" that patient data can be broadly shared for treatment, payment, and health care operations: "the Privacy Rule permits the use and disclosure of PHI for TPO without express individual permission."[37]

Although this statement is clear and factually correct, other ONC statements obscure the depth of data sharing: "The HIPAA Privacy Rule generally permits the use or disclosure of PHI for *limited specific purposes* (such as treatment, payment, and health care operations—often referred to as TPO) without an individual's permission."[38] (Emphasis added.) Statements like this convince Americans that they have privacy when they have none.

Furthermore, although HIPAA's minimum-necessary provision requires covered entities to limit the use of protected health information to only what is necessary, limit the amount of PHI disclosed to only what is necessary, and limit requests for PHI to only what is necessary to accomplish a business purpose, this minimum-necessary requirement "does not apply to treatment disclosures of information."[39] And given the breadth of the term "health care operations," the authorized sharing for business purposes may also not feel very "minimum."

"Limited Data Set" Loophole

HIPAA also has a special loophole for researchers, government public health agencies, and the 2.2 million covered entities and business associates conducting health care operations. It's called the limited data set (LDS). Patient consent for use and disclosure of this data is not required. Counterintuitively, the data set is not a limited set of data, nor is it a de-identified set of data.[40] Instead, it's a comprehensive set of patient data minus sixteen identifiers—excluded information includes name, email address, Social Security number, biometrics, telephone, vehicle ID, and full-face photos—that can be used without patient authorization or consent for three broad purposes: research, health care operations, and public health.[41]

Reidentification is possible. Johns Hopkins calls LDS "a limited set of identifiable patient information." The following unique identifying numbers, characteristics, or codes that remain in the data set could potentially allow reidentification when matched with other public databases:[42]

- Dates such as admission, discharge, service, date of birth, date of death
- City, state, five digit or more zip code, and
- Ages in years, months or days or hours[43]

Johns Hopkins therefore cautions that "this information is still protected health information or 'PHI' under HIPAA. It is not de-identified information."[44] And CMS freely admits the identifiability of this patient data:

> Limited Data Sets (LDS) contain beneficiary level health information but exclude specific direct identifiers as outlined in the Health Insurance Portability and Accountability Act of 1996 (HIPAA). *LDS are considered identifiable even without the specific direct identifiers.* Since the information is considered identifiable, it also remains subject to the provisions of the Privacy Act of 1974. These data are identifiable because of the potential for identifying a beneficiary due to technology, particularly in linking and reidentifying data files.[45] (Emphasis added.)

All disclosures of the LDS require a signed data-use agreement (DUA) between the covered entity and the person requesting the data.[46] The DUA requires data users to promise not to reidentify or contact the subject of the data.[47]

Those creating, sharing, or receiving a "limited data set" (LDS) are not required to track or account for these disclosures and uses of the data.[48] This means clinics and hospitals need not provide patients with an accounting of any disclosures of their medical records if the sharing happened using HIPAA's "limited data set" rules.

Data Sharing on Auto Pilot

HIPAA-permitted data sharing of so-called "protected" health information (PHI) is ongoing. Think 24/7, 365 days a year. The ONC "roadmap" reports: "HIPAA Rules support electronic exchange of health information in an automatic way, with rules that run 'in the background.' This ensures our nationwide care delivery system continues to function. *How PHI is shared 'in the background' without written permission is made transparent to individuals through Notices of Privacy Practices.*"[49] (Emphasis added.)

This is no doubt a surprise to most Americans. Using the word *privacy* in this context deceives. Despite ONC's declaration that sharing has been "made transparent," most patients never read the clinic or hospital Notice of Privacy Practices. Many likely assume the "HIPAA privacy form" they sign at the doctor's office actually means their privacy will be protected.

They're in good company. In meetings with congressional health care staffers in 2015, CCHF asked each one what it meant when they signed the HIPAA privacy form. Almost to a person, they believed the form kept their information confidential, just between them and their doctor. They too were in the dark. However, if a patient reads the Notice of Privacy Practices, it becomes clear: they have no privacy.

Those who wrote the HIPAA "privacy" rule acted strategically. The rule requires doctors and hospitals to ask patients to sign a form acknowledging that they have received the Notice of Privacy Practices. The acknowledgement—initially on a separate form referred to as the "HIPAA privacy form" but now often tucked into the patient consent form as a single sentence—perpetuates the myth that HIPAA protects privacy. The same is true for the Notice of Privacy Practices. It contains the word *privacy*, leaving most to believe it is what it says, rather than reading it to see what it really is. A more honest title would be "Notice of Federally Authorized Disclosures for Which Patient Consent Is Not Required."

A picture tells a thousand words. In 1997 Paul D. Clayton, PhD, and other committee members at the National Research Council published a book to serve as a guide to writing the HIPAA privacy rule. As theDataMap, a project of The Data Privacy Lab at Harvard

University, describes, the picture below "is a reproduction from the book; it depicts flows of patient information about a hypothetical, but typical, patient named Alice. The figure shows representative, not comprehensive, descriptions of flows of health information between organizations in a pre-HIPAA era based on ad hoc knowledge of committee members."[50]

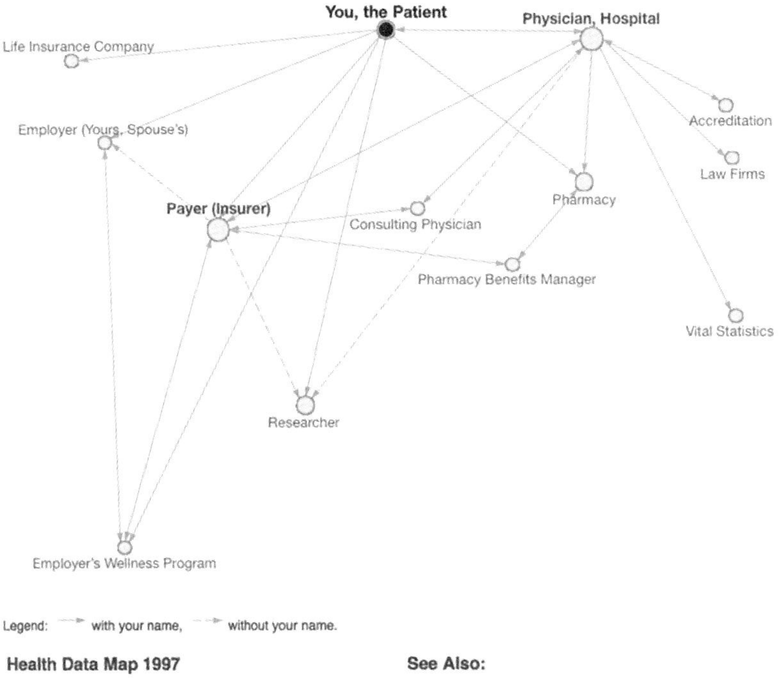

Source: The Data Privacy Lab at Harvard University. Published with permission.

The graph below shows the state of data sharing in 2010 as authorized by HIPAA and extrapolated by Harvard's privacy researchers.

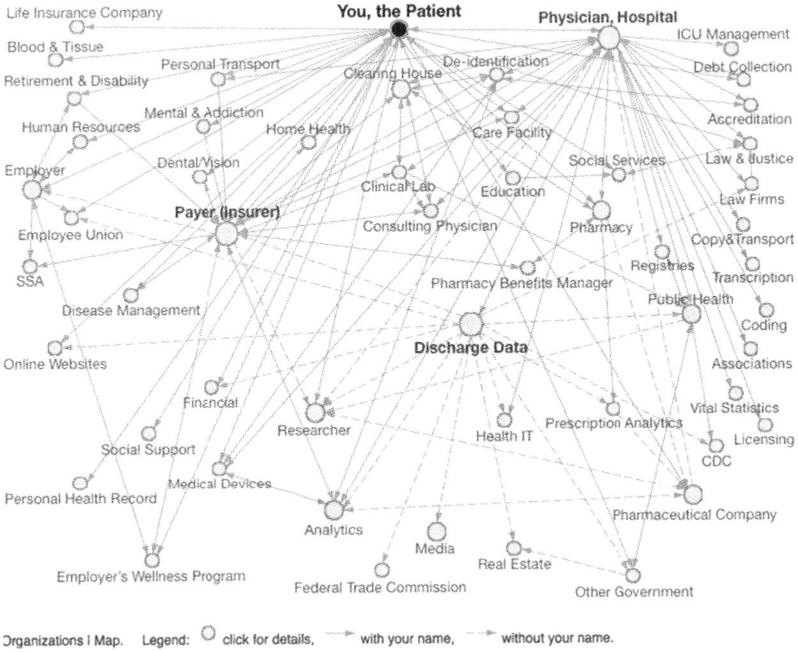

Source: The Data Privacy Lab at Harvard University. Published with permission.

Again, if patients actually read the Notice of Privacy Practices, rather than blindly signing the acknowledgement that they have received it, they might realize how widely their data can be shared without their permission. But most have never read or even asked for a copy of it.

Clearly, the HIPAA privacy rule is a no-privacy rule. As HHS notes, whether an individual signs a clinic's HIPAA privacy form or refuses to sign, his or her private medical data can be shared *without* consent, for treatment, payment, health care operations, government surveillance, research, twelve national priority purposes, and more.[51]

Thus, unless a state legislature has used state preemption authority to enact a medical-privacy law that prohibits some or all of the data sharing permitted under HIPAA, health plans, researchers, government agencies, and others can share and use volumes of private medical records without patient consent. The online-accessible EHR makes the sharing easy.

Clearinghouses Want to Share Data

Data clearinghouses, part of the administrative infrastructure of health care, handle about 90 percent of all health care claims transactions in the US.[52] Proposed legislation, the "Ensuring Patient Access to Healthcare Records Act of 2017," would allow clearinghouses to use and share patient data without express patient consent for the purpose of "enhancing treatment, quality improvement, research, public health efforts and other functions."[53]

Deemed "business associates" under HIPAA, clearinghouses today can only process nonstandard health information data into standard data elements[54] solely for claims processing[55] and only under business associate data-use agreements that limit the use of the data.[56] In 2016, three corporations with clearinghouses established the "Claim Your Health Data Coalition"[57] to work for repeal of the business associate designation. If enacted, clearinghouses would be able to "use and disclose protected health information in the same manner as other covered entities under the HIPAA Privacy Rule."[58] This means without the restrictions of patient consent or data-sharing agreements. Comprehensive health care records including "every healthcare event going back decades" is the goal, writes Dan Johnson, executive vice president of Health Strategy at Experian Health. This goes against public opinion. A 2015 survey regarding health information exchange found only 57.3 percent of respondents willing to share identified information for health care.[59]

Adrian Gropper, MD, writing in *The Health Care Blog,* issues this warning against the legislation: "By giving the infrastructure business the right to use and sell our data without consent or even transparency, we are enabling a true panopticon—an inescapable surveillance system for our most valuable personal data."[60] He adds, "Privatizing involuntary surveillance via clearinghouses is even worse than having the government do it. At least the government would be subject to some public interest constraints."[61]

This troubling bill could also be used to establish a national patient ID system. In *Health Management Technology,* Johnson writes, "Archived data from multiple clearinghouses would be linked through a non-vendor-specific universal patient identifier (UPI) algorithm. A

UPI would associate all relevant health data with a unique individual." He says clearinghouses already help create unique patient IDs for each individual health system, and that Experian Health began working with the National Council for Prescription Drug Programs in 2016 to standardize patient IDs across pharmacy systems nationwide.[62]

"Refuse to Sign HIPAA" Campaign

Citizens can actively engage on this issue. First, ask state legislators to enact true privacy laws that protect patients from HIPAA. Second, refuse to sign the HIPAA form and/or the Notice of Privacy Practices acknowledgement statement, whether it is presented in paper or electronic format.

Medical and administrative staff often believe that a signature is a federal HIPAA requirement, and they're afraid of federal penalties. However, HHS tells patients they're not required to sign. The law only requires clinics and hospitals to make a "good faith effort" to get a signature. Patients can say no. The HHS website explains:

> The law requires your doctor, hospital, or other health care provider to *ask* you to state in writing that you received the notice. (Emphasis added.)
>
> - The law does not require you to sign the "acknowledgement of receipt of the notice."
> - Signing does not mean that you have agreed to any special uses or disclosures (sharing) of your health records.
> - Refusing to sign the acknowledgement does not prevent a provider or plan from using or disclosing health information as HIPAA permits.
> - If you refuse to sign the acknowledgement, the provider must keep a record of this fact.[63]

HHS's two-page "Understanding the HIPAA Notice" says patients who refuse to sign *cannot* be denied access to treatment:[64]

> Understanding the HIPAA Notice 2
>
> **4. Know What You are Signing.**
>
> The law requires your doctor, hospital, or other health care provider to ask for written proof that you received the Notice of Privacy Practices, or what they might call an "acknowledgement of receipt." The law does not require you to sign the acknowledgement form.
>
> If you choose not to sign, your provider must keep a record that they did not get your signature, but they still have to treat you.
>
> If you choose to sign, you have not given up any of your rights or agreed to any special uses of your health records. You are just stating you got the Notice.
>
> To learn more, visit **www.hhs.gov/ocr/privacy/**.

Interestingly, on October 9, 2017, the "Understanding the HIPAA Notice" was no longer on the HHS website—except in Chinese (two versions), Vietnamese, Korean, Russian, Spanish, and Tagalog. The HHS document where links to the notice could once be found in English and eight other languages[65,66] has also disappeared. HHS's own "Get it. Check it. Use it" HIPAA web page,[67] last reviewed by HHS in September 2017, included a link to the document under "Learn More" but ended at "Page Not Found."

Citizens' Council for Health Freedom (CCHF) has a nationwide public campaign encouraging individuals to not sign the HIPAA form or the statement. Those who refuse to sign refuse to participate in the deception that HIPAA protects privacy, exercise their legal right to refuse, enlighten clinic staff, and prohibit the clinic from waving the signed form under their nose after they complain about a disclosure.

When you're asked to sign, just say, "I don't sign that form," and hand it back with a smile. If they have it on an electronic pad, don't sign it. Ask for the paper copy so you can determine what you will and will not sign. Some patients experience pushback from the staff and looks of disapproval. Ask for the manager if necessary. Some will ask you to write "refuse" and initial it. Refuse that too. That's their responsibility. Here is just one person's story of the many CCHF receives from around the country:

> I was a new patient to see a Doctor of Chiropractic in a specialty field. I refused to sign HIPAA form—[the] nurse told him. He angrily came out of his office and announced, "It's the law." I said, "So you don't want me?" He kept repeating it's the law. I've always refused to sign the HIPAA form. First time I've been dismissed out of hand. . . . Guess it's just him afraid to make waves.[68]

If you face this kind of situation, be calm, be kind, but refuse to sign. Protecting privacy is key to protecting freedom. When you get home, use CCHF's special website (**hipaahurtme.org**) to report what happened. CCHF is using personal stories to restore patient privacy and consent rights.

National Medical-Records System

Every Medical Record Available Online

The EHR mandate is advancing a national medical-records system, an "interoperable health information exchange" for the entire United States.[69] It has been described as a "network of networks."[70] It's not yet ready for prime time—it may never be—but it's moving forward.

The latest initiative to implement the information exchange is the Trusted Exchange Framework and Common Agreement (TEFCA). After its release on January 5, 2018,[71] Office of the National Coordinator for Health Information Technology (ONC) head Don Rucker said, "This is really a network of networks concept." The goals of the framework are patient access to data, population-level data exchange, and open and accessible application programming interfaces (APIs).[72] TEFCA establishes "Qualified Health Information Networks," which agree to the Common Agreement and can locate and exchange patient data on demand or using an automated process.[73]

As envisioned, the patient's "health information is not limited to what is stored in electronic health records (EHRs) but includes information from many different sources (including technologies that individuals use every day) and provides a longitudinal picture of their health." The system would also allow public health agencies and researchers to "rapidly learn, develop, and deliver cutting edge treatments by having secure, appropriate access to Electronic Health Information."[74]

Fully implemented, this nationwide network would mean the computerized record of every health care encounter, wherever it took place, would be accessible to your health care institutions and practitioners (and disclosed to others for "health care operations" and more)—even if you didn't want one doctor to know about the other or if you want a fresh, unadulterated second opinion about your illness. HIPAA enables the system to be built.

Purveyors of EHRs are pushing to have "full medical histories" online.[75] David Kibbe, MD, MBA, president and CEO of DirectTrust, an independent nonprofit trade group supporting direct exchange of patient data, said in 2013, "We are much closer than most people realize to achieving widespread health information exchange over the Internet that is secure, easy to use, and capable of connecting people working in unaffiliated healthcare organizations, health information organizations, and across multiple vendors' products."[76]

Public Opposes National Data System

On November 15, 2004, just seven months after President Bush used an executive order to create the ONC, the federal government issued a request for information on how to achieve nationwide interoperability and exchange of patient data. It was titled "Development and Adoption of a National Health Information Network."[77] The government received 512 responses from individuals and organizations (nearly five thousand pages).[78]

When HHS issued a report on the responses in June 2005, the title of the document was "Summary of Nationwide Health Information Network (NHIN) Request for Information (RFI) Responses."[79] HHS replaced *national* with *nationwide* in the description. Perhaps they felt *nationwide* had less of a big-government feel. HHS reported receiving many responses from individuals opposed to creation of a national patient ID and concerned about privacy and ownership of medical records. Later, the department also changed the acronym from NHIN (pronounced "en-hin") to NwHIN.

According to the HHS report, "Approximately 85 percent of responses from individuals expressed strong concerns about the potential loss of privacy" and "fifty-three percent of health professionals responding to the RFI also expressed concerns about the potential loss of privacy that could occur through a NHIN."[80] The concerns warranted their own section in the report: "Due to the number and length of comments on privacy and security aspects of a NHIN across multiple categories of RFI questions, this section was created to summarize these topics as presented by the respondents who commented on them."[81] In fact, 55 percent of the respondents were from individual consumers or individual health care professionals, according to this data chart presented in the report:[82]

Type of Respondent	Count	Percent
Individual Consumers	174	**34%**
Individual - Health Professionals	108	**21%**
Vendors - Software, hardware, system integrators	95	**19%**
Associations - Medical, Patient Interests, Vendors	54	**11%**
Multistakeholder Respondents	16	**3%**
Provider Organizations (Hospitals, clinics, labs, homecare, hospice, pharmaceutical firms, etc.)	16	**3%**
Research Org (think tanks, non-hospital Universities, etc.)	15	**3%**
RHIOs	10	**2%**
Payers (HMO, PPO)	9	**2%**
Standards Development Organizations	7	**1%**
Federal, State, Local Government agencies	4	**1%**
Foundations	4	**1%**
Total	**512**	**100%**

eHealth Exchange

Attempts to build the NHIN in the 1990s were unsuccessful. All seventy pilot projects to establish Community Health Information Networks (CHINs) failed. However, President Bush's April 2004 executive order reignited plans for a national health-data system.[83] A national coordinator for health IT was selected and requests for information (RFIs) were issued to stakeholders.[84] Contracts were awarded for development of national health IT standards and EHR certification criteria and the American Health Information Community was created to provide the secretary of HHS with recommendations on "how to accelerate the development and adoption of health information technology and the Nationwide Health Information Network (NwHIN),"[85] a transitional name for the system that is no longer used.

The Congressional Research Service gave an overview: "The National Health Information Network (NHIN) is envisioned as a 'network of networks'; that is, a nationwide, Internet-based architecture that interconnects state and regional health information exchanges (and other networks). It will be built on a secure platform using a shared set of standards and policies to permit interoperable health information exchange among providers, consumers, and others involved in supporting health care."[86]

In 2012 the governance of the NwHIN moved from the ONC to a nonprofit entity called Healtheway, which in 2015 changed its name to one most of the public would never connect with health or data: The Sequoia Project. As part of this transition to a public-private partnership, which was created among four federal agencies and "dozens of private sector organizations,"[87] NwHIN was "rebranded" the eHealth Exchange. Here is how Healtheway described these entities in 2012:

- **Nationwide Health Information Network (NwHIN):** A set of standards, services, and policies deemed by ONC as NwHIN.
- **eHealth Exchange:** A community of exchange partners who, via a contractual relationship, share information using NwHIN or other standards, services, and policies.
    - Started as an NwHIN program initiative in 2007
    - Transitioning to public-private partnership in 2012
    - Rebranded as *eHealth Exchange*
    - Healtheway assuming operational support, starting in Oct 2012
- **Healtheway:** [A] non-profit organization chartered to support the eHealth Exchange[88]

According to The Sequoia Project, which now oversees the system, the eHealth Exchange is "a group of federal agencies and non-federal organizations."[89] As of October 2017, Sequoia lists more than two hundred participants, including Alaska eHealth Network, Allina Health, CMS, Cleveland Clinic Foundation, CliniSync, CVS MinuteClinic, US Department of Defense, Kaiser Permanente, Kentucky Health Information Exchange, Mayo Clinic, Sanford Health, SSA, University of Miami, and Veterans Health Administration.[90]

eHealth Exchange—How It Works

The eHealth Exchange is not a centralized database per se. It's a "federated architecture, which means the network does not have a central hub through which all data passes. Rather, participants are able to securely connect and share data over the Internet in a standardized and seamless manner," reports The Sequoia Project.[91] It could also be called a "distributed database system"[92] in which the data stays at the original provider's location and the health information organizations (HIOs) that govern data exchange on eHealth Exchange only have a "pointer" to that data to show where it can be found.[93]

On its website, ONC notes: "Current eHealth Exchange participants include large provider networks, hospitals, pharmacies, regional health information exchanges and many federal agencies, representing 40% of all US hospitals, tens of thousands of medical groups, more than 8,000 pharmacies and 100 million patients."[94] The Sequoia Project reports its most popular use is "connecting the private sector providers and state and regional HIEs [health information exchanges] to federal agencies."[95]

This 2010 graphic in the HHS "Architecture Overview" shows how the NHIN is expected to work as a "network of nodes" that share data over the Internet.[96] (Note: Healtheway updated the graphic in 2013, changing the title from NHIN to eHealth Exchange and removing some of the details seen below.[97]) The six-sided figures attached to the Internet (represented by the oval) are the NHIN Nodes, which HHS describes as Health Information Organizations (HIOs) that participate "in the exchange of health information with other nodes on the NHIN via a NHIN Gateway."[98]

Figure 1: The Network Approach

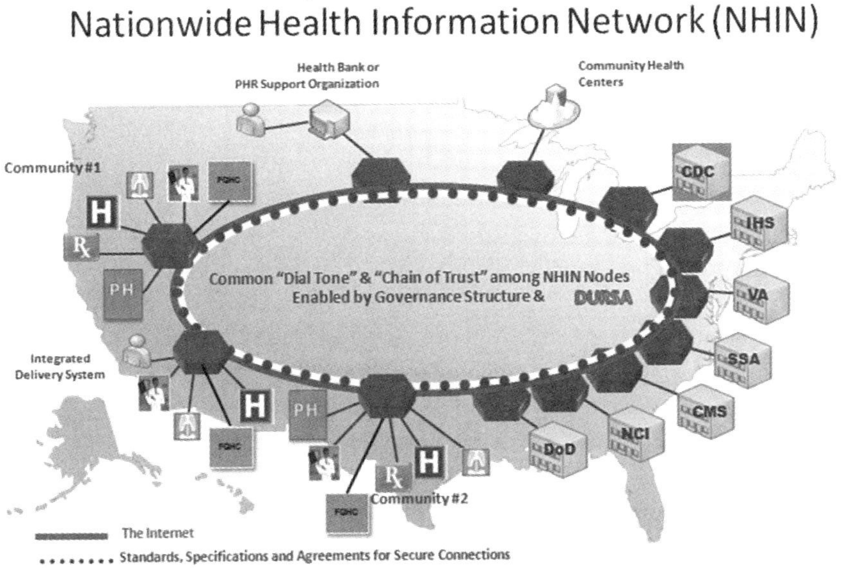

The Gateway is described as NHIN technical specifications implemented for exchange of patient data across the NHIN. As HHS explains, "an HIO's implementation of a NHIN Gateway enables each NHIN Node to maintain autonomy inside their domain, while adhering to NHIN specifications for inter-node communication."[99] The nodes can be as simple as a single computer or as complex as a server with multiple clients.[100] The nodes are "addressable" and defined as "the source or the recipient of an HIE 'transmission.'"[101]

Nodes may "include EHRs, lab information systems, PHRs, interface engines, etc."[102] For example, 250 provider facilities in Minnesota are hooked up to four HIOs as of August 2017. They include clinics, hospitals, medical centers, Indian Health Boards, County Social Services, radiology groups, anesthesia groups, a pathology lab, and more.[103] Data exchange over the Internet is governed by a Data Use and Reciprocal Support Agreement (DURSA), or as Healtheway calls it, a "shared trust framework and rules of the road."[104]

There are significant costs for hooking up (on-boarding) to the eHealth Exchange. While ONC was financially and operationally supporting the eHealth Exchange, participants were not charged during trial implementations, testified Michael Matthews, chair of the Healtheway board of directors, in January 2013.[105] Once it began operating independently, its sustainability model included fees. In 2012 annual *membership* fees for founding members ranged from $5,000 to $50,000, based on annual revenue.[106] Current annual *participation* fees for health systems and HIOs are in the chart below.[107] Participant testing fees range from being included in the participation fee to $11,000, depending on the test. The product-testing fee for vendors is $34,000. [108]

Annual Revenue	**Annual Participation Fee (Effective through 6/30/18)**	**Annual Participation Fee (Effective 9/1/2018)**
>$500 Million	N/A	$27,000
$100 Million to less than $500 Million	N/A	$25,000
$10 Million to less than $100 Million	N/A	$19,000
$10 Million or More	$19,000	N/A
$1 Million to less than $10 Million	$9,950	$11,000
< $1 Million	$5000	$5,000

Sequoia is working on an initiative to make patient medical records available during disasters. Using funding and technical support from CMS, ONC, the HHS Assistant Secretary for Preparedness and Response, the California Association of Health Information Exchanges, and research company MITRE Corporation, Sequoia is building the Patient Unified Lookup System for Emergencies, or PULSE. According to the website of *Health Data Management*, the goal is "to retrieve patient data from health information exchanges, hospitals and delivery systems, pharmacies and other sources using Sequoia's national exchange standards, and to match patients to their data."[109] A demonstration project is taking place in California. The funding and technical support will likely give Sequoia additional resources to expand the eHealth Exchange, and perhaps to build a national patient-matching system (see National Patient ID below).

State Health Information Exchanges

EHRs are critical to participating in health information exchange, which requires "the capacity to effectively store and manage clinical data electronically."[110] Without EHRs, this would be impossible. State health information exchanges (HIEs) for exchanging data between physicians, clinics, hospitals and others "are critical to the Obama administration's plans to digitize the healthcare system and make patient records available across the range of care settings," reported *Healthcare IT News* in 2015.[111]

The 2009 HITECH Act provided more than $30 billion in incentive funding for EHRs and $100 million[112] for state HIEs. In addition, the four-year State Health Information Exchange Cooperative Agreement Program (State HIE Program) to "establish HIE capacity among hospitals and healthcare professionals,"[113] provided $564 million to organizations in fifty-six states and territories.[114] In 2015, additional federal HIE grants totaling $28 million were given to states, territories, or state-designated entities that "work to expand coordination of care efforts so providers all over the country can begin to *modify their standards of care* using health IT and health information exchange," reported the ONC.[115] (Emphasis added.)

Changing the practice of medicine is the clear goal of the EHR mandate, state health information exchanges, and the eHealth Exchange. Sometimes, as the ONC did, the government actually admits it.

A 2016 report commissioned by the federal government has a map detailing which states had enacted laws to advance HIEs and EHRs as of 2013 in three categories:[116] *Laws Enacted to Promote Both EHR and HIE:* California, Connecticut, Delaware, Illinois, Maine, Maryland, Massachusetts, Minnesota, Mississippi, New Mexico, North Dakota, Oregon, and Vermont. *Laws Enacted to Promote Only HIE:* Arizona, Iowa, Kansas, Oklahoma, Arkansas, Florida, Hawaii, Kentucky, Nevada, New Hampshire, New York, North Carolina, Pennsylvania, Rhode Island, Texas, Utah, West Virginia, and Washington. *No Laws Enacted to Promote EHR or HIE:* Alabama, Alaska, Colorado, Georgia, Idaho, Indiana, Louisiana, Michigan, Missouri, Montana, Nebraska, New Jersey, Ohio, South Carolina, South Dakota, Tennessee, Virginia,

Wisconsin, and Wyoming. For further updates, readers are advised to check their own state laws.

State HIEs were part of the federal government's coercive three-prong approach: EHR mandate, MU mandate, and HIE mandate, with penalties for enforcement. The ONC wanted the State HIE Program up and running "to ensure that all eligible providers within every state have at least one option available to them to meet the HIE requirements of MU in 2011."[117]

Although a 2014 RAND study found more than one hundred operational HIEs,[118] most government HIEs are expected to fail. In late 2013, 72 percent of provider groups, payers, and insurers surveyed predicted "as few as 10 of the current public HIEs will still be around" in 2017.[119] By the end of the federal HIE grant program, seven HIEs were no longer operational and according to a study commissioned by the ONC, "grantees expressed concerns about the financial sustainability of their HIE efforts."[120]

Examples of failures include the dissolution of Wyoming's HIE after the federal grants were gone. Connecticut's HIE closed in 2014 after "wasting" $4.3 million in grants, wrote its executive director. Tennessee received $11.6 million but shut the HIE down in 2012.[121]

Funding is not the only problem. HIEs, according to the majority of stakeholders interviewed by Black Book Market Research, have flawed business models and fail to provide "meaningful connectivity."[122] For example, in January 2018, reports surfaced that Vermont's HIE was struggling. Despite receiving $44.3 million in state and federal funds, only 19 percent of eighty-nine "stakeholders" said it was meeting their needs and most had lost confidence in Vermont Information Technology Leaders (VITL), the organization running the HIE. VITL had not updated the HIE's plan for five years and didn't have its own long-term plan in place.[123]

But some HIEs appear to be thriving. In January 2018, the Strategic Health Information Exchange Collaborative (SHIEC) announced nationwide expansion of the "Patient Centered Data Home." The PCDH is a data-sharing and notification system that enables sharing of patient data between local, regional, and state-level HIEs. In short, it's HIE-to-HIE interoperability. HIEs in the PCDH system use the patient's zip code to determine if the patient is receiving care in their home region or another state. If the patient is out of state, a notification is sent to the exchange that's considered the patient's "data home." If the home HIE has records to share an automatic alert is generated, allowing the other exchange to request the records. A similar alert is generated from the "away" HIE after the patient is treated, notifying the home HIE of new records for the patient.

The national rollout follows a trial rollout among seventeen HIEs in three regions. The nationwide network was created by connecting the three regions. It includes a national, legally binding agreement for sharing data across state lines.[124] The network preserves state HIE consent options for patients. "The infrastructure that we're building with the Patient-Centered Data Home gives patients confidence that their records can follow them across the health system while adhering to their privacy preferences," says David Kendrick, a SHIEC board member and CEO of the MyHealth Access Network in Oklahoma.[125]

Consent Options for HIE

HIPAA does not require patient consent for the electronic exchange of health information. "HIPAA does not create legal obstacles for sharing information through an HIE. . . . This is because HIPAA contains exceptions that allow a covered entity to share information (without consent) for treatment, payment or healthcare operations," said Andrea Leeb, RN, JD, Chief Privacy Officer at Cal INDEX, at the April 2016 HIE in EMS Summit.[126] Congress also specifically designated HIEs as business associates,[127] which generally requires a data-use contract with the health care provider, but no consent from the patient.[128]

However, some states require affirmative, *opt-in* patient consent for the exchange of clinical data through the state's health information organization, such as Massachusetts requires for Mass HIway.[129] These states are exercising their right to create stronger state privacy laws under the state-preemption provision of HIPAA. Others, like California, do not.[130] Milken Institute School of Public Health has a list of each state's opt-in or opt-out policies, last updated in September of 2016.[131]

However, unless state law specifically prohibits it, some patients may not be able to keep their data out of the HIE even if they have consent or dissent options: "Data is always flowing to the HIE after the hospital is live. The consent concerns whether or not a treating physician can actually access the data, not what data is available," explains the Ohio Health Information Partnership.[132]

Furthermore, some data sharing may continue even if the patient has opted out. Per HealthShare Exchange (HSX): "Your opt-out does not prevent direct sharing of your health information from provider to provider through the exchange. It also does not prevent the sharing of your information outside of the exchange in the traditional ways permitted by law. Thus, it does not prevent a provider from seeking or sending information about you through other electronic or non-electronic methods. . . . Opting out does not prevent the HSX Encounter Notification Service from alerting your primary care provider, insurer, or care-management organization about emergency services or inpatient treatment you have received."[133]

Opt-in requirements protect patients, which threatens HIEs. Linda Reed, chief information officer at Atlantic Health System, a founding member of the health information exchange Jersey Health Connect, said the exchange grew quickly because patients had to explicitly *opt out*. Had the state's HIE proponents not convinced New Jersey's governor to accept opt-out as the standard, "we would have just had to close up shop."[134] But opt-out provisions do not recognize the privacy and property rights of patients. Opt-out laws claim the patient's data as government or business property, keep patients in the dark about the data sharing, and put the burden on patients to learn about and stop the intrusion. As a result, many patients may not know about the HIE or the opt-out option.

There are various consent models for health information exchange, according to the Office of the National Coordinator for Health Information Technology:[135]

Table 1. Consent Models

Model	Explanation
No Consent	Health information of patients is automatically included in and available through electronic exchange; patients cannot opt out.
Opt-out	Default is for all or some set of patient health information to be eligible for electronic exchange automatically, but the patient can opt out completely.
Opt-out with exceptions	Default is for health information of patients to be included in electronic exchange, but the patient can opt out completely or allow only selected data to be included.
Opt-in	Default is that **no** patient health information is automatically made available for electronic exchange; patients must actively express consent to participate, but if they do so, then their information must be all in or all out.
Opt-in with restrictions	Default is that **no** patient health information is made available for electronic exchange, but the patient may allow a subset of select data to be included.

Costly Connections

Having an HIE available is one thing. Hooking up to it is another. Providers must pay expensive "interface" fees to the EHR vendor.[136] To ease the financial burden, several states used federal HIE funding to cover the cost of building interfaces between provider EHRs and the HIE. States also used the funds for one-time "onboarding" connection costs or monthly subscription fees to the HIE.[137]

A price list provided by HealthlinkNY, the New York health information exchange shows how pricy electronic connections can be. The following tables of data taken from their 2015 "Services & Pricing Package" are costs for exchanging clinical data and radiology imaging data.[138] A note about the acronyms: PACS stands for Picture Archiving and Communication System (X-rays); C-CDA stands for Consolidated Clinical Document Architecture (clinical data); and ADT is a "single data feed that electronically transmits" Admission, Discharge and Transfer information. "ADT w/Consent" indicates whether the patient has consented to have their clinic or hospital access their health data, which is housed in the HIE.[139]

Interfaced Connection Options	Average Cost
C-CDA: Add-on Connection via Hub Model	$2,700
C-CDA: New Connection (Non-Hub Model)—Connection prices include an ADT w/Consent feed.	$32,500
Standard Hospital Connection (Multi-feed Package)—Connection prices include an ADT w/Consent feed.	$29,400

Individual Facility PACS Imaging Connections	Setup Cost	Annual Cost
Extra Large Facility—Over 300,000 imaging studies/year	$30,800	$36,960
Large Facility—Between 100,000 and 300,000 imaging studies/year	$22,000	$26,400
Medium Facility—Less than 100,000 imaging studies/year	$14,300	$17,160
Small Software-only Connection—Less than 24,000 imaging studies/year	$5,000	$9,900

According to the HealthlinkNY package, the average time to establish an interface between the health care provider's EHR and the state exchange ranges from three to twelve weeks. The cost of any additional project management services beyond the "included hours" in the HIE service and pricing package amounts are billed at $200 per hour.[140]

Despite all the dollars spent, government HIEs are not popular. In 2014, HIEs were used in only 2 to 10 percent all of encounters, according to RAND.[141] Another study found just 30 percent of state HIEs have health insurers participating, with 86 percent of payers saying they "refuse to pay the annual fees of public exchanges." [142] Accountable Care Organizations (ACOs) established by the Affordable Care Act (ACA) are driving payers and providers to build private exchanges. According to a 2016 study, 94 percent of payers planned "to totally abandon their involvement with public HIE initiatives and work within regions or states to bolster private enterprise HIEs, which more directly meets their need in engaging in accountable care contracts with providers." Furthermore, 93 percent of providers "are considering cooperating with payers on HIE initiatives to satisfy the growing need for enhanced data sharing under accountable care organizations."[143]

Meanwhile, Republicans are concerned that the HIE dollars spent under the HITECH Act may have been wasted. In January 2015, US Senators Lamar Alexander (R-TN), Richard Burr (R-NC), and Mike Enzi (R-WY) asked the Government Accountability Office (GAO) to review the health information exchanges to see what the nearly $600 million in taxpayer dollars bought.[144] Within days *Healthcare IT News* reported that an agency spokesperson said the review had begun.[145]

Payers Want a Single Network

According to a 2015 study in the *Journal of the American Medical Informatics Association*, many third-party payers of medical care believe America's approach to health information exchange has impeded payer involvement in public HIEs. In general, only 40 percent of HIE efforts nationwide have one or more payers providing financial support.[146] There is no sustainable business model yet. The federal funds have run out, and payers don't wish to keep the HIE boat afloat.

Furthermore, insurers think engaging with multiple state and regional networks is costly and complex. The study says public and private payers have five common principles for an optimal HIE, including a single network, broad access by payers to clinical data, no hoarding of data, financial support for HIE in proportion to the value they receive, and data exchange framed by the "triple aim" of improved patient experience of care, improved health of populations, and reduced per capita cost of health care. [147]

Notably, industry players aren't waiting for government to perfect the eHealth Exchange. Kibbe's DirectTrust network includes "over 100,000 health care organizations using more than 350 different EHRs."[148] With the 21st Century Cures Act requiring ONC to develop a Trusted Exchange Framework and Common Agreement to facilitate interoperability—essentially a single on-ramp[149]—CHIME and DirectTrust are partnering to ensure secure data exchange at "every location in the healthcare system where a patient's data and information might be needed."[150] Also, in December 2016, Carequality and CommonWell Health Alliance announced plans to work together to increase health IT connectivity nationwide.[151] Jitin Asnaani, executive director of CommonWell, said: "We believe this connectivity between CommonWell and Carequality will continue to move the country forward on its path to achieving nationwide data exchange by bringing together such a sizeable majority of providers and patients that there will be no turning back for American health care."[152]

Government Lax on Data Security

How secure is patient data in these public HIEs and how secure would it be in a national medical-records system? Forty percent of 800 Californians surveyed in 2015 said HIEs hurt data privacy and security.[153] Are they right? Consider one of the largest IT systems in the United States: Healthcare.gov, the national government information technology system for Obamacare enrollment.

David Kennedy, a cyber-intelligence expert and CEO of TrustedSec, told the CNBC website: "When you develop a website, you develop it with security in mind. And it doesn't appear to have happened this time. . . . It's really hard to go back and fix the security around it because security wasn't built into it."[154] At a congressional hearing, three witnesses said the exchange should be shut down.[155]

The security experts said Healthcare.gov runs on 500 million lines of code, which is twenty-five times bigger than Facebook, one of the world's busiest sites. "When your code base is that large it's going to be indefensible," said Morgan Wright, CEO of Crowd Sourced Investigations to *Reuters*. "Do you want to defend the Great Wall of China or a very small line?"[156]

In March 2016 the GAO reported "316 security-related incidents" at Healthcare.gov between October 2013 and March 2015.[157] The GAO also reported weaknesses in federal technical controls for data flowing through its Federal Data Services Hub, as well as a lack of federal oversight of the security and privacy of data processed by the state-based exchanges that connect to the data hub. A year earlier, GAO had testified that CMS had failed to improve security and privacy of Healthcare.gov, or to conduct privacy-impact assessments recommended by the GAO.[158] Tom Walsh, founder of the consulting firm tw-Security said, "The government should lead by example and implement better security practices."[159]

National Patient ID

Unique Patient Identifier

National data systems often require national identification systems. The 1993 Clinton Health Security Act required the federal government to issue health security cards with a unique patient identifier (UPI) "for the purpose of providing or assisting the eligible individual in obtaining an item or service that is covered." Had the law not failed, its National Health Board would have established standards for the card, including "the information to be encoded in electronic form on the cards."[160]

Just two years after the Health Security Act failed, the UPI became law in the Administrative Simplification section of HIPAA. When the US Department of Health & Human Services held a hearing in 1998 to solicit suggestions for implementation, your author testified against it, the *New York Times* covered the story,[161] and Congressman Ron Paul, MD (R-TX) used a 1999 appropriations bill to prohibit all funding for the creation of a national ID "until legislation is enacted specifically approving the standard."[162] The prohibition was added every year to the annual appropriations bill.[163]

The prohibition was so strong that individuals who wanted to discuss it were told by federal officials and congressional aides, "If we bring it up again, the meeting would be over because they could be perceived as breaking the law."[164] But the industry push continued. In 2012, concerned about emerging attempts to bypass the prohibition, CCHF issued a report on the history and continued push to establish a national patient ID.[165]

An opening to establish the UPI came unannounced in December 2014. For the first year since 1998, the annual prohibition against "planning, testing, piloting, or developing a national identification card" was not included in the appropriations bill for 2015.[166] A softer, more permissive version appeared:

> Sec. 510. None of the funds made available in this Act may be used to promulgate or adopt any final standard under section 1173(b) of the Social Security Act providing for, or providing for the assignment of, a unique health identifier for an individual (except in an individual's capacity as an employer or a health care provider), until legislation is enacted specifically approving the standard.[167]

Most people likely missed the switch, but Carl Bergman, the managing partner of EHRSelector.com, wrote, "Unlike Paul's absolutist text, the new rider makes Congress the last, biggest step in a formal ID process. The new language lets ID development go ahead, but if HHS wants to adopt a standard, Congress must approve it." In short, HHS could create a final standard but could not impose it. Bergman suggested the language would allow the National Institute of Standards and Technology (NIST) to develop a voluntary, industry standard and calls on "ONC, NIST, etc., to use this new freedom."[168]

By this time, national patient ID proponents had begun working on various patient-matching strategies, but this was not their preference. In 2015, the GAO reported, "Representatives from five [interoperability] initiatives noted that a national patient identifier, which HHS identifies as currently prohibited under law, is needed to fully address this challenge."[169]

"We need a unique patient identifier," pleaded Richard Milani, the chief clinical transformation officer at Ochsner Health System in New Orleans, at a July 7, 2015, event in Washington, DC, sponsored by the EHR Association. Milani also called for unique provider addresses, which according to Politico Pro, "he analogized to a phonebook for health care." However, sharing patient data for non-clinical purposes should be curtailed, he said. "There's a fear that you're mining data.... That's inappropriate." [170] Yes, but not illegal. HIPAA permits it.

In March 2015, the College of Healthcare Information Management Executives (CHIME), which "has lobbied . . . for a universal federal patient ID number,"[171] offered a $1 million prize to anyone who could come up with a 100 percent accurate patient identification system for the nation.[172] At least two hundred companies and individuals registered to receive more information about the CHIME National Patient ID Challenge, with the grand-prize winner announcement scheduled for November 3, 2017.[173] It should not be missed that three of the four finalists based their proposals on biometric technology.[174] However, on November 15, CHIME announced it was suspending the challenge because it "did not achieve the results we sought to this complex problem."[175]

The annual prohibition against a unique patient ID was not resurrected in the 2016 appropriation bill, which passed in late 2015; however, it did not include language specifically authorizing UPI development. This was no doubt a disappointment to UPI proponents, but they continued undeterred. On February 8, 2016, US Senators Patty Murray (D-WA) and Lamar Alexander (R-TN) introduced the Improving Health Information Technology Act, which included a GAO study on patient matching:

> Not later than 1 year after the date of enactment of this Act, the Comptroller General of the United States shall conduct a study to review the policies and activities of the Office of the National Coordinator for Health Information Technology and other relevant stakeholders to ensure appropriate patient matching to protect patient privacy and security with respect to electronic health records and the exchange of electronic health information.[176]

Industry achieved success in 2017. Nineteen years after Dr. Paul's prohibition, on May 5, 2017, President Trump signed into law the Consolidated Appropriations Act, 2017.[177] It included language that twenty-five groups had requested of Congress and the US Senate in an April 5, 2017, letter.[178] The organizations signing the letter include the American Medical Association (AMA), America's Health Insurance Plans (AHIP), the American Health Information Management Association (AHIMA), CHIME, the euphemistically titled Confidentiality Coalition, Healthcare Leadership Council, HIMSS, Intermountain

Healthcare, Medical Group Management Association (MGMA), Premier Healthcare Alliance, and The Sequoia Project.[179]

Like the 2014 law, the 2017 law specified again that none of the funds could be used to adopt or provide for "the assignment of, a unique health identifier for an individual (except in an individual's capacity as an employer or health care provider), until legislation is enacted specifically approving the standard." However, it provided more than $60.3 million for the "development and advancement of interoperable health information technology."[180]

Then, in an accompanying report that explains Congress's intentions, in a section titled "Unique Patient Health Identifier," language nearly identical to language in the April letter authorizes HHS to "provide technical assistance to private-sector led initiatives to develop a coordinated national strategy that will promote patient safety by accurately identifying patients to their health information." It specifies that the prohibition on a unique patient ID "does not prohibit HHS from examining the issues around patient matching."[181]

Proponents of a national patient identification number were elated. "After Nearly Two Decades, a Win in Congress for Patient Data Matching" heralded a post by HIMSS.[182] The website EHR Intelligence went further: "National Patient Identifier Gains Congressional Support."[183] Interestingly, the federal government had already engaged in the process. On April 28, 2017, just twenty-three days after the multigroup letter and seven days before President Trump signed the bill, the Patient Matching Algorithm Challenge was announced with $75,000 in prizes "powered by" ONC, Capital Consulting Corporation, MITRE Corporation, and Just Associates.[184]

Two states aren't waiting. Indiana's Regenstrief Institute is "building a new automated tool to accurately match patient records" using a five-year $1.7 million federal grant from AHRQ. It will use the Indiana Network for Patient Care, the largest inter-organizational health data repository in the country, which is operated by the Indiana Health Information Exchange.[185] And acting on behalf of the New Jersey Department of Health, the New Jersey Innovation Institute received a $2.9 million grant in 2015 to develop a patient identification database, reports the *Personal Injury Law Journal* blog.[186] "The so-called 'Master Patient Index' initiative endeavors to compile the health history of every person in the state and assign him or her a unique identifier."[187] These kinds of initiatives could lead to a national patient ID—state by state empowered with federal funds. Notably, New Jersey is required by state law to participate in the National Health Information Network.[188]

Meanwhile, in early September 2017, the same week that credit reporting company Equifax announced the hack of personal information affecting 145.5 million people[189]—later increased to more than 147 million[190]—credit bureau Experian announced that it was working to convince EHR companies to incorporate its Universal Identity Manager into their systems as a unique patient identifier solution, reported *Modern Healthcare*.[191]

One month later, at a panel discussion hosted by ONC, health IT policy expert Jeff Smith shared his opinion on the state of interoperability telling ONC that "making healthcare data digital and computable is a prerequisite for interoperability" and that "the asymmetric adoption and upgrades of health IT systems across the nation's hospitals and physician offices would dog interoperability." He added, in a later post on *Medium*, "[W]hile I neglected to mention it on the panel, it seems to me that without improved patient matching and linking of patient data, all of our efforts will be for not [sic]—especially as more and more datatypes enter the picture."[192]

One provider of cloud-based services for medical practices and health systems, athenahealth, is working on a unique plan to identify patients and build a networking platform, "so that eventually with everyone there you kind of pull out the pin and everyone is connected," says Jonathan Bush, athenahealth's CEO and president. As reported by the website Healthcare Dive, athenahealth is working "to create a national patient index across the U.S. and a national calendar that acts like Open Table or TripAdvisor. In theory, a patient could make an appointment with any doctor on athenaNet or any doctor not on athenaNet that wants to use the athenaNet calendar."[193]

Meanwhile, as detailed earlier, Congress has proposed legislation that would allow health care clearinghouses to use and share patient information without patient consent. Since clearinghouses have medical claims data on approximately 90 percent of all health care transactions, and because they already help establish organization-specific unique patient IDs for health care systems, the bill could potentially lead to a universal patient identifier.[194]

The American public has not consented to a national patient ID that will link all their data into a single lifelong, longitudinal record. However, since HIPAA mandates it, and because Congressman Paul's prohibition is all but gone, powerful forces are working to establish it.

Patient Biometrics and Augmented Identification

Some say it's time to uniquely identify patients by biometrics, which could include fingerprints, facial recognition, iris and palm scans, behavioral patterns, and DNA. Dan Cidon, chief technology officer of NextGate, writes, "Instead of looking at a NPI as the definitive answer to solving our patient ID issues, the industry should focus on a pragmatic, multi-faceted approach to improve patient matching—one that moves beyond probabilistic algorithms." He suggests supplementing today's technologies with biometrics, such as using smart phones to capture "biometric signatures."[195]

Will the public support using their own body as an identifier? A 2017 survey found 26 percent of millennials more likely to hand over their biometric data for identity, compared to 19 percent of baby boomers. However, only 14 percent of those born after 1998 support biometric identification, according to the website Nextgov.[196]

These young Americans will have a battle on their hands. Biometric identification can start early. Hospitals have recently begun taking high-resolution footprints of newborns. McLaren Northern Michigan hospital reports, "The digital footprints and security photo can be stored efficiently in the newborn's electronic medical record. And, much like fingerprints, footprints are a biometric identifier, unique to each baby, so they can be used for identification throughout a lifetime."[197] The Newborn Safety System, which also captures the mother's fingerprints, was developed by CertaScan Technologies in line with recommendations from the National Center for Missing and Exploited Children. The system is already being deployed in hospitals in twenty-four states.[198] Concerned parents may want to think twice before subjecting their newborns to this biometric identification scheme.

Furthermore, "augmented identification" facilitated by biometrics is in the works,[199] even though Eduard Goodman, global privacy officer at CyberScout, warns that biometric identification could lead to "extrapolated uses of biometrics" and "misuse of its data collection."[200] IDEMIA, a company with close to 3 billion euros in revenues and fourteen thousand employees,[201] calls itself "the global leader in trusted identities."[202] The corporation is involved in data collection for the TSA Precheck program at American airports,[203] has contracts with various federal agencies, and distributes identification documents for governments all over the world, including biometric IDs to more than one billion people in India[204] and state driver's licenses in forty-two states, which increasingly include a REAL ID-compliant biometric facial scan.[205] For more information, see CCHF's report: "Exposing Idemia: The Push for National Biometric IDs in America."[206]

Privacy Threat of REAL ID

Another way to establish a national patient ID is through REAL ID, which US Senator Lamar Alexander (R-TN) once called a "national identification card."[207] REAL ID has been unpopular and controversial, and it's been called unconstitutional commandeering.[208] Legislators from several states have sent letters to President Trump asking for relief from the law that "federalizes driver licensing," creates a "national identity registry," and usurps power reserved to the states.[209] In short, it's a violation of states' rights under the Tenth Amendment.

Although the 2005 federal REAL ID Act mandates that states comply with federal specifications for all driver's licenses and identification cards, including a facial biometric standard,[210] the US Department of Homeland Security (DHS) admits it's a voluntary program for the states.[211] REAL ID includes a national hub for the collection of data on every individual with a state driver's license or identification card.[212]

This new national ID can easily become a national *patient* ID. In January 2018, the daughter of an eighty-nine-year old Maryland woman wrote that her mother's doctor would no longer be able to see her if she didn't have "a new photo ID, now required by some doctor's offices." As she explained in a *Carroll County Times* op-ed, "Her expired license no longer sufficed. Her doctor refused to see her again if she did not get the new ID immediately."[213]

The REAL ID Act authorizes the secretary of DHS to expand the official purposes for which it must be used: "'Official purpose' is defined under §201 of the Act to include access to Federal facilities, boarding federally regulated commercial aircraft, entry into nuclear power plants, and such other purposes as established by the Secretary of Homeland Security."[214] Given how heavily health care is federally regulated, the secretary could unilaterally choose to make health care access an "official purpose," thereby establishing a national patient ID. More than fifty-five million Americans are Medicare recipients[215] and 74.5 million Americans are recipients of Medicaid and the Children's Health Insurance Program (CHIP).[216]

Note: The aforementioned IDEMIA offers identity services to states to become REAL ID compliant.[217] For more details and little-known facts about REAL ID, such as the fact that DHS says, "Individuals without a REAL ID-compliant document will still be able to enter Federal facilities and board commercial aircraft,"[218] go to the REAL ID page on the CCHF website: http://www.cchfreedom.org/issue.php/39.

Big Data and Big Business

Selling Patient Data

Data in medical records is valuable. OCR Director Roger Severino told HIMSS 2018 conference attendees that having patient data is like "holding a bar of gold" that should be guarded "like Fort Knox."[219] Unknown to many Americans, the holders of medical records often sell patient information to commercial databases. As Adam Tanner writes in *Scientific American*, "At present, the system is so opaque that many doctors, nurses and patients are unaware that the information they record or divulge in an electronic health record or the results from lab tests they request or consent to may be anonymized and sold."[220]

In an article titled, "How Data Brokers Make Money Off Your Medical Records," Tanner discusses data brokers engaged in a multi-billion-dollar business. IMS Health, a $9 billion company in 2016 and one of the largest brokers in medical data, recorded $2.6 billion in revenue in 2014, writes Tanner, a fellow at Harvard University's Institute for Quantitative Social Science. He explains,

> Nowadays IMS automatically receives petabytes (1015 bytes or more) of data from the computerized records held by pharmacies, insurance companies and other medical organizations—including federal and many state health departments. Three quarters of all retail pharmacies in the U.S. send some portion of their electronic records to IMS. All told, the company says it has assembled half a billion dossiers on individual patients from the U.S. to Australia.
>
> IMS and other data brokers are not restricted by medical privacy rules in the U.S., because their records are designed

> to be anonymous—containing only year of birth, gender, partial zip code and doctor's name. The Health Insurance Portability and Accountability Act (HIPAA) of 1996, for instance, governs only the transfer of medical information that is tied directly to an individual's identity.[221]

However, anonymity is a ruse. Chesley Richards, director of the Office of Public Health Scientific Services at the Centers for Disease Control and Prevention (CDC), told Tanner, "It is getting easier and easier to identify people from anonymized data." Tanner concurs: "Once upon a time, simply removing a person's name, address and Social Security number from a medical record may well have protected anonymity. Not so today. Straightforward data-mining tools can rummage through multiple databases containing anonymized and nonanonymized data to reidentify the individuals from their ostensibly private medical records."[222]

Iqvia, with $8 billion in revenue in 2017, has arrangements with 120,000 sources around the world to get anonymous data, reports *Modern Healthcare* in an article about third parties harvesting patient data. The data comes from providers, payers, and pharmacies, but rarely from EHR vendors. However, the data from hospitals are "technically arriving via a technology partner." Furthermore, EHR vendors often have contracts with clinics and hospitals that allow them to sell patient data. "It's the EHR vendor who's aggregating provider data, then de-identifying them, and then, at their discretion, monetizing or commercializing them," says Scott Kolesar, the health technology innovation leader for the US at Ernst & Young. While Epic Systems does not yet sell the patient data in their vast EHR system or include a contractual clause allowing them to, according to the article, "Practice Fusion's provider user agreement includes provisions that allow it to sell de-identified information 'for any purpose without restriction.'" According to Tanner, the company has sold longitudinal data sets for $50,000 to $2 million.[223]

Doctors, nurses, and patients "will not remain in the dark about these practices forever," says Tanner. "I have found growing unease about the ever expanding sale of our medical information not just among privacy advocates but among health industry insiders as well."

He notes, “The entire health care system depends on patients trusting that their information will be kept confidential.”[224]

Monetizing Data

In 2015 the Mayo Clinic announced that it was switching to the Epic EHR system. In January 2016 Mayo announced it was selling its 62,000-square-foot Rochester, Minnesota data center to Epic for $46 million. Epic will lease the data center back to Mayo for at least four years, with an option to continue indefinitely.[225] A few months before the announcement, Carl Dvorak, Epic’s president, said his corporation was “working actively with Mayo Clinic to offer some of their clinical content as a paid-for subscription.” Some of the money will go to Epic as payment for managing that process for Mayo but “the app store will allow them to monetize solutions,” he told *Healthcare IT News*.[226]

That’s not the only collaboration. In 2015 Epic announced it will be working with the Mayo Clinic and IBM Watson Health “to apply the cognitive computing capabilities of the Watson supercomputer to electronic health records,” as the *Milwaukee Business Journal* reports.[227] Epic plans to integrate Watson’s capabilities into its clinical decision support (CDS) platform. “Clinicians will be able to share clinical data with Watson and, using that data, Watson will help develop patient-specific treatment plans and personalized chronic disease management plans,” reports the website HIStalk.[228] Watson will be used to conduct “thorough analysis of medical factors” in patient records that could affect a patient’s health and wellness, the *Journal* adds.[229]

Do patients have the right to refuse to be under this analytic microscope? In a legal analysis focused on health data, Wendy Mariner contends that hospitals and practitioners “typically review EHR data to analyze the cost and quality of care that they have provided to their patients.” She then cautions, “Where the analyses are designed to provide generalizable knowledge to improve patient care in general, rather than to inform the reviewers’ own practices, they could be considered health services research that requires patient consent under state law.”[230] However, since some states conform their state medical privacy laws to the permissive federal HIPAA "privacy" rule, such consent may not be required.

Wearable Surveillance Is Big Business

Analysis of individuals 24/7 will be enabled by the technology that increasingly enamors the American public. Venture funding for health IT in 2015 surpassed $4.3 billion, with 50 percent in six categories that included health care consumer engagement, wearables and biosensing, and personal health tools.[231] According to a Market Reports press release, "Diagnostic wearable medical devices are used to monitor, control, and track an individual's vital signs at regular intervals. . . . Diagnostic wearable medical devices monitor physiological data through remote or wireless communication and transmit this information to medical professionals or the user."[232]

Supporters of shifting the focus of health care institutions from patient care to "population health" see many opportunities coming their way from wearables, patient portals, and patient-generated information reports *HealthITAnalytics*:

> Although wearables have been around for a few years now, their burgeoning popularity with patient populations will bring the Internet of Things to new heights this upcoming year. These devices, made popular by products such as the FitBit or AppleWatch, have the power to monitor patient health from a remote location . . . helping to reduce costs and maintain patient and population health. . . .
>
> "Wearable sensors hold promise for both outpatient and inpatient monitoring as they continuously monitor health status less obtrusively, capture and provide more data to clinicians, and possibly enable patients to leave the hospital sooner and prevent readmissions," the authors of the [ECRI Institute] report write. "Wearable sensors have potential to cut the cord for inpatient physiologic monitoring and can

potentially provide continuous, unobtrusive monitoring pre-, intra-, and post-surgery."[233]

Apple Health acts as a "centralised dashboard for all your wearable tech and fitness app data powered by the HealthKit developer framework," claims James Stables in *Wareable*.[234] At least twenty-two fitness apps work with Apple Health, he writes.

But who owns and has control over personal data collected from wearables and the increasingly broad array of Internet-based mobile health apps? As Americans grapple with this issue, the European Commission is working on a privacy code of conduct for mobile health apps. *Politico* reports: "Apps that collect and use data to predict or measure health risks would fall under the voluntary code. Developers must gain informed consent and use data for 'specific and legitimate purposes.'"[235]

Meanwhile, uses for wearables are expected to grow. Google is creating a contact lens that will measure the glucose level of a diabetic's tears, and the Apple Watch may someday measure blood oxygen. Proponents of importing data from wearables to EHRs say this is inevitable. Bob Wachter, MD, says, "I think we're going to rethink what an EHR is over time. . . . These things won't be separable. There's a whole world of consumer-facing data collection that will involve everything from a sensor to a wearable to perhaps a survey you fill out every day that shows up in your email. . . . At the end of the day, all these things need to connect."[236]

This is not true. Nothing needs to connect, and 24/7 data collection is not inevitable. Once Americans realize that HIPAA doesn't protect their privacy but allows their private data to be broadly shared, how will they respond? Will we see #DeletePatientPortal emerge?

Tracking America's Children

On November 21, 2017, the American Academy of Pediatrics (AAP) announced its commitment to spend $583,000 to develop and establish the Clinical Health Information and Longitudinal Data (CHILD)

Registry over the next five years. As reported by *Becker's Hospital Review*:

> To develop the CHILD Registry, the AAP will capture children's health data through EHRs, health payers and existing pediatric disease registries. The organization's goal for the project is to collect, store and analyze health data from all U.S. children, including information related to well-child and sick visits, chronic disease management and specialty care. . . . The registry will also include a patient portal to allow parents and patients to submit their own data.[237]

This brings up at least two questions. Will parents be asked for consent before their child's data is submitted? And will AAP try to secure and include data from government home-visiting programs?

Using federal grant funding, public health nurses, social workers, and paraprofessionals visit the homes of many pregnant mothers and families with newborns and young children,[238] collecting data on the families.[239] Former Congressman Henry Hyde (R-IN), chairman of the House Judiciary Committee, in an October 1998 letter to colleagues, called home-visiting "cradle to grave tracking of newborns" and "big brother intervention as we have never seen before."[240] The ACA has provided approximately $400 million in grants each year for home-visiting programs.[241]

Privacy Rights, Consent, and Coercion

Americans Support Consent Requirements

Federal policy and the actions of corporations and government officials often don't align with public opinion on privacy rights.

Surveys show strong public support for patient-consent requirements. In September 2017, a study discussed the factors that influence patients' willingness to electronically share private medical information—which, ironically, is called *protected* health information (PHI) under HIPAA. The researchers sought to better understand how to "represent a patient's interests more accurately in sharing settings, instead of treating patients like predetermined subjects." They concluded, "Privacy concerns are a central stage in modern society and the crown jewel is the sharing of PHI." The authors state that privacy concerns had "the most influence on individuals' intentions to share" and "privacy concern is a major barrier to sharing PHI with providers."[242]

In a 2015 survey, 75 percent of 800 Californians said their participation in a health information exchange (HIE) depended most on privacy and security considerations. Fully 89 percent preferred opt-in consent or opt-in with "break the glass" access in an emergency. But almost a quarter would prohibit sharing data without consent even in an emergency. In addition, 40.3 percent said HIEs worsen privacy and 42.5 percent said they worsen security. Regarding EHRs, 52.4 percent said electronic health records worsen privacy and 42.7 percent said they worsen security.[243]

In a 2000 Gallup Survey titled, "Public Attitudes Toward Medical Privacy," patient consent and protection of medical records from outside access was the clear choice of Americans:

- **78** percent feel it is very important that their medical records be kept confidential.

- **93** percent say that medical and government researchers should not be allowed to study an individual's genetic information unless they first obtain his or her consent.

- **92** percent oppose allowing government agencies to see their medical records without their permission.

- **82** percent object to insurance companies gaining access without permission.

- **67** percent oppose researchers seeing their medical records without the patient's permission.

- **91** percent oppose a federal requirement to assign everyone a medical identification number, similar to a Social Security number, to create a national medical database.[244]

According to Sue Blevins, then president of the Institute for Health Freedom, "The Gallup survey results show that individuals clearly do not want government agencies or private groups accessing their medical information without their permission . . . Any new law or regulation—whether federal or state—that strips Americans of their right to determine who sees their medical records is going against the will of the majority of citizens. Consent has always been viewed as a fundamental human right and the Gallup poll confirms that Americans strongly support that right when it comes to determining who can access their medical and genetic information."[245]

Black Book surveyed 12,090 consumers in late 2016 and found the following, according to Healthcare Informatics:

- 57% report "being skeptical of the overall benefits of health information technologies, such as patient portals, mobile apps, and electronic health records, mainly because of recently reported data hacking and a perceived lack of privacy protection by providers."

- 87% of patients were unwilling "to comprehensively divulge all their medical information."
- Respondents were concerned "that their pharmacy prescriptions (90%), mental health notes (99%) and chronic condition (81%) data is being shared beyond their chosen provider and payer to retailers, employers, and or the government without their acknowledgement."
- 89% report withholding health information during provider visits.[246]

Furthermore, respondents to the 2015 California survey were more likely to agree to share de-identified information for research (76.2 percent) than to share identified information for healthcare (57.3 percent). On the question of research, 69.8 percent valued individual control over societal benefit. And 44.8 percent said consent should be required for each research project before EHRs are accessed electronically. Only 7.9 percent said there was no need to ask permission.[247] Patient privacy concerns extend to mobile devices. In 2016, researchers found 44 percent of those surveyed were completely unwilling to share diagnostic information using the devices and only 24.8 percent were very willing to share the information.[248]

In a 2013 survey on patient concerns about privacy, 69 percent of nearly 2,100 respondents were very or somewhat concerned about privacy of medical records, of which 75 percent were very or somewhat concerned about the security of medical records. As expected, the study found only 8 percent withheld information from a health care provider due to these concerns.[249] Most patients in need of treatment will do what's necessary to receive it, even if they may have privacy concerns. Essentially, they have no choice. It would be interesting to see how the results of this survey might change if people realized that HIPAA does not protect their privacy but allows vast sharing of information.

Ten years before the EHR mandate, a 1999 survey conducted by Princeton Survey Research Associates for the California Health Care Foundation found 15 percent of the population taking steps to protect their privacy:

> In total, 15% of national adults and 18% of California adults say they have done something out of the ordinary to keep personal medical information confidential. The steps people have taken to protect medical privacy include behaviors that may put their own health at risk or create financial hardships. These behaviors include: going to another doctor; paying out-of-pocket when insured to avoid disclosure; not seeking care to avoid disclosure to an employer; giving inaccurate or incomplete information on medical history; and, asking a doctor to not write down the health problem or record a less serious or embarrassing condition.[250]

The public's opposition to data being shared without consent for research is also well known. As Wendy Mariner writes about a "rigorous" 2008 survey on research and consent conducted by Harris Interactive and Alan Westin for the Institute of Medicine:

> Only 1% of respondents were willing to allow researchers to use their personal information without their consent, while 8% were willing to give a general consent to such use. . . . Thirty-eight percent wanted the right to consent to or refuse each use, while 13% would not allow research use under any circumstances.[251]

The First Violation

When does a disclosure violate privacy? Alan Westin, former Columbia University Professor of Public Law and Government and author of *Privacy and Freedom*, defines privacy as "the claim of individuals, groups or institutions to determine for themselves when, how and to what extent information about them is communicated to others."[252] But in an article on health information privacy and the Constitution of the United States, Wendy Mariner writes, "As Professor Nicolas P. Terry notes, discussions of health information privacy often conflate privacy protection with preserving the confidentiality of information already obtained, with or without a person's permission." Mariner correctly underscores the key issue: "The threshold question is whether identifiable data should be collected without consent in the first place. If not, its collection is an invasion of privacy."[253]

For example, the ACA requires "any federally conducted or supported health care or public health program, activity or survey" to gather and report (without the consent of patients) "data on race, ethnicity, sex, primary language, and disability status for applicants, recipients, or participants . . . [and] any other demographic data as deemed appropriate by the Secretary regarding health disparities." The law requires the HHS secretary to develop a standard for the collection of data that "at a minimum":

i. Collects self-reported data by the applicant, recipient, or participant; and

ii. Collects data from a parent or legal guardian if the applicant, recipient, or participant is a minor or legally incapacitated

The secretary, who is required to analyze the data collected to detect and monitor trends in "health disparities" must ensure that "all data collected . . . is protected . . . under privacy protections that are at least as broad as those that the Secretary applies to other health data under [HIPAA regulations]." The secretary of HHS must also protect the data "from all inappropriate internal use by any entity that collects, stores, or receives the data."[254]

In line with Mariner's concerns, the statute requires protection of privacy, but only *after* the law compels the health care provider to gather the data. This means that providers must do everything possible to compel patients to pick a race, choose an ethnicity, and so on before they can see the doctor or be admitted to the hospital.[255] Patients have no idea their choices are being reported to the government and could be used for purposes that have nothing to do with their visit.

In the case of this particular data collection, there's more afoot than meets the eye. In 1999, the US Commission on Civil Rights issued an extensive report on "health disparities." Two commissioners dissented saying the report advocates "not only a whole new bureaucracy, but a national strategy to achieve a 'leveling' in health care delivery, research, and financing. . . . the report is a thinly veiled endorsement of universal health care."[256]

So the next time you hear claims that HIPAA requires government or others to keep your data private, keep in mind that the collection of the data is the first violation of your privacy, unless you provide it willingly, without coercion and with fully informed written consent. Once your private information has been taken, by force or otherwise, the word *privacy* simply means keeping your data secure in someone's data system for their uses—or for the multitude of disclosures permitted by HIPAA.

Fourth Amendment or Third-Party Doctrine?

How does the US Constitution address medical record disclosures? You might be surprised to learn that the courts and the federal government have devised a loophole to access your medical records, despite the protections of the Fourth Amendment, which reads:

> The right of the people to be secure in their persons, houses, papers, and effects, against unreasonable searches and seizures, shall not be violated, and no Warrants shall issue, but upon probable cause, supported by Oath or affirmation, and particularly describing the place to be searched, and the persons or things to be seized.[257]

That loophole is called the "Third Party Doctrine." In a scholarly law article titled, "Reconsidering Constitutional Protection for Health Information Privacy," Wendy Mariner says the doctrine, "permits the government to obtain information from a third party without the data subject's consent." Furthermore, she writes,

> The third-party doctrine presumes that information held by third parties, like hospitals and health insurers, no longer qualifies as the person's "papers or effects" protected by the Fourth Amendment.... For decades, the third-party doctrine has operated to close the courts to claims that information provided to government by a third party violates the Fourth Amendment—primarily in the criminal context."[258]

"In contrast," she writes, "government agencies, such as health departments, seek mandatory reporting laws to collect health information for civil purposes. Civil reporting laws require information about a population, none of whose members are suspected of any criminal offense." Thus, government databases, such as the state All-Payer Claims Databases and state prescription-monitoring programs "invite data mining," she cautions. "The appeal of analyzing information already collected is almost irresistible. If one searches hard enough, something will certainly be found. Thus, the mere existence of a database attracts new users and uses."[259]

With some hope, she notes, "judicial hints have encouraged critics of the third-party doctrine to argue that the Fourth Amendment does not give government entirely free rein to obtain information about a person simply because the information is in the hands of a third party."[260] She writes the article to encourage a reassessment of whether and how other Amendments might protect personal health information. This would include all data gathered by the EHR. In 1928, US Supreme Court Justice Louis Brandeis wrote a compelling statement about privacy and the US Constitution. Now would be a good time to follow his admonition:

> The protection guaranteed by the Amendments is much broader in scope. The makers of our Constitution undertook to secure conditions favorable to the pursuit of happiness. They recognized the significance of man's spiritual nature, of his feelings, and of his intellect. They knew that only a part

> of the pain, pleasure and satisfactions of life are to be found in material things. They sought to protect Americans in their beliefs, their thoughts, their emotions and their sensations. They conferred, as against the Government, the right to be let alone—the most comprehensive of rights, and the right most valued by civilized men. To protect that right, every unjustifiable intrusion by the Government upon the privacy of the individual, whatever the means employed, must be deemed a violation of the Fourth Amendment.[261]

Coercive Consent Forms

The EHR mandate, HIPAA, Meaningful Use, and MACRA have led to coercive data-gathering mechanisms. When patients schedule an appointment, the data collecting begins. Some patients are asked to provide information using the clinic or hospital's Internet portal. Some are sent a bundle of paper forms to complete. Others arrive at the clinic or hospital where they are handed an iPad that collects "structured data" (no write-in answers) and will not advance from one question to the next without an answer.

Patients are often asked to sign on an electronic pad with no idea what they're signing. Some are told it's the HIPAA form. But with no words to read, it could be anything. Patients should request a paper copy of whatever the form is, and only sign that form if they wish to. Contracts between the electronic pad vendors and health care facilities may include agreements to testify in court that the patient was a willing signer (had the stylus in his or her hand), that it's the patient's signature according to independent handwriting experts, that it's a legally signed document, and more.[262] No one should sign an electronic pad that does not show every word of the form or requested consent. The patient's signature makes it a legal document. A similar concern was shared during an interview-based study on the use of e-consent: "I know things can change online. If it's something I signed—this is a hard copy. You can see what I signed. Sometimes online, things change."[263]

Beware of iPad cameras. One person titled "Anonymous" commented on a "submit ideas for document signing" Web page for the Practice Fusion EHR: "Let us create our own waiver or consent forms and then allow the patient to sign on iPad.... Allow the camera on the iPad to take a photo of the patient while signing."[264] Patients who are not interested in the clinic or hospital entering a photo into the EHR (which could also be circulated by the HIE) should consider bringing an adhesive note to cover up the camera as soon as the iPad is in their hands.

Although the HIPAA rule allows most sharing of patient data without patient consent, it requires patient *authorization* for "uses and disclosures of protected health information not otherwise allowed by the Rule," reports HHS.[265] However, HIPAA prohibits compound authorizations—those in which two authorizations are combined into one with a single signature—reported the Institute of Medicine. In addition, "it is generally not permissible to condition treatment on the provision of an authorization."[266]

Considering the vulnerable status of most patients in need of care, many clinic and hospital consent forms are coercive. Some may violate HIPAA's prohibition against compound authorizations. CCHF has received copies of forms from across the nation with multiple consent provisions and only one signature line. For example, the "Consent for Services" form at Minnesota-based North Memorial Clinic has a list of nine items, including consent for treatment and consent for release of medical records "regardless of when generated" for medical or scientific research. Just above the signature line, the form states, "By signing below, I consent to *all of the above* and I acknowledge that I have received a copy of the North Memorial Notice of Privacy Practices." [Emphasis added.][267] This is not true consent because sick and injured patients must "consent" to all nine items if they want treatment. Patients can prohibit the clinic from sharing their data for research, but only if they submit a written objection. A true consent form would include simple "yes" and "no" checkboxes for each item being requested of the patient.

V

Government Intrusion

Research at the Bedside

Controversial ACA Research Institute

The Obama administration understood the power of data mining. The 2009 ARRA, or "economic stimulus" bill, not only imposed the $30 billion EHR mandate, it also dedicated at least $1.1 billion for "comparative clinical effectiveness research" (CER) using patient data. Further, the law established the Federal Coordinating Council for Comparative Effectiveness Research, comprised of fifteen senior federal officials to advise HHS on CER. The Institute of Medicine, which was mandated to determine priority research topics, developed a list of one hundred topics across twenty-nine research areas.[1]

However, with enactment of the ACA in 2010, the Federal Coordinating Council was dissolved and the Patient-Centered Outcomes Research Institute (PCORI) was established in law as a nonprofit government-funded corporation to conduct the mandated CER activities. PCORI's advisory group includes seven federal agencies.[2]

During the 2009 Senate debate over the bill, Senator Pat Roberts (R-KS) warned about the government using the federally funded research to ration care or impose cookie-cutter treatments. While he said he's all for it [CER], he doesn't want the government to use it to ration health care and called it "very dangerous territory."[3]

Senator Roberts introduced The Four Rationers Repeal Act of 2015 to repeal four federal agencies included in the ACA, including PCORI. Roberts warned, "The government can now use taxpayer dollars to invest in ways to reduce patient access to care. . . . The reality is they're going to reduce patient's ability to access the care they want and need, all hidden under the cloak of innovation." He's concerned that PCORI's research "will be abused to arbitrarily deny patients access to potentially lifesaving treatments or services."[4]

There is cause for concern. Peter Orszag, director of the Congressional Budget Office in 2007 told Congress that CER might not yield any direct savings for many years, but suggested "Medicare could use information about comparative effectiveness to promote higher-value care."[5] Indeed, one year later he suggested to Congress: "to alter providers' behavior, it is probably necessary to combine comparative effectiveness research with aggressive promulgation of standards and changes in financial and other incentives."[6]

Jerome Groopman, MD, a professor of medicine at Harvard Medical School, points out the potential harm: "Over the past decade, federal 'choice architects'—i.e., doctors and other experts acting for the government and making use of research on comparative effectiveness—have repeatedly identified 'best practices,' only to have them shown to be ineffective or even deleterious."[7] Yet former Senate Majority Leader Tom Daschle (D-SD) once suggested establishing a Federal Reserve-type body for health care, that would use CER to set standards for federal health care programs.[8] Orszag thought similarly, as reported by *Politico* just two days after ARRA and the CER program became law:

> The next step on health care, [Orszag] said, is a set of "changes to Medicare and Medicaid to make them more efficient, and to start using those programs more intelligently to lead the whole health care system."
>
> With a growing body of research finding some practices more cost-effective than others, the program's reimbursement rules can be used to force changes at those hospitals—a sort of back door to health care reform.
>
> "Medicare and Medicaid are big enough to change the way medicine is practiced," he said.[9]

Millions in Federal Research Database

By September 2015 PCORI hoped to have created "a giant repository of medical information from 26 million to 30 million Americans" to use for comparative effectiveness research.[10] In 2014, PCORI invested more than $250 million to develop PCORnet, and in 2015, PCORnet received $142.5 million to expand the network.[11] By May 4, 2017, there were 46 million in the network.[12] Few if any of them know.

PCORnet has thirty-three research partners, including "13 Clinical Data Research Networks (CDRNs), based in healthcare systems such as hospitals, integrated delivery systems, and federally qualified health centers, and 20 Patient-Powered Research Networks (PPRNs), operated and governed by groups of patients and their partners."[13] CDRNs include the Mayo Clinic, which received a three-year, $10-million grant to participate,[14] and the Greater Plains Collaborative, a network of twelve medical centers in eight states with a total population of sixteen million patients.[15]

Seven health systems in New York City are participating, with a goal of aggregating data on a minimum of one million patients. The systems will "extract data from their EHRs or clinical data warehouse platforms,"[16] including diagnoses, blood tests, X-rays, insurance claims, surgeries, and some genetic samples.[17] A centralized data processing facility will "match patients while preserving anonymity across multiple EHRs as a way of creating an integrated and complete view of longitudinal clinical data":

> The Informatics Center will leverage two health information exchanges' existing electronic master patient indices, patient matching algorithms, and patient de-duplication techniques provided by vendors . . . to align data contributed by systems to NYC-CDRN.
>
> The central database will link to other sources including public and commercial claims data; patient-reported and patient-generated data, including data actively collected through surveys and passively collected through mobile devices; genomic data allowing for novel links to biologic and molecular disease markers; and other publicly available data.[18]

Proponents say patients' identifiable data are retained by hospitals and not included in the database, but this gives no comfort. First, as noted, de-identifying the information does not make it anonymous because it could be reidentified. Second, the subjects of the data have had their information shared for research without their consent. Third, the project treats data as though patients have no ownership rights to the most private information about themselves.

The *Washington Post* notes the troubling distinction between the database and typical research: "Hospitals and other organizations participating in the project don't have any plans to explicitly inform patients about this. If researchers wanted doctors to collect additional data as part of a clinical trial, the researchers would clearly have to get a patient's consent." According to the *Post*, certain privacy experts claim "the general consent forms that patients sign when they get treatment should allow the use of data already collected in the aggregate."[19] However, this is not consent, patients are not being given a choice, and some patients may refuse if consent was requested.

On May 4, 2017, PCORI announced the release of "refreshed data and expanded conditions of interest." "We are pleased to offer researchers a more robust view of the data from more than 100 health institutions and the millions of Americans PCORnet represents," said its executive director Joe Selby, MD, MPH.[20]

Research to Restrict Care?

It is no accident that the EHR mandate was enacted before the Affordable Care Act. Nineteen times the Act mentions "comparative clinical effectiveness research" and "comparative effectiveness research" (CER) is mentioned four times.[21,22] Section 6301 of the law focuses on CER and establishes PCORI, as well as the Patient-Centered Outcomes Research Trust Fund (PCORTF) to fund its activities. Such research is enhanced by electronic access to patient data.

PCORI issued its first grants in December 2012, totaling $40.7 million over three years.[23] In May 2013 PCORI announced $88.6 million for CER over three years.[24] In 2016, the PCORI board approved

$153 million for "28 comparative clinical effectiveness research (CER) studies and seven related projects for improving CER methods." The money targeted conditions and problems that "impose high burdens on patients, caregivers and the healthcare system."[25] On August 15, 2017, the PCORI Board of Governors approved $119 million for twenty CER studies.[26]

The ACA requires PCORI to establish a research agenda by identifying "national priorities for research" that focus on chronic conditions and "the effect on national expenditures associated with a health care treatment, strategy, or health conditions." PCORI must also consider the "National Strategy for Quality Improvement in Health Care" in Section 399H of the ACA.

To assist PCORI in securing data to conduct research, ACA section 6301 requires the HHS secretary to take two actions: 1) make data available from Medicare, Medicaid, the Children's Health Insurance Program (CHIP), and public health data networks, and 2) develop clinical registries and health outcomes research data networks to develop a "comprehensive, interoperable data network to collect, link, and analyze data on outcomes and effectiveness from multiple sources, including electronic health records."[27]

Despite assertions to the contrary—"Materials, forums, and media used to disseminate the findings, informational tools and databases shall . . . not be construed as mandates, guidelines, or recommendations for payment, coverage, or treatment"[28]—the law clearly permits PCORI's research to be used to restrict payment for and access to care.

ACA section 1182 states that rationing is prohibited—HHS must not use CER to make coverage, reimbursement, or incentive decisions that treat "extending the life of an elderly, disabled, or terminally ill individual as of lower value than extending the life of an individual who is younger, nondisabled, or not terminally ill." But the law also states that this prohibition on value-based rationing "shall not be construed as preventing the Secretary from using evidence or findings from such comparative clinical effectiveness research in determining coverage, reimbursement, or incentive programs . . . based upon a comparison of the difference in the effectiveness of alternative treatments in extending an individual's life due to the individual's age, disability, or terminal illness."[29] Thus, the secretary is allowed to determine "effectiveness" and use those determinations to deny coverage and reimbursement.

Interestingly, the law attempts to create statutory distance between PCORI and the federal government. It states PCORI "is neither an agency nor establishment of the United States Government." But then the legislation adds, "The Institute shall be subject to the provisions of this section" of the ACA and must make an annual report to Congress and the president. Furthermore, PCORI must give preference to research done through the federal Agency for Healthcare Research and Quality (AHRQ) and the National Institutes of Health (NIH). Finally, the Office of Communication and Knowledge Transfer at AHRQ is required to broadly distribute the research findings of CER. In short, PCORI is a nonprofit in name only. It's really an arm of the federal government.

Who Funds PCORI?

As noted, the stimulus bill appropriated $1.1 billion for CER. Of this, $400 million went to HHS, $400 million to NIH, and $300 million to AHRQ.[30] That was just the start. One year later, also as noted, Obamacare established PCORI and gave it a ten-year budget of $3 billion, reports Bloomberg Government.[31] The *Washington Post* pegs the total revenue stream at about $500 million per year.[32]

The funding comes from the "general fund of the Treasury,"[33] siphoning dollars from the Medicare trust fund and a fee on insurers. From 2010 through 2012 the PCORI Trust Fund received a total of $210 million from the general fund. For 2013-2019 PCORI will receive general-fund appropriations of $150 million per year plus the net revenue from fees imposed on health insurance and self-insured plans. In addition, in fiscal year 2013, the PCORI Trust Fund received $1 per Medicare Part A and Part B recipient from Medicare. For 2014-2019, the amount transferred from Medicare is $2 per recipient.[34]

Learning Health System

The federal government would also like research to be ongoing in the exam room and at the bedside—through the EHR. In June 2014 ONC issued its "10-Year Vision to Achieve an Interoperable Health IT Infrastructure," a paper supporting broad adoption of health IT so "health information can be easily and appropriately shared to support multiple uses." In line with the ACA drive to comparative effectiveness research, ONC states, "the national priority of cost-effective care requires information about quality and use of services to be available to consumers, providers, payer, and employers." And almost as an afterthought, ONC adds, "Further, physicians expect health IT to enable and support patient care."[35] While most Americans may believe that's the primary purpose of the EHR, as it was with the paper medical record, this statement shows how others may consider patient care just one purpose of many.

The ONC also launched a new goal: to allow the health care system to "continuously learn," which "should also enable lower health care costs, improved population health, truly empower consumers, and drive innovation." ONC further writes, "An interoperable health IT ecosystem should support critical public health functions such as real-time disease surveillance and disaster response, and data aggregation for research and value-based payment that rewards higher quality care, not necessarily a higher quantity of care."[36]

On January 30, 2015, with the EHR mandate in place and a majority of clinics and hospitals in compliance, ONC released a draft of an EHR-based "interoperability roadmap."[37] The roadmap describes the health care system as a "learning health system." HHS Secretary Sylvia Burwell said, "A successful learning system relies on an interoperable health IT system where information can be collected, shared and used to improve health, facilitate research, and inform clinical outcomes."[38] Here is ONC's online description:

> This draft Roadmap proposes critical actions for both public and private stakeholders that will advance our nation towards an interoperable health IT ecosystem, advance research and ultimately achieve a learning health [system]. Health IT that

> facilitates the secure, efficient and effective sharing and use of electronic health information when and where it is needed is essential to better care, smarter spending and a healthier nation.[39]

This is government-speak at its worst. For those who can read between the lines, it portends a nationwide data-sharing system that meets the agendas and purposes of people other than patients and their doctors.

ONC took the public's comments through April 3, 2015, and put them online, spread over seventeen web pages.[40] Approximately 20 percent of almost 250 comments objected to the interoperability plan. Most of the 20 percent were from individuals. Perhaps that's why there's a special section on the page listing "statements of support for advancing an interoperable learning health system"—from corporations, government agencies, health care organizations, and the data industry.[41]

On October 6, 2015, the final ONC interoperability roadmap[42] was released along with a colorful infographic.[43] Although the agency said comments on the draft roadmap "demonstrated that there is a great deal of confusion" about when data can be legally exchanged without patient consent," it omitted any mention of the opposition voiced by many commenters. The only link to these comments appears to be a link on the roadmap web page, which is also where there are three links to "Statements of Support" and the roadmap graphic shown here appears.[44]

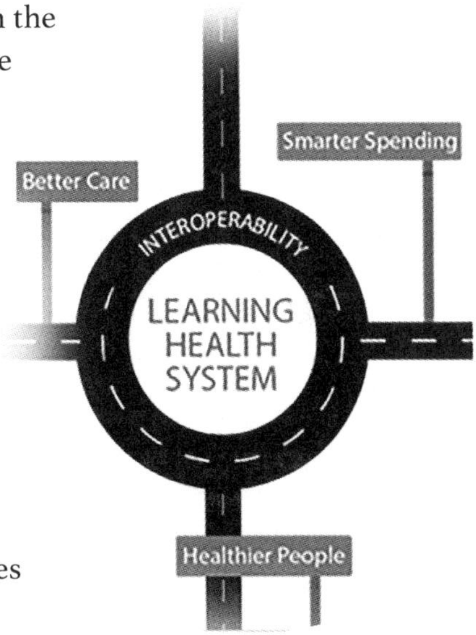

The term "learning" is essentially a euphemism for exam-room surveillance, at-the-bedside research, ongoing analysis, and standardization of care. ONC envisions a future of "seamless sharing and use of electronic health information" at the individual, population and longitudinal level, all 50 states "aligned in policy" (no state privacy laws), and financial "incentives" to advance interoperability.[45]

When ONC released its final roadmap, there were documents labeled "Version 1.0" and "Final Version 1.0."[46] In them, ONC suggested patients could be given the option of "Basic Choice"—essentially the right to opt out of certain data sharing, thus dissent, not consent—but did not encourage it. It also acknowledged the public's concerns about privacy, but said, "policy debates about the degree of control that individuals should have over health information are ongoing and will continue into the future."[47] Tellingly, it wrote the following about sharing and use of protected health information (PHI) for treatment, payment, and health care operations (TPO):

> Of particular importance to a learning health system is the fact that the Privacy Rule *permits* the use and disclosure of PHI for TPO without express individual [patient] permission (called "consent" in this Roadmap and in other venues).[48]

In fact, the ONC notes, "the HIPAA Privacy Rule does not require permission for information to be shared."[49] That's true, but as I discussed earlier, state legislatures have the power to restrict unconsented sharing of patient data under HIPAA's state preemption authority as well as the Tenth Amendment.

ONC hopes states will not act. It asks all state governments and "stewards of health information" (health care organizations, HIEs, etc.) to revise these more protective regulations and policies by 2024 "to align with the consensus on non-sensitive information that is permissible to exchange—or access, use and disclose." Whose "consensus" would that be? ONC is particularly focused on sharing data without the individual's written consent for treatment, payment, and health care operations (TPO) to establish "consensus background rules for the nation."[50] As a reminder, the HIPAA definition of *health care operations*—the *O* in *TPO*—is nearly four hundred words long. Perhaps under the Trump administration, ONC's focus will change.

However, Gopal Khanna, the new director of AHRQ under President Trump, wants to catalyze "the evolution of learning health systems." He envisions "a health care delivery system that lives within a larger ecosystem of data—a system that provides a 'whole-person,' or 360-degree view of patients." This, he writes in an AHRQ blog post, "requires thinking beyond the walls of the traditional health care delivery system."[51]

On September 5, 2017, AHRQ and PCORI announced $8 million in grants to promote a sustainable learning health system workforce. One objective of this research program is identification, recruitment, and training of "clinician and research scientists who are committed to conducting patient-centered outcomes research in healthcare settings." The training programs "embed the scholars at the interface of research, informatics, and clinical operations within learning health systems."[52] This research at the bedside will be funded by taxpayers, but may or may not be known or consented to by patients.

In October 2017, the American Medical Association announced its own national health-data system to support "a continuous learning environment to enable interoperable technology solutions and care models that evolve with real-world use and feedback." The Integrated Health Model Initiative (IHMI) will "help the health system learn how to collect, organize and exchange patient-centered data . . . and transform the data into a rich stream of accessible and actionable information."[53] The initiative, which includes the American Medical Informatics Association, Cerner, Epic, IBM, PCORI, and as of January 3, 2018, ten other collaborators,[54] will allow the data to be "easily extractable," says AMA CEO James Madara.[55]

Federal "Common Rule" for Research

The federal government often permits patient consent to be waived for federally funded research. A 2015 proposed revision to the Federal Policy for the Protection of Human Subjects Rule ("Common Rule"), issued by sixteen federal agencies, excluded government agencies and private entities from consent requirements for analysis and research using biospecimens (e.g., blood, urine, organs, and DNA) and medical data, including EHR data, claims data, and data in state health surveillance systems.[56]

Exceptions to consent requirements were pervasive. The proposed rule included nine exemptions—research that was not subject to the rule, except as specified. It also included twelve exclusions—research that was considered outside the scope of the rule and thus "deemed not research."[57] In addition, the institutional review boards (IRBs) could still waive consent requirements as they've done for years. In public comments on the proposed rule, Citizens' Council for Health Freedom called these loopholes.[58]

The federal government made clear its objection to being constrained by its own regulation. The agencies claim "collection and analysis of data, biospecimens and records by a criminal justice agency, public health surveillance activities, and surveillance, collection and analyses of data and biospecimens for national security purposes" should be carried out "without any hindrances that satisfying the Common Rule regulatory requirement might impose." They also argue that some activities fall into a "gray area that encompasses some activities that arguably might be judged to be research" but then claim these activities as "part of inherently governmental functions" in which "the principles of beneficence and justice outweigh any intrusions on individual autonomy that the regulations might have prevented."[59]

On January 19, 2017, the Obama administration issued the final Common Rule. It eliminated "exclusions" but in the definition of research, it deemed four activities not to be research, including public health surveillance. It exempted certain secondary research uses of identifiable private information or identifiable biospecimens from consent requirements.

Research conducted by or on behalf of the federal government including "government-generated or government-collected information obtained for nonresearch activities," was deemed as secondary research for which consent is not required.[60] This could include newborn DNA stored by states after newborn (genetic) screening.

Research on "Baby DNA" Without Consent

Newborn screening is a state government genetic-testing program. Newborn test results and dried blood spots, taken by pricking the newborn's heel, are stored long-term or indefinitely by many states after the screening is done, without parental knowledge or consent.[61] Parents are not pleased. At least five lawsuits against state health departments have been filed, the most recent in Michigan.[62]

In 2014, Citizens' Council for Health Freedom (CCHF), which has opposed this storage since discovering it in 2003, secured a parent consent amendment for the Newborn Screening Saves Lives Reauthorization Act of 2014.[63] It required consent for the use of newborn dried blood spots for federally funded research, did not allow consent to be waived, and deemed this to be human subjects research. Indiana State University Senior Biology Major Samantha Zent, who researched the storage of newborn blood, said that until the 2014 law "there was no federal mandate that required hospitals and research entities get parental consent to use the child's sample in research."[64] The consent requirements went into effect on March 16, 2015.[65]

But the final Common Rule *eliminated* the consent requirements. As part of the Senate negotiations to get the genetic privacy amendment added to the bill, the statutory language requiring parental consent was only in force until the final rule was issued, at which time CCHF expected the protection to be retained by the rule.[66] However, the final rule states:

> The [Newborn Screening Saves Lives Reauthorization Act of 2014] made a number of changes relevant to the HHS regulations for protecting research subjects, including asserting that research with newborn dried blood spots (DBS) that is federally funded . . . is to be considered research with human subjects, and that the provisions allowing IRBs [institutional review boards] to waive consent would not apply. By statute, the changes made by this law applied only until changes to the Common Rule are promulgated. Thus, the changes made by this statute will no longer apply after the effective date of this rule, January 19, 2018.[67]

Many commenters, according to the final rule, felt that "important research involving newborn screening would be halted or inhibited" under the proposed rule. Under the final rule, "secondary research with nonidentified newborn DBS would be treated in the same way as secondary research with any other type of nonidentified biospecimen. Such research would not be considered research with human subjects under the final rule, and thus would not be subject to the rule."[68]

Most parents do not support this decision. A 2009 survey of parents regarding researcher use of newborn dried blood spots (CCHF calls it "Baby DNA") found only 28.2 percent were somewhat or very willing if no consent was obtained. The rest of the parents essentially said, "Not without my permission":

> In this survey of a nationally representative sample of parents, we found that over three-quarters of parents would be willing to permit the use of their children's NBS samples for research purposes if their permission was obtained prior to such use. However, if permission was not obtained prior to the use of these NBS samples for research purposes, more than half of parents would be "very unwilling" to permit use of their child's sample. These findings indicate the importance of considering parental permission in future plans to use NBS samples for research purposes.[69]

The four federal "Newborn Sequencing in Genomic Medicine and Public Health" programs have discovered similar parental resistance. The NIH's five-year, $25 million program "explores the trio of technical, clinical and ethical aspects of genomics research in the newborn period."[70] Genomic sequencing "examines the complete DNA blueprint of the cells," reports NIH. Two of the projects, BabySeq and NC Nexus, have faced challenges enrolling participants into the programs, despite early indications of interest by the families.[71] Only 7 percent of more than 2,400 couples approached have agreed to participate, including only 24 of 345 sick babies in neonatal intensive care and 138 of 2062 healthy babies, reports *Science*.[72] Newborn babies in the BabySeq program are "tested for nearly 2,000 conditions."[73] The San Francisco–based project, NBSeq, got institutional review board

(IRB) approval to analyze the DNA in the de-identified dried blood spots of newborns,[74] which are stored by the State of California without consent after newborn screening, but parents may request the blood spots be destroyed and therefore not used for research.[75]

Parent concerns include confidentiality and privacy, fear of future discrimination for life, disability or long-term care insurance, and getting unclear or unfavorable results.[76] Regarding the possibility of insurance discrimination, geneticist Robert Green with the BabySeq project told *Science*, "A lot of that is literally 50 years in the future and they are concerned."[77] He told CBS New York, "We can't predict what kind of discrimination is going to be occurring by the time your child grows up. . . . We can't predict whether some sort of privacy breaches [will occur], and we most importantly can't predict the information is accurate."[78]

Parents thinking long-term about protecting their child should also consider this: a sequenced newborn grows up with exposed DNA—and with no ability as an adult to reclaim the privacy of their genetic code. As Dave Archard, chair of the Nuffield Council on Bioethics, said, "Babies do not get a say in this, making it especially important that they, and others, are not disadvantaged in their future lives by a decision taken at birth."[79]

Hands Off My EHR

Adults are also concerned about research that digs deep into their DNA and EHR. The federal *All of Us* genetic research program, previously known as the Precision Medicine Initiative, has hit a snag. "In early testing of its consent form, about 20 percent of patients failed to agree to share their electronic medical records with researchers," reports Politico Morning eHealth in October 2017. Some estimated it was as high as 30 percent.[80] NIH has "invested in a state-of-the-art biobank and built 'big data' IT systems to transfer and store data,"[81] and plans to use the EHR as one way to collect the medical information of an expected one million participants. "Those records are a crucial part of All of Us; without them scientists won't be able to correlate things like genetic mutations, environmental pollutants and exercise patterns with the subjects' health outcomes. The power to predict which genes, pollutants, foods or activities affect health would be lost," reported *Politico*.[82]

About four thousand people signed up for the beta-testing phase of this ten-year study, for which the Obama administration requested $309 million in fiscal year 2017.[83] The program's FAQ only says: "If you have an electronic health record, we may ask for access." Now 30 percent of the participants appear to be in the "none of us" camp when it comes to the EHR. Therein lies the value of a written consent form. The details are laid out for prospective participants to make an informed decision. National rollout of All of Us and nationwide enrollment began on May 6, 2018.[84]

Affordable Care Act Experiments

"ACA Innovation Center"

The Affordable Care Act established a new government agency to conduct research on the American people without their consent. The Center for Medicare & Medicaid Innovation (CMMI, or Innovation Center) will "test innovative payment and service delivery models to reduce program expenditures."[85] Several models give preference to or mandate use of EHRs.[86]

The HHS secretary may choose from eighteen models in the statute (called "opportunities") but is not limited to them. For example, one model uses salaried doctors rather than doctors paid a fee for their services. Another model provides varying payments for physicians according to their adherence to "appropriateness criteria" for ordering advanced diagnostic imaging services,[87] such as CTs, MRIs and PET scans.[88] And another provides "payment incentives" for care coordination and "appropriateness of care." This Oncology Care Model (OCM) "is working with EHR vendors in a workgroup to review data needs for OCM implementation and strategies to support practices in reporting data to the OCM Data Registry."[89]

The implications for privacy and the practice of medicine under the CMMI models are made clear in a proposed Medicare payment rule posted on July 11, 2014, which states that the secretary of HHS and CMS "must be able to determine specifically which individuals are receiving services" through the experimental models of payment and health care delivery.[90] The proposed rule also says these patients—"the subjects of the intervention"—will be "compared to clinically, socio-demographically, and geographically similar matched individuals."[91]

And if the intrusion wasn't clear enough, the agency writes, "To carry out this research we must have access to patient records not generally available to us."[92] Certain models "will conduct quality measurement across all patients regardless of payer" and require "the ability to identify all individuals subject to the model test regardless of payer."[93] CMS uses more than one thousand words on more than one page of three-column text to rationalize government access to identifiable patient data.[94] At the end of the "Access to Identifiable Data for the Center for Medicare and Medicaid Innovation Models" section they write: "We invite public comment on this proposal to mandate the production of the individually identifiable information necessary to conduct the statutorily mandated research under section 1115A of the Act."[95]

This proposed access would impact *every patient.*

Every patient seen at the participating clinic or hospital, whether publicly subsidized, privately insured, or cash paying, would have their private information reported to the government. Furthermore, the federal government requires submission of "identifiable health and utilization information for patients of private payers" from clinics and hospitals participating in the experiment "when an explicit purpose of the model test is to engage private sector payers."[96] In short, the federal government is demanding personally identifiable health data on the privately insured for government research without the patient's consent.

Most private payers today are involved in Medicare and Medicaid. Thirty-nine states (including Washington, DC) have Medicaid contracts with managed care organizations.[97] In addition, most of the 17.6 million individuals in Medicare Advantage—31 percent of all Medicare enrollees in 2016[98]— likely enrolled in the 2,034 private Medicare Advantage plans offered for 2017 enrollment, such as Aetna, Blue Cross and Blue Shield affiliates, Cigna, Humana, Kaiser Permanente, UnitedHealthcare, and Wellcare.[99]

For illustrative purposes, below are examples of just some of the types of information that could be required to carry out an evaluation, and for which the evaluator would need patient-level identifiers:

- Utilization data not otherwise available through existing Centers for Medicare & Medicaid Services (CMS) systems.
- Beneficiary, patient, participant, family, and provider experiences.
- Beneficiary, patient, participant, and provider rosters with identifiers that allow linkages across time and data sets.
- Beneficiary, patient, participant, and family socio-demographic and ethnic characteristics.
- Care management details, such as details regarding the provision of services, payments or goods to beneficiaries, patients, participants, families, or other providers.
- Beneficiary, patient, and participant functional status and assessment data.
- Beneficiary, patient, and participant health behaviors.
- Clinical data, such as, but not limited to lab values and information from EHRs.
- Beneficiary, patient, and participant quality data not otherwise available through claims.
- Other data relevant to identified outcomes—for example, participant employment status, participant educational degrees pursued/achieved, and income.[100]

The final rule, issued in November 2014, noted the many concerns expressed about this requirement. The rule received 2,945 comments, including from various entities that wanted separate assurance that the required data sharing would not violate the HIPAA privacy law. HHS responded by saying the data would be subject to HIPAA requirements, whether in the hands of CMMI or their "evaluation contractors," acting as HIPAA business associates. But their response included a troubling admission:

> We respectfully disagree that sufficient assurances have not been provided. *The disclosure would be required by a regulation, so it would be "required by law" under HIPAA.* See 45 CFR 164.512(a) and the definition of "required by law" at 45 CFR 164.103. A HIPAA covered entity is permitted to disclose protected health information as required by law under these provisions so long as the disclosure complies with and is limited to the relevant requirements of the law. A separate minimum data necessary determination is not required under the HIPAA Privacy Rule for required by law disclosures under 45 CFR 164.512(a). See 45 CFR 164.502(b)(2).[101] (Emphasis added.)

Thus, under the permissive HIPAA rule, HHS demands full disclosures of patient data, including identifying information, characteristics, treatments, outcomes—not only from Medicare and Medicaid patients, but from any patient that a participating clinic or hospital has under its care.

Hospitals Forced to Experiment on Patients

As of March 2018, CMS has implemented thirty-seven innovation models.[102] One model in particular has generated significant controversy and dissent.

On November 24, 2015, the CMS Innovation Center finalized a rule to "test" a new way of paying for hip and knee joint replacements for Medicare patients for the next five years, starting on April 1, 2016.[103] In the final rule creating a payment model for comprehensive joint replacement (CJR), Medicare officials designated eight hundred hospitals[104] in sixty-seven metropolitan regions to participate.[105] Participation was mandatory, not voluntary, a fact that upset hospitals, which told CMS that it had no statutory authority to force them to participate. CMS responded in the final rule by claiming:

> We disagree with commenters that we lack the legal authority to test the CJR model as proposed and specifically, to require

> the participation of selected hospitals. . . . Such a design will allow for testing of how a variety of hospitals will fare under an episode payment approach. . . . The information gained from testing of the CJR model will allow CMS to more comprehensively assess whether . . . episode payment models are appropriate for any potential national expansion.[106]

Here's how it works. Medicare will determine the cost of a government-defined "episode of care" for hip and knee joint replacements and reattachment of lower extremities.[107] If a hospital, at the end of the year when costs are reconciled, has stayed under the determined cost for all its patients, the hospital will receive a reconciliation payment. If the hospital spent more than the specified cost, the hospital will have to pay the government back.

Notably the "episode of care" is not limited to the actual cost of the procedure and postsurgical care. An "episode of care" can last for ninety days after discharge and includes the cost of treatment given to the patients for conditions directly related to the joint replacement and for chronic conditions that may be affected by the procedure or postsurgical care.[108]

CMS admits this is an experiment on patients, that it will be collecting data electronically, that no consent is required, that prior notice is unnecessary, and that no acknowledgement of a notice of the experiment is required—leaving it more likely that patients will not know what is happening.

The proposed rule suggested allowing patients to opt out of data sharing. However, CMS in the final rule states, "we have decided not to finalize our proposal to allow beneficiaries the opportunity to decline having their data shared." Specifically, Medicare recipients receiving joint replacements "will automatically be included in the model" and "will not have the option to opt out of inclusion in the model." They will also not be able to "opt out of having their beneficiary-identifiable data shared" through "interoperable exchange of health information." Instead the agency will "make a robust effort to reach out" to educate patients about the CJR model, starting at the time of admission to the hospital.[109]

Responding to commenters who wrote that patient notification should be earlier, the agency wrote, "We do not agree that the point of admission is too late." Additionally, because the final rule does not specify any mechanism proving patients have been notified and because no signature is required to indicate that the patient has agreed to participate, most Medicare recipients will not realize they have been entered into an experiment.[110]

Should patients worry that their joint replacements will be of lower quality to cut costs? Should they expect shorter stays or limits on access to certain care as a method of keeping the cost as low as the government determines it should be? CMS says, "Issues associated with care stinting, provision of substandard care, or denial of medically necessary care are serious matters."[111] The regulation permits the agency to "take action" against hospitals or their collaborators if these situations are found, but did not impose a separate financial penalty.[112]

However, after President Trump's inauguration, the implementation of all new and pending rules was halted for sixty days and agencies were encouraged to consider delaying regulations beyond the sixty-day period.[113] On March 21, a new interim rule delayed the pending July expansion of the CJR model to hip and femur fractures until October 2017.[114] But on August 17, CMS issued a proposed rule to give hospitals a "one-time option to choose whether to continue their participation in the model."[115] If a hospital wanted to *opt in* to the program, it had to send a written "participation election letter" by January 31, 2018, according to the American Hospital Association.[116]

However, when the final CJR rule was issued on December 1, CMS modified the opt-out provision, giving only certain hospitals a one-time option to choose whether or not to participate. Mandatory participation was reduced from hospitals in sixty-seven metropolitan areas to hospitals in thirty-four areas, the geographic areas with the highest payments for lower extremity joint replacements, and certain low-volume and rural hospitals in those areas are not required to participate. CMS estimated that 370 hospitals would be under the participation mandate and that sixty to eighty hospitals would voluntarily participate, for a total of 430 to 450 hospitals for the last three years of the experiment.[117]

Patients who enter participating hospitals will be automatically enrolled in the "test" and its data-sharing requirements. Medicare promises that it will warn patients but what good is a warning when they are being admitted to the hospital with a broken hip? And how will they warn them? And if they wanted to go elsewhere, what ambulance would transport them to a hospital outside the metropolitan area? There are many questions, but clearly patients would be given little notice of the medical experiment taking place at their bedside.

ACOs: Seniors Secretly Enrolled

Accountable Care Organizations, established by the ACA's Medicare Shared Savings Program,[118] also have control of America's physicians as a top priority—through the EHR. In 2017, 850 ACOs provided care to more than 28 million people, with 570 ACOs participating in CMS models, including the Shared Savings Program, Next Generation ACO Model, and the Comprehensive ESRD [End-Stage Renal Disease] Care Model.[119] As John C. Goodman, now president and CEO of the Goodman Institute for Public Policy Research once wrote,

> There is one thing that ACOs will indisputably accomplish. They will drive doctors into organizations where their behavior can be controlled. For the first time in our history both the practice of medicine and the way money is spent on medical care will fall under federal control.[120]

Goodman wrote, "ACOs are HMOs on steroids."[121] David Himmelstein, MD, a professor at the City University of New York at Hunter College, said ACOs are "essentially the modern version of HMOs."[122] ACOs are classified as alternative payment models (APMs) in which groups of physicians, hospitals, and others band together "assuming accountability for the quality of care and financial outcomes of the populations they serve."[123]

Data exchange is key. As part of the responsibilities of participants, one ACO agreement found online says the ACO participant "must have the capability to exchange clinical and demographic information electronically with ACO" and shall provide patient clinical data to the ACO for various purposes, including "to advance the health of the population through measurement and evaluation and modification to improve the efficiency and effectiveness of the ACO Care Models."[124]

These populations are senior citizens enrolled in "Original Medicare," the *non*-HMO/PPO version.[125] Instead of choosing Medicare Advantage, the HMO/PPO version, they chose Original Medicare, often at a higher price.[126] However, these seniors may be *assigned* to the ACO by the federal government without notification.[127] As Kaiser Health News reports, "You may even be in one and not know it."[128] The nine million assigned individuals reported as of January 2017 are likely to be senior citizens who specifically chose *not* to be in a Medicare HMO but have been secretly assigned to the ACO version of an HMO.[129] They had no choice and they've not been told. The assignment process is mind-boggling to read, but it clearly happens outside the purview of the individual being assigned. It does, however, require the individual to be receiving care from a practitioner or facility already participating in an ACO.

There are seven criteria of eligibility. If you're in Original Medicare, you could be assigned to the ACO in which the clinicians and facilities participating in the ACO "have provided the plurality" (greater proportion) of your *primary care services* as compared to other clinicians and facilities in and outside of ACOs.[130] These practitioners are all identified by taxpayer identification numbers (TINs) and CMS knows whether the doctors you see and the hospitals you use are in an ACO or not. In explaining this, CMS says it "treats ACOs as a collection of TINs" to determine if a recipient has received a larger amount of primary care services from the ACO.[131] Based on this calculation, an individual could be assigned to an ACO. These secretly assigned individuals can obtain care wherever they want to, but the ACO doctors bear part of the financial risk of that care. The doctor's income can rise if the population's total cost of care (total Medicare Parts A and B FFS [fee-for-service] expenditures) is lower than the benchmark, or drop if the population's costs are higher than the benchmark—even if the patient goes elsewhere for care.

When the doctor takes on a risk-bearing (insurance) function without the patient's knowledge and express consent, a conflict of interest between the patient and the doctor is established. ACOs want to keep this conflict hidden. FierceHealthcare reports 426 ACOs were surveyed about physician payment and specifically asked "whether doctors were financially penalized for ordering tests or making referrals that can increase costs." Only thirty-nine ACOs (9.2 percent) provided some information despite repeated attempts to get a response.[132]

The EHR is essential to every element of the ACO.

To determine each recipient's likely health care costs, which are used to set a benchmark for the ACO, the federal government generates individual "risk scores" based on patient data. Each year CMS considers the changes in the Medicare recipient's health status and demographic factors and adjusts the benchmark. This is called risk adjustment.[133]

Using this calculation and others, the ACO will either share in the savings or share in the losses sustained by CMS. Depending on the chosen risk model—one-sided ("carrot only") or two-sided ("carrot and stick")[134]—"shared savings payments" can be as high as 20 percent of total benchmark expenditures and "shared losses" for exceeding the benchmark can be as high as 15 percent—which must be paid back to the government.[135] Shared-savings payments are reduced by law under sequestration (mandatory across-the-board discretionary spending cuts to federal domestic and defense spending from 2013 to 2021[136]), but CMS plans to adjust variables in the equation to ensure that "sequestration applies only once to ACO shared savings."[137]

How's the ACO experiment working? Thus far, the 561 Medicare Shared Savings Program ACOs are not saving taxpayers money. According to an analysis released by consulting firm Avalere in March 2018, instead of saving Medicare about $2 billion by 2016 as the Congressional Budget predicted in 2010, federal spending has increased by $384 million from 2013 to 2016 because most ACOs have chosen the bonus (carrot-only) model.[138]

CMS shares aggregate information on the ACO's assigned population and financial performance at the start of the agreement period, quarterly during the year, and at the end of each performance year.[139] To secure the most payment in this alternative payment model, Dan

Moriarity, the chief information officer of Atrius Health, shares a succinct list of ACO essentials:

To be an ACO you need three things:

1. A common EHR
2. A robust data warehouse
3. A care coordination platform

If you don't have those three elements, you are flying blind.[140]

Becker's Hospital Review agrees, emphasizing the need to measure the health status of the population: "Due to the heavy reliance on data sharing ACOs require, the presence of a sophisticated electronic health record and a health information exchange implementation strategy is needed."[141] Kaiser Health News adds, "Because hospitals usually have access to capital, they may have an easier time than doctors in financing the initial investment, for instance to create the electronic record system necessary to track patients."[142] Aledade, a company founded in 2014 by Farzad Mostashari, MD, former national coordinator of health information technology in the Obama administration, was built to fill the need. Aledade's software collects "patient data from a variety of sources, creating a helicopter view. Doctors can see which specialists a patient has visited, which tests have been ordered, and, crucially, how much the overall care might be costing the health care system," reports the *New York Times*.[143]

A provision in the Bipartisan Budget Act of 2018 may make this easier. ACOs will be able to start paying patients up to $20 a year for primary care visits. "The money, so the theory goes, would encourage patients to get their care within a particular ACO so the provider group can control and coordinate their care."[144]

Since these senior citizens may not know they're in an ACO, they may choose to go elsewhere for care. As CMS states, "Nobody—not your doctor, not your hospital—can tell you who you have to see."[145] But the ACO will be informed about every visit and every doctor and hospital the patient uses. CMS tells Medicare patients:

> To help you to get the best-coordinated and highest quality care, Medicare will share certain information about your medical care with your doctor's ACO, including medical conditions, prescriptions, and visits to the doctor. This is important to help the ACO keep up with your medical needs and track how well the ACO is doing to keep you healthy and helping you get the right care. Your privacy is very important to us. You can tell Medicare not to give your doctor's ACO information that your doctor needs to coordinate your care by calling 1-800-MEDICARE (1-800-633-4227). TTY users should call 1-877-486-2048. Unless you take this step, your medical information will be shared automatically with your doctor's ACO for purposes of care coordination and quality improvement.[146]

This language may be intended to engender fear ("information your doctor needs"), but regardless of what choice the individual makes, the information will still be shared with and used by the government. As CMS tells providers, "A beneficiary's decision not to have this information shared, however, does not affect the provider's participation in the ACO or CMS' use of the patient's data for the purpose of assessing the ACO's performance on quality or cost measures."[147] In other words, CMS will continue to analyze the health status and costs of each individual.

"ACOs aren't the end game," said Chas Roades, chief research officer at The Advisory Board Company. "He says the ultimate goal would be for providers to take on full financial responsibility for caring for a population of patients for a fixed payment, but that will require a transition beyond ACOs," reports Kaiser Health News."[148]

This dangerous idea would turn doctors and hospitals into "insurers," at risk for every dollar they spend on patient care. Or as John Goodman warns, "ACOs are the portal through which we will all march toward a truly nationalized health care system."[149] All powered by the EHR.

The Population Health Agenda

Shifting the Focus

Computerized data has enabled the government and other third-party payers to demand physicians change the way they practice medicine. The doctor's focus is shifting from the patient in front of him or her to the entire population of patients that could appear in the doctor's office. This is called "population health." Calculating the health risk of each individual in the American health care system is required for the ACA "risk adjustment" program,[150] and it's considered critical to achieving population health.

ONC claims interoperable EHRs are key to "the national priority of better and more affordable health care, leading to better population health." The agency plans to use the EHR mandate to "transform care into a model that enhances access and truly addresses health *beyond* the confines of the health care system."[151] (Emphasis added.)

Think about that word "beyond."

In an article titled, "Care Beyond the Clinic: Health Lessons from Electronic Health Record Data," the Robert Wood Johnson Foundation touts community assessment plans as public health efforts in which the EHR is used to track and monitor entire populations of people for "data-informed population health activities."[152] The report states, "The assessment data is richer when fed by clinical data through EHRs. This data lets health officials track health status changes longitudinally and by community."[153]

Karen B. DeSalvo, MD, MPH, national coordinator of health IT in the Obama administration and now a professor at the University of Texas at Austin in Dell Medical School's Department of Population Health,[154] envisioned a health IT system where patients learn how their information can be shared and how it will be "effectively and safely used to benefit their health and that of their community."[155]

This brings up a few questions. Are patients asked or just informed? Who is in the patient's community? How big is that community? What if the patient doesn't want to help their "community" this way? Who decides what data is shared? Who in their community gets what data? And who will decide the answers to these questions?

A summary of comments given during a workshop called "Population Health Implications of the Affordable Care Act," includes this statement: "Although there is no precise definition of population health, Flores continued, it can be viewed as an approach that treats the population as a whole (including the environmental and community contexts) as the patient." [156] George Flores, MD, MPH, is the program manager for The California Endowment, the state's largest health foundation.[157]

This is troubling. As David S. Oderberg, professor of philosophy at the University of Reading in the United Kingdom, says, "Given that care and cure are the primary duties of medicine and health care generally, what is best for someone other than the patient can never be the primary objective of the health care professional as health care professional."[158] Michel Accad, MD, a cardiologist based in San Francisco, writes in his *Alert & Oriented* blog: "Medical care can only have one end, the care of a given patient. A dual mandate to simultaneously care for individuals and populations is inherently confused."[159]

But Flores says, "Health largely depends on conditions where we live, learn, work, and play, not just on the medical treatment we receive. . . . Health is not just in pills and surgeries and hospitals. We need to think more broadly than that."[160] Similarly, during a *Politico* panel discussion on population health, Joshua Sharfstein, MD, former Maryland secretary of health and now associate dean of public health practice and training at Johns Hopkins Bloomberg School of Public Health, said the Maryland health information exchange gave doctors tools to "know what was happening to their patients even if they weren't seeing them." Doctors can "see where they are in the system through the different information feeds." Sharfstein says population health is doctors "thinking about their whole population of patients, not just the ones in front of them, but the ones who are part of that population that really do need their help."[161]

The population health workshop report says the Affordable Care Act "provides unprecedented resources to prevent illness and keep people healthy and includes, for the first time, a National Prevention Strategy," as well as incentives that will "shift health care from today's high-volume and high-cost health care system focused on personal service to a future system that stresses healthy lifestyles and healthy environments."[162] Would this shift financial resources away from caring for the sick and injured?

Judy Murphy, chief nursing officer at IBM, told an audience at the HIMSS 2018 conference, "We're managing everyone. We're not just worrying about the people that we see in front of us, and it's a real important difference. . . . Because we can't always treat everybody all of the time, [we need to] be able to predict those people that we . . . absolutely need to get at, and prioritize them to the top. That's where this predictive layer comes in, where we're actually using the data to look at predictive modeling and forecasting." She added, "Part of our efforts sometimes [are] in understanding how we can actually predict which people are going to be catastrophic, so that we make sure, even though we want to intervene with everybody, that we at least make sure that we intervene on the ones that are probably going to move into that very sick side."[163]

Everything About You in the EHR

What could this ultimately look like? According to the workshop summary, the ACA is an opportunity to transfer "funds now spent on medical care to social and infrastructure investments that can both stabilize the nation's fiscal health and improve the well-being of its citizens."[164] Dr. Stephanie Mayfield Gibson, former state health commissioner for Kentucky and former senior vice president of population health for KentuckyOne Health says, "An accountable health system embodies the belief that if you want to achieve comprehensive health, you have to address basic human needs, often referred to as social determinants of health," such as housing, employment, economic well-being, food stability, education, and freedom from violence, reports *Hospitals & Health Networks*.[165] Some health organizations, reports Kaiser Health News, "are now asking patients much more general questions: Do you have trouble paying your bills? Do you feel safe at home? Do you have enough to eat?"[166]

This information could soon be gathered through a detailed coding system mandated by the federal government called ICD-10. (See next chapter.) A group of authors in *Health Affairs* write, "The ICD-10 provides an expanded set of codes reflecting patients' social characteristics in the form of 'z-codes.' Although z-codes are not yet used routinely by health care systems, together the mandate for ICD-10 adoption and its potential for coding and billing on social determinants of health make the ICD-10 an attractive option for a standardized approach to data aggregation." Already the National Association of Community Health Centers has begun working to link data from social screening to existing patient data captured in ICD-10 codes.[167]

When asked to describe the difference between public health and population health, Sharfstein said:

> I think population health is the way that health care systems are thinking about public health now. Generally speaking, when people use the term, public health, they're talking . . . about population health. I think it's a very similar concept. It's the term that people in health care use when they're doing some of the things that people in public health do.[168]

In short, the private and public sectors are merging together. Private health plans and public health departments are coalescing to oversee and intervene in private lives.

The EHR is the facilitator for this combined intrusion. "The fundamental building block of population health management is an EHR," writes *Health Data Management* magazine. Or to be more precise:

> As the industry shifts to outcomes-based payment models, providers still must deliver care patient by patient, but they

must also monitor those patients most likely to throw budgets off course.

That requires a population-based approach, in which *providers track patients* by either clinical risk, financial risk, or some combination of the two.

Upholding the idea requires insuring that preventive screenings are complete, that patients with certain conditions follow care guidelines and treatment plans, and that care is coordinated among different settings. The I.T. requirements are steep, but manageable, experts say. An EHR, a patient registry, analytics capacity and rudimentary data exchange are prerequisites.[169] (Emphasis added.)

"Slice and Dice" Analytics

Marc Probst, vice president and chief information officer at Intermountain Healthcare and a panelist at the *Politico* discussion, says "data is a really important component of achieving any level of population health so that you know where to focus your resources, but also you know how to modify your practice to best serve the community that you're in."[170]

The population health management (PHM) market is booming. In North America, it generated revenues of $1.01 billion in the fourth quarter of 2016, up 17 percent year over year, and up 8 percent from the third quarter.[171] PHM is expected to grow into a $31.9 billion business worldwide by 2020 as hospitals and health care systems switch their focus to population-based delivery and payment systems, reports Healthcare Informatics.[172] The global market in December 2015 was just $14 billion. Perhaps this is why Amazon is teaming up with Cerner, an EHR company to "help health-care providers better use their data to make health predictions about patient populations," announced CNBC. The partnership is focused on HealtheIntent, Cerner's population health product that allows hospitals to collect and analyze "huge volumes of clinical data." Amazon has already "taken steps" to comply with HIPAA.[173]

Patrick Combes, global technical leader of healthcare and life sciences at Amazon Web Services told *Healthcare IT News*: "Looking ahead, AWS is interested in how we can work with longitudinal health records and leverage them for population health and analysis efforts. . . . As we're seeing it, it's possible for the cloud to act as a permanent home for all patient records and enable the shift away from event-based records to a more holistic view of patient health, supporting value-based care initiatives." He adds, "the cloud offers a complete analytics pipeline that can ingest, manage, and analyze any type of data—whether it is structured data, unstructured data, or streams."[174]

Eric Schmidt, technical advisor and former executive chairman of Alphabet Inc., likes the cloud too. At the HIMSS 2018 conference, he said, "Get to the cloud. Run to the cloud. Right? Don't stop, don't walk, don't think about it. Just run, take an airplane, fly to the cloud." [175]

Schmidt said, "The arrival of the EHRs is a major story in the last decade because ten years ago they didn't exist in the form that we know today. We forget that they didn't exist. And before that it was impossible to get the health care data."[176] He said, "A lot of people think that there are at least 150,000 observations per day on patients that are just ignored per patient because they're all real time. There's no way to track them and store them and so forth. Can you imagine when we have the combination of sensor data plus continuous behavioral data, which you're going to get from your smartphone and the various smartwatches that are coming, plus all the molecular data and so forth? This data explosion is profound." [177] Schmidt summed up his goal: "We can't predict our own fates, but machines can. That's what I want as I age: I want the computer and all this work I've done over my whole career to make sure that I have a healthy life."[178]

At the same conference, National Coordinator for Health IT Don Rucker, MD said this about smartphones and apps today, as reported by *Healthcare IT News*: "Either you're looking at things that don't have medical data, or you're looking at things that just have medical data. You're not looking at things that synthesize knowledge about our environment and our lives and our behaviors with medical data. That is really the opportunity here."[179]

Carl Dvorak, president of Epic, the nation's largest EHR system, clarifies his view on the subject: "When I think of population health, I think of algorithms. . . . We need a support system for the algorithmic workers and the caseworkers to sift, sort, slice, dice, and understand their population, and for case managers and proactive outreach in order to have a work queue, to have a dashboard, to have a patient list to help do the outreach to help motivate people."[180]

Psychiatrist Kenneth Davis, MD, the CEO of Mount Sinai Health System says the ACA will encourage physicians to manage populations, for which a "hospital's health-care delivery network will be paid a certain amount to care for a given population, and no more." Such populations could include "a company's employees and their families, a union's members, a group of individuals who purchase a like product on the insurance exchanges, or a group of Medicare or Medicaid beneficiaries."[181] Under this system of capped payments, detailed private data on individuals would be critical. He wrote in the *Wall Street Journal*,

> Individual fee-for-service health care is transforming to population health management. This is a welcome development because fee-for-service often gives physicians an incentive to overutilize resources and treat illnesses rather than to maintain patients' good health. . . .
>
> Hospitals will also need to track patient conditions and treatments through sophisticated electronic medical records. . . . For example, through large patient populations, one can apply supercomputer resources to mine the data collected on them and create predictive models of diseases. We can identify patterns in clinical syndromes and link them with genetic data and lifestyle behaviors to help individuals better understand their risk of illness, and customize a prevention or treatment strategy.[182]

He calls this "population health management." But many would call it Big Brother. This is data mining deep into people's lives—likely with a dose of coercion on the side to keep them healthy.

Digging into DNA

Speaking of deep, consider how far this predictive modeling and population management could go. Australian researchers are working to develop a test to "identify newborns who have the greatest risk of growing up obese." The test could be incorporated into newborn screening, the government's genetic testing program—even though the lead researcher, Peter Meikle, admits, "we are not really talking about a genetic disease, we are talking about the risk of disease somewhere down the track."[183]

Dr. Bradley Schaefer, director of genetics at the University of Arkansas for Medical Sciences, says, "There are studies now looking at the implications of doing whole genome sequencing on the newborn screening blood-spots. Think about what that means. By the second day of a person's life you can know their whole genetic makeup and all that entails."[184] Eric Green, MD, PhD, director of the National Human Genome Research Institute (NHGRI), underscores the danger of such predictive analysis:

> One could imagine a future where a child's genome is sequenced at birth, it goes into their electronic health record and every time they go to see their doctor, their doctor looks up what their sequence is and looks for what kind of medications to give them, diseases to look for, and so forth. . . . But it raises a whole host of ethical issues. The ethical questions are very different for sequencing a healthy newborn as opposed to an acutely ill one.[185]

Adults should keep this in mind as well. Intermountain Healthcare has created a global DNA registry called the GeneRosity Registry. Hoping to use the genetic data for studies "to determine which patients are at risk for developing genetic health problems," Intermountain is asking adults who have been tested by AncestryDNA, MyHeritage, or 23andMe to upload the genetic results into GeneRosity Registry. They hope to gain data on genes, environment, and lifestyles.[186]

In Chicago, NorthShore University HealthSystem is encouraging patients to get genetic testing as a part of their annual physical. "The hospital uses an algorithm that scans a patient's EHR information to determine the appropriate tests," reports FierceHealthcare. [187] Because most primary care physicians won't know what genetic tests to order, "the primary care doctor just has to basically click on the suggestion," says Peter Hulick, MD, director of NorthShore's Center for Personalized Medicine.[188] To lower the financial risks hospitals face due to government payments that are increasingly "value-based" rather than service-based, this is one way NorthShore is proactively working to keep patients healthy "rather than focusing solely on treating them when they become ill."[189] This may sound wise, but it could mean a future with less money, time and services available for the people who are actually sick and injured.

One State's Push to Population Health

The Minnesota Department of Health (MDH) health IT staff agree that EHRs are key to monitoring populations of people inside and outside the exam room:

> Some local health departments have explored, in partnership with their local healthcare providers, the use of data housed within electronic health record (EHR) systems. This partnership is . . . enabled by near-universal adoption of EHR systems among Minnesota's hospitals and clinics. . . . EHR data have the opportunity to play a large role in supporting population health activities beyond the boundaries of a health organization's patient population. EHR data have the potential to provide timely and complete data for subpopulations, geographic areas, and health conditions that are typically underrepresented in traditional assessment methods.[190]

In short, EHRs are perfect tools for tracking. MDH provided twelve e-health grants in 2006, primarily to rural communities to plan for or implement EHRs or HIE.[191] In 2007, with support from a Republican administration,[192] the Democrat-controlled Minnesota legislature mandated EHR use by all health care providers with no exceptions[193]—the only state in the nation to do so, according to Citizens' Council for Health Freedom research, although Massachusetts comes close with its policy of aligning licensure with EHR "proficiency."[194] In 2008, mandatory electronic reporting of patient outcomes, care processes, and other quality measurement data were added.[195] The EHR mandate took effect on January 1, 2015.

However, with the help of mental health professionals, Citizens' Council for Health Freedom secured legislation during Minnesota's 2015 legislative session to exempt solo and cash-based practices. The chair of the civil law and data practices committee held an informational hearing in a room filled with concerned psychologists, social workers, and others. MDH testified in support of keeping the law in place and asked the committee instead to steer providers "complaining about the cost" to the department where they could access grants to help manage the transition from paper records to the EHR.[196]

The exemption was amended to an omnibus health care bill with the help of chairwoman Representative Peggy Scott (R) and Representative Tara Mack (R), passed the last day of the session, passed shortly before the legislature adjourned, and became law.[197] With eleven authors and coauthors, bipartisan support included Republican authors Representative Glenn Gruenhagen and Senator Warren Limmer, and Democrat coauthors Representatives John Lesch and Peter Fischer.[198] Even without a statewide EHR mandate in law, states should consider passing this kind of protection to prevent regulators and health plans from requiring small practices to use an EHR.

Tracking Americans in Sickness and Health

Real-Time Surveillance

The Centers for Disease Control and Prevention is preparing to build direct lines into EHRs. As FierceHealthcare reports, the CDC "is focusing on efforts to improve data collection capabilities by accessing information buried in EHRs and utilizing cloud-based applications."[199] The CDC already "captures data from nearly 60% of US hospital emergency department visits," notes *Public Health Reports*.[200] This is public health surveillance, which has been defined as the "continuous, systematic collection, analysis and interpretation of health-related data needed for the planning, implementation, and evaluation of public health practice."[201]

An article written by nine individuals with either an MD or MPH or both after their names, including Thomas R. Frieden, MD, MPH, former director of the CDC during the Obama administration, says, "In the future, public health surveillance will depend increasingly on the secondary use of existing data and information found in rapidly evolving health care information systems, as well as nonhealth information systems with data on social determinants." They report that HHS's Shared Nationwide Interoperability Roadmap includes three areas of focus for the CDC to improve public health surveillance: implementing shared information technology services, developing the surveillance workforce, and harnessing electronic health records and health care information technology systems.[202]

To build interoperability between the public and private sector the CDC "is moving toward greater use of shared digital data services and an interoperable, integrated, cloud-based data platform." The nine authors note, "Electronic case reporting (eCR) is the automated electronic generation and transmission of reports of potential cases of reportable conditions from the electronic health record to state and local public health authorities for review and action. eCR can allow state and local health departments to conduct *real-time surveillance* without burdening health care providers." (Emphasis added.) In other words, it will be invisible, happening in the background. Out of sight, out of mind. Planning for eCR began in 2016.[203]

Digital Bridge, a collaboration among health care organizations, public health agencies, and health information technology organizations, is a big part of this plan. Its goal is "to ensure our nation's health through a bidirectional information flow between health care and public health."[204] "Health care" means the private sector, and "public health" means the government. The collaborative is building a standardized eCR approach for infectious disease reporting through "streamlining interoperability between EHR systems and the IT systems public health agencies use to monitor disease trends and respond to outbreaks."[205] Digital Bridge is funded by the Robert Wood Johnson Foundation and the deBeaumont Foundation with management by the Public Health Informatics Institute and Deloitte.[206] It is unlikely that this bidirectional data sharing will end with infectious disease.

ICD-10 Tracking Codes

In line with Big Brother tracking, Congress mandated a new and highly detailed health coding system for diagnoses and treatments recorded in the EHR and used on insurance claims. Its purpose is much bigger than securing payment. "ICD-10 is the foundation for health care reform," said Jeff Hinson, a CMS regional administrator during a conference call for providers in Colorado.[207]

ICD-10 is shorthand for a mouthful of words: the International Classification of Diseases, Tenth Revision, Clinical Modification (ICD-10-CM) and its corresponding Procedural Code System (ICD-10-PCS), which is used only for hospital inpatient procedures. For outpatient procedures, Current Procedural Terminology (CPT) codes are used.[208]

The new detailed ICD-10 data collection and recording system "incorporates much greater specificity and clinical information," which will enhance the "ability to conduct public health surveillance," say federal officials.[209] If you haven't found a physician who's opted out of the government and health-plan reimbursement systems, such as can be found in The Wedge of Health Freedom (JoinTheWedge.com), detailed recording of your data began October 1, 2015.[210]

"Walked into a Lamppost? Hurt while Crocheting? Help Is on the Way" is the catchy title of one of the best articles on the details captured by the coding system. As the *Wall Street Journal* reported in 2011, "Today, hospitals and doctors use a system of about 18,000 codes to describe medical services in bills they send to insurers. . . . A new federally mandated version will expand the number to around 140,000—adding codes that describe precisely what bone was broken, or which artery is receiving a stent."[211]

The frustration of one internist is palpable:

> We are now working with 17,000 diagnosis/billing codes—absolutely ridiculous. There are nine codes for abdominal pain (right upper, left upper, right lower, left lower—you get the idea). And the government has recently increased the number of codes from 17,000 to 155,000. The bottom line—300 codes would probably cover everything. It could be printed in a four-page leaflet, not three large volumes. It is unnecessarily complicated and it does absolutely nothing to improve patient care.[212]

This international coding system will indicate precisely where you were injured (e.g., chicken coop, opera house, which of nine rooms in a mobile home) and what procedure was done to exactly what body part and on what side of the body.

There are also codes for "bizarre personal appearance" and "very low level of personal hygiene." There's a code for the first time you walk into a lamppost and another code for a "subsequent encounter" related to that lamppost injury. There are codes for knitting injuries,

Type A behavior pattern, problems with in-laws, being struck by an orca, and injuries due to water skis on fire. There are nine codes for being injured by a macaw.

The level of detail becomes clearer still with the realization that what was a single code for a badly healed fracture in the former ICD-9 edition (in place since 1979) became 2,595 different codes in ICD-10.[213] Lest there be any doubt, CMS clarifies, "The ICD-10 transition is a mandate that applies to all parties covered by HIPAA, not just providers who bill Medicare or Medicaid."[214] That means all patients using insurance or government programs will have detailed information collected using a code of three to seven characters.[215] It also means more people have become employed as medical coders. The *New York Times* reported in 2017: "Membership in the American Academy of Professional Coders has swelled to more than 165,000, up 10,000 in the past year alone."[216]

The number of codes makes life difficult for busy physicians. One physician said that even though she knows what she wants to order for a patient, she can't do it unless she can figure out which ICD-10 code on the computer has all the treatment orders included in it. She said it's time-consuming, but she must pick through the various codes until she can get the one that lets her order all the tests and procedures she wants to order.[217]

The American Medical Association (AMA) asked Congress to repeal the ICD-10 requirement, calling it a "costly, unfunded mandate for practicing physicians."[218] The AMA said the mandated transition to ICD-10 would cost small physician practices between $56,639 and $226,105. Large practices would be hit with costs between $2 million and $8 million.[219] Some spent more. For example, Cedars-Sinai spent $15 million to comply with the 2014 deadline.[220] By 2012, an estimated $22 billion had been invested or budgeted for implementation of ICD-10, according to CMS.[221]

The transition for doctors and hospitals is complicated and fraught with financial fears and reduced productivity.[222] The World Health Organization (WHO), which copyrighted the system, claims ICD is "the foundation for the identification of health trends and statistics globally" and "the diagnostic classification standard for all clinical and research purposes."[223]

Supporters in the United States have broader purposes. The Coalition for ICD-10 said ICD-10 improves "quality measurement, public health surveillance, clinical research, and healthcare payment through research, education, advocacy, and mobilization."[224] The organization's twenty-six coalition members include American Health Information Management Association (AHIMA), American Hospital Association, American Medical Billing Association (AMBA), American Medical Informatics Association (AMIA), America's Health Insurance Plans (AHIP), College of Healthcare Information Management Executives (CHIME), and the Health IT Now Coalition (sixty-four corporate and nonprofit members[225]).[226]

Sue Bowman, senior director of coding policy and compliance at AHIMA, says the more granular data provided by the new code set is necessary to implement "value-based purchasing" and accountable care organizations (ACOs).[227] Patient profiling by code began nationwide on October 1, 2015. Less than two years later, 815 proposed code changes were approved by CMS, including new codes, revised codes and deleted codes. They became effective October 1, 2017.[228]

Patients Scored for Risk

ICD-10 codes will be accepted for risk adjustment (RA)—the ACA-mandated creation of risk profiles of people enrolled in insurance.[229] The RA program "applies to non-grandfathered plans in the individual and small group insurance market, both inside and outside of the exchanges, with some exceptions." In short, RA uses "enrollees' individual risk scores" to determine which health plans have higher-risk enrollees and which have lower-risk enrollees. According to the calculation, the RA program "redistributes funds from plans with lower-risk enrollees to plans with higher-risk enrollees."[230]

HHS has issued a rule requiring a sophisticated data-based system for calculating and reporting individualized risk scores. According to the rule, states that operate an Obamacare exchange "may establish a risk adjustment program, or have HHS do so on its behalf."[231]

If the federal government does RA for the state, health plans must provide HHS with de-identified data, including enrollees' individual risk scores. If a state operates its own RA program, it is required to "only collect information reasonably necessary" to determine individual scores and must not collect personally identifiable information. Each year, these plans must provide HHS with access to the data through a "dedicated data environment (i.e., an EDGE server)."[232]

An EDGE server is an Enhanced Data GSM Environment, which "stores data files on remote servers with the specific purpose of streaming them over the internet," explains Brandon on ServerFault.com. Other explanations come from Shawn Quillman ("squillman") and LawrenceC, who explain that an EDGE server resides on the "edge" between two networks, typically a private internal network and the Internet, or a foreign network.[233]

From 2016 onward, if a health plan fails to create a "dedicated distributed data environment" from which HHS can access the health plan's enrollee data, HHS will issue penalties (payment adjustments), starting in 2018.[234] The Center for Medicare & Medicaid Services at HHS will evaluate data quality made available on the EDGE server by the following criteria:[235]

Data Quality Evaluation Metrics	
Key Metrics	**Area**
Percent of all enrollees with at least one Hierarchical Condition Category (HCC)	**Risk Adjustment**
Average number of conditions per enrollee with at least one HCC	
Issuer average risk score	
Average number of diagnosis codes per medical claim	
Average premium per member per month	
Percent of individual market enrollees with reinsurance payments	**Reinsurance**
Average reinsurance payment per enrollee receiving reinsurance payment	
Claims per enrollee ratio	**EDGE Claims/Enrollment**
Percent of enrollees without claims	
Percent of medical claims that are institutional claims	
Percent of claims that are pharmacy claims	

"An enrollee's risk score is derived from demographic and health status factors, which requires the use of enrollee identifiable information," reports HHS.[236] To build the data parameters for risk adjustment, HHS used a Medicare Advantage database and a source most Americans know nothing about: the Truven Health Analytics 2010 MarketScan Commercial Claims and Encounters database and the MarketScan expenditure database, which contains:

> enrollee-specific claims utilization, expenditures, and enrollment across inpatient, outpatient, and prescription drug services from a selection of large employers and health plans. The database includes de-identified data from approximately 100 payers, and contains more than 500 million claims from insured employees, spouses, and dependents.[237]

As a reminder, de-identified data is no longer subject to HIPAA if it is de-identified following the HIPAA-required procedures. As HHS clarifies in a guidance document: "De-identified health information created following these methods is no longer protected by the Privacy Rule because it does not fall within the definition of PHI [protected health information]."[238]

HHS also notes that the risk-adjustment audit process may require health plans to have "more extensive access to provider medical documentation."[239] While HHS could require plans to "comply with any request for data for any audit or validation preformed [sic], including relevant source enrollment documentation, all claims and encounter data, and medical record documentation," a 2016 RA rule says, "CMS will use the smallest possible sample size that will provide a statistically valid sample" of information on enrollees.[240] The shared data, which HHS admits is of a "sensitive nature," will be used to "validate the enrollment, demographic, and health status data of each enrollee."[241]

A new federal database, authorized by the ACA and located in the CMS Data Center in Baltimore, Maryland, and at various contractor sites, will keep this sensitive information. The CMS Risk Adjustment Data Validation System (RAD-V) will collect and retain the following personally identifiable information on current or former enrollees of health plans until they become "inactive": demographic, geographic, medical and/or health care information, date of birth, gender, and dates of service.[242]

CMS will also collect identifiable information about individual health care providers, including but not limited to: name, Individual Taxpayer Identification Number (ITIN) or Employer Identification Number (EIN), and National Provider Identifier (NPI).[243]

CMS may disclose the information outside of the agency as described in a list of six "routine uses," including to other federal agencies with "a need to know," the US Department of Justice (DOJ), and CMS contractors—and "to parties outside the agency, without the individual's consent, for any of the purposes authorized directly in the Privacy Act."[244] The Privacy Act of 1974 "governs the collection, maintenance, use and dissemination of certain information about individuals by agencies of the federal government." Despite its title, there are twelve exceptions and ten exemptions to the rule's "No Disclosure Without Consent" requirements.[245] One exception is "routine uses." The DOJ notes that "the routine use exception because of its potential breadth, is one of the most controversial provisions in the Act."[246] It's also its biggest loophole.

Medicare Annual Wellness Visit

The ACA requires that everyone over the age of sixty-five submit to an annual wellness visit (AWV) for health risk assessments and personalized prevention plan services. This is essentially a mandatory inspection: "The Secretary shall establish procedures to make beneficiaries and providers aware of the *requirement* that a beneficiary complete a health risk assessment prior to or at the same time as receiving personalized prevention plan services."[247] (Emphasis added.) Senior citizens do not know about this law and the author finds no enforcement provisions in the law (e.g., fines or denial of services) but CCHF is now hearing from seniors who have been denied access to their doctors after refusing to comply. One concerned individual received this response from a practice administrator:

> You expressed discontent at having to fill out paperwork for your annual well exam. I have attached two documents. The

> first one is from [insurer] for a patient that is over 65, and you can see how [insurer] is definitely looking at records for all patients, and especially those over 65 that have Medicare, and we MUST comply. That is because [insurer] will receive a bump in payment from CMS/Medicare dependent on how we document the care we give to you and how physically fit you are at the time. The second document is from CMS/Medicare and it shows what they require from us and how again we share information with you the patient. They want us, your family doctor, to let you know what we see you need now and what you may need in the next 5–10 years. They both want to know if you've been immunized, if you have had a mammogram, if you have had a colonoscopy, and more. These are all measures (HEDIS) that we are required to provide/offer you to meet their [insurer/Medicare] expectations, and medical coverage is typically covered by your insurance company. . . . Rest assured, we take all this very seriously, for your benefit.[248]

The first document was a medical records request letter from the insurer asking the clinic to provide "access to specific member medical records to facilitate a risk adjustment chart review. As you may know, risk adjustment is the payment methodology used by the Centers for Medicare and Medicaid Services (CMS) and the Department of Health and Human Services (HHS) for our Medicare Advantage and Commercial members. The purpose of these chart reviews is to verify that information to be reported to [insurer] and ultimately to HHS and CMS in claims or encounter data includes all pertinent diagnosis codes at the accurate levels of specificity."[249] Notably, under the risk-adjustment mechanism, the more diagnosis codes the higher the "bump in payment" could be.

The patient also mailed CCHF a copy of the documents she was required to fill out or submit to as a prerequisite to seeing the doctor: "Medicare Annual/Subsequent Wellness Visit" and "Patient Health Questionnaire" and "Six Item Cognitive Impairment Test (6CIT)" as well as a "2016 Medicare Patient Checklist" which included a "list of required 2016 ACO Quality for patient" to "ensure this Medicare

Patient has receive all required screening/met all care requirements." In the final 2010 Medicare rule on the annual wellness visit, CMS noted the following: "Many commenters expressed support for CMS' proposal to waive the beneficiary deductible and coinsurance for the AWV. The commenters noted that this waiver would likely encourage more beneficiaries to receive an AWV."[250] Thus, there's no enforcement. Department officials simply hope seniors will submit to the annual inspection if it's free.

According to eMDs, the practitioners receive an average reimbursement of $172 for the initial visit and an average of $111 for all subsequent visits (every twelve months).[251] To receive the reimbursement, a list of required elements includes detection of cognitive impairment, review of functional status, and end-of-life planning (verbal or written information regarding the individual's ability to prepare an advance directive and whether the physician is willing to follow the individual's wishes in the advance directive).[252]

Medicare "Star Ratings"

CMS also reimburses Medicare Advantage plans using "star ratings." Plans are rated on data reported to the federal government, such as whether seniors get their flu shot and how well they manage their diabetes, reports Axios.[253] CMS says the ratings span five broad categories: outcomes, intermediate outcomes, patient experience, access, and process.[254] "Medicare doles out 5% bonus payments to insurers that have at least four stars (out of a possible five)."[255] Plans are paid about $10,000 per member annually on average to cover seniors, reports Kaiser Health News. The 5 percent bonus adds $500 per member. In 2016, $3 billion was available for plans, with United Healthcare expected to receive $1.4 billion.[256]

Hospitals have expressed concerns about using five stars to quantify their quality and performance. They say the program "puts a heavy reporting burden on hospitals and doesn't present information in a way that is helpful to patients," reports Healthcare Dive. In

December 2017, CMS issued a new rating formula, but the jury is still out.[257]

Star ratings have also led to denial of care, as reported by the *New York Times* about a Veterans Administration hospital in Oregon: "In 2016, administrators began cherry-picking cases against the advice of doctors—turning away complicated patients and admitting only the lowest-risk ones in order to improve metrics." As a result, the Roseburg Veterans Administration Medical Center's rating rose from one star to two stars and the director received a bonus of $8,120.[258]

The All-Payer Claims Database

In many states, every time a patient uses health insurance to receive care, the insurer registers the claim with the state's all-payer claims database (APCD), which collects data on health care utilization and spending.[259] However, care paid for using cash is not reported.

The first APCD began in Maryland in 1995.[260] By December 2016, at least eighteen states had APCD laws and sixteen databases were operational, but not all mandate data submission.[261] At least six states encourage voluntary submission: California, Michigan, Oklahoma, South Carolina, Virginia, and Wisconsin. So far, eight states haven't made any movement toward an APCD: Alabama, Georgia, Indiana, Mississippi, Missouri, Nevada, North Dakota, and South Dakota.[262]

What is claims data? It's not every ounce of data in the EHR. Mike Doyle at Health Catalyst defines claims data as "the structured (coded) data that a healthcare provider may transmit to, or receive from, a payer or clearinghouse, and which are intended to justify payment for services rendered on behalf of a specific patient of the provider organization."[263] It includes charges, payments, patient demographics, provider identification, and diagnoses and treatment codes, such as ICD-10 and CPT codes. Once deidentified, it can be sold.[264]

Supporters of linking EHRs and APCDs gave the following information in a report prepared for the Agency for Healthcare Research and Quality:

> Comprehensive data sets linking clinical and claims data will become more widely available in the future, but to date such sets are available from only a limited number of States or regions. A recent [2011] report on APCDs states that currently, five States with existing or developing APCDs are collecting patient identifiers that would allow linking the dataset to other outside data sources, such as clinical data from EHRs or an HIE, four States do not currently allow patient identifiers to be collected, and five States are either examining the issue legislatively or are unable to disclose whether or not they are collecting patient identifiers.[265]

But APCDs have a new challenge. One health insurer, acting as a self-funded employer, filed a lawsuit against the chair of Vermont's Green Mountain Care Board, *Gobeille v. Liberty Mutual*, claiming its third-party administrator, Blue Cross Blue Shield of Massachusetts, wasn't required to send its employee data to the state's database.[266] Liberty Mutual, which runs self-funded plans in all fifty states, claimed that the federal Employee Retirement Income Security Act (ERISA), which exempts self-insured employers from having to follow fifty different state laws, exempts it from the Vermont disclosure statute.[267]

The US Supreme Court agreed in a 6-2 decision on March 1, 2016, writing, "Pre-emption is necessary to prevent States from imposing novel, inconsistent and burdensome reporting requirements on plans"—a win for self-funded employers and patients throughout the country.[268] It could get even better. Two experts writing in the *New England Journal of Medicine* warned that a win for Liberty Mutual would mean self-insured corporations could ignore other state data-submission laws.[269] A win could shut down government health information exchanges, they wrote. Liberty Mutual's victory could also hamper plans for establishing the eHealth Exchange, which, as noted, is being created by incorporating state HIEs into a national medical-records network.

However, the US Department of Labor, under the Obama administration, responded to the lawsuit by proposing regulations that would require self-insured companies to send summary data annually to the federal government.[270] Some want DOL to require that

ERISA plans report their claims data to APCDs.[271] Given the Trump administration's freeze on new regulations, this troubling proposal may be on hold. Meanwhile, three organizations—the National Academy for State Health Policy, the National Association of Health Data Organizations, and the APCD Council—are developing a "Common Data Layout (CDL) for the collection of claims data in a single national standard format . . . applicable to both self-insured and fully insured plans," reports *Health Affairs*. That said, the article says APCDs "have been significantly diminished after Gobeille" and implementation of the DOL's rule, if finalized, "will depend upon the leadership of the Trump administration."[272]

The Physician Compare Database

The federal government collects patient data to profile physicians. The Affordable Care Act requires development of Physician Compare, a CMS website that currently uses patient data from Medicare claims[273] to compare group practices that have at least two physicians.[274] The website—medicare.gov/physiciancompare—launched in December 2010, and will eventually be used to compare individual physicians and other health care professionals.[275] The data collected electronically for inclusion on the website are:

- Measures collected under the Physician Quality Reporting System (PQRS)
- Assessment of patient health outcomes and functional status of patients
- Assessment of the continuity and coordination of care and care transitions, including episodes of care and risk-adjusted resource use
- Assessment of efficiency
- Assessment of patient experience and patient, caregiver, and family engagement

- Assessment of the safety, effectiveness, and timeliness of care
- Other information as determined appropriate by the Secretary[276]

Such "other information" apparently includes Meaningful Use of electronic health records. HHS notes in the proposed rule, "With the Physician Compare redesign, we . . . included a notation and check mark for individuals that successfully participate in the Medicare EHR Incentive Program."[277]

The "quality comparison" data on Physician Compare are generated from a federal data system known to clinics and hospitals—the Provider Enrollment, Chain and Ownership System, or PECOS[278]—and from medical claims[279] sent to Medicare by physicians under fee-for-service, non-HMO Medicare, called Original Medicare. [280] According to HHS, the PECOS information "is the sole source of verified Medicare professional information," and the primary source of administrative information on Physician Compare.[281]

HHS further explains, "The primary goal of Physician Compare is to help consumers make informed health care decisions. If a consumer does not properly interpret a quality measure and thus misunderstands what the quality score represents, the consumer cannot use this information to make an informed decision."[282]

This claim is faulty. First, quality is in the eye of the beholder, not the assessment of a government data collector. Second, these quality scores reflect physician compliance with government-prescribed quality and process measures, which cut into the time doctors can spend with patients and limit treatment options. As Barry Christopher, MD, a practicing neurosurgeon in Oklahoma, wrote in public comments to CMS, "A physician's 'compliance score' is tied to 'resource use.' Physicians will be increasingly pressured to make decisions that save resources for Medicare instead of decisions that are in the best interest of their individual patients." [283] Third, measuring quality is difficult. "It's very hard to distinguish what is variation in provider quality, who are good and bad providers, from differences in the patients that they serve," says health policy researcher Eric Roberts. He worries that doctors with sicker poorer patients will be scored lower and unfairly penalized.[284] Fourth, current EHRs may not be cut out for the task. A study reported in April 2018 concludes, "The current state of EHR measurement functionality may be insufficient to support federal initiatives that tie payment to clinical quality measures."[285] Fifth, studies show few people use physician scorecards[286]—in 2015, a study found only 10 percent had seen and 6 percent had used information on physician quality.[287] Sixth, health plan networks dictate patient choice of physician regardless of quality scores. Surely there are better uses of taxpayer dollars.

State Health Surveillance Systems

If your doctor, hospital, or clinic is seeking full reimbursement for Medicare services, your confidentiality will be compromised. Stages 1 and 2 of Meaningful Use require the ability to exchange data with public health departments. Requirements or options for data sharing include submitting electronic data to immunization registries, to public health agencies, to cancer registries, and to specialized registries.[288] See section II.

Mandated electronic reporting—and the interfaces required to connect—provides state public health officials with easy access to private data, as well as expanded data collection possibilities. For example, a baby's birth certificate seems rather innocuous, but it has become a method for expansive data collection. In a report titled, *Profiled from Birth: Not Just a Birth Certificate*, the following points are highlighted:

- Parents don't know more data is being collected by the state than is necessary to register the birth of the child.
- Using the child's birth as an opportunity, states collect a wide array of data on children, mothers and families, such as education levels, race, behaviors, last employment and income.

- Data is used to conduct research and analysis without parent consent.
- "Birth Certificate Worksheets," labor, delivery, prenatal and mother's medical records are used to gather the data.
- One state allows parents to refuse to provide data not required for registration, but parents may not be told.[289]

The report, issued by our organization, Citizens' Council for Health Freedom (CCHF), includes a spreadsheet with the various data elements collected by twenty-eight states and Washington, DC. Before mothers and fathers begin to answer questions on the birth certificate form, they might consider where the data is going—typically to the state health department—and how it will be used. The report provides action steps that can be used to protect the family's privacy.

Other state surveillance systems begin at birth as well, including state immunization registries, newborn screening databases, and birth-defect registries. In addition, there are state surveillance systems for Alzheimer's disease, asthma, autism, brain injury, blindness, burns, cardiovascular disease, cerebral palsy, chronic disease, diabetes, disability, ER visits, hospital discharge, HIV, injury, morbid obesity, body mass index, occupational disease, Parkinson's disease, poisoning, sexually transmitted diseases, stroke, trauma, vaccinations, violent injury, and more.[290] For more information on state data-collection systems, check out CCHF's fifty-state report on health surveillance: *Patient Privacy and Public Trust: How Health Surveillance Systems Are Undermining Both.*[291]

Prescription Drug Monitoring Programs

One state surveillance system deserves special mention. If you have received a prescription for pain medication or purchased a pseudoephedrine product such as Sudafed, you are likely in the database. As described by the Congressional Research Service (CSR):

> Prescription drug monitoring programs (PDMPs) maintain statewide electronic databases of prescriptions dispensed for controlled substances (i.e., prescription drugs of abuse that are subject to stricter government regulation). Information collected by PDMPs may be used to support access to and legitimate medical use of controlled substances; identify or prevent drug abuse and diversion; facilitate the identification of prescription drug-addicted individuals and enable intervention and treatment; outline drug use and abuse trends to inform public health initiatives; or educate individuals about prescription drug use, abuse, and diversion as well as about PDMPs.[292]

All fifty states have implemented a PDMP, although Missouri's program was established by an executive order issued in July 2017 after years of legislative opposition. Republican Governor Eric Greitens claimed it was "a step" toward solving the opioid crisis. But Jeff Howell, director of government relations for the Missouri State Medical Association, said, "It looks to be more a law enforcement tool than it does to be a patient treatment tool. We like to think part of the reason to have a PDMP is to have a clinical tool that subscribers can use to treat patients."[293] A majority of these central databases are administered by state pharmacy boards, but some states house them in agencies such as consumer protection, substance abuse, professional licensing, law enforcement, and departments of health.[294]

Surveillance could expand well beyond opioids. On January 1, 2018, Nebraska became the first state to require reporting of all dispensed prescription drugs to the PDMP. Maryland-based DrFirst is under contract to capture prescription information and send it to the PDMP, providing "a complete view of a patient's prescription history," says Deb Bass, CEO of the Nebraska Health Information Initiative.[295]

Here's how the typical surveillance process works. Personally identifiable information and prescription data on each patient receiving a controlled substance (as defined by each state) is submitted to the database without patient consent. Depending on the state, required submitters include hospitals, sole practitioners, wholesale distributors, and even out-of-state, mail order, and Internet pharmacies. Access to patient information also depends on the state, but can include pharmacists, practitioners, law enforcement, licensing and regulatory boards, state Medicaid programs, state medical examiners, and research organizations.[296]

States share patient data with other states. As of December 2013, reports CSR, forty-five states allowed for sharing PDMP information on some level—with PDMPs in other states, with authorized PDMP users in other states, or both. Research into the effectiveness of PDMPs is limited due to challenges such as defining effectiveness, accounting for differences among state PDMPs, and potential confounding factors such as the impact of other initiatives on lowering drug abuse, and economic downturns or upturns.[297] A study in *JAMA (Journal of the American Medical Association)* says evidence of lower rates of prescription drug abuse and altered prescribing practices is "mixed and inconclusive."[298] Surprisingly, one federal study found "the likelihood of abuse was actually higher in states with PDMPs than in states without PDMPs, but that proactive PDMPs inhibited the rate of increase in prescription drug abuse."[299]

Interestingly, the Associated Press says the PDMP's tracking of pseudoephedrine purchases has "created a vast and highly lucrative market for profiteers to buy over-the-counter pills and sell them to meth producers at a huge markup."[300] Rob Bovett, the district attorney in Lincoln Country Oregon, says buying less than the legal limit or using fake IDs "are the two things that completely evade and eviscerate the electronic tracking systems."[301] Counterintuitively, "the pharmaceutical industry has spent several million dollars to fund the tracking systems," reports the Associated Press. "For drug makers, that is far cheaper than one alternative—making the medication available only by prescription." Oregon and Mississippi have already done so.[302]

PDMPs have experienced "mission creep." For example, the Minnesota program was enacted in 2007 ostensibly as a helpful tool for physicians to voluntarily use to reduce doctor shopping for controlled substances.[303] Collection of patient and prescriber data began January 1, 2010.[304] But legislators regularly expanded the law. Changes were made in 2008, 2009, 2010, 2013, 2014, and 2016.[305] Over time, the state legislature required longer retention of the data, granted permission to use the data for research studies and trend analysis, provided law enforcement access with a search warrant, allowed licensing boards to conduct a "bona fide investigation of a complaint received by the board that alleges that a specific licensee is impaired by use of a drug for which data is collected," and mandated that all prescribers and pharmacists register with the system and maintain a user account whether they use it or not. There are twelve categories of "permissible users" authorized to access the system within certain parameters.[306] In 2017 and 2018, to reduce addiction to opioids, there was an unsuccessful push to mandate that all physicians use the PDMP.[307] As of March 2015, twenty-two states required prescribers to check the PDMP before writing a prescription for a controlled substance.[308] Michigan's mandate began in June 2018.[309]

The Minnesota PDMP demonstrates how intrusiveness can expand. In 2014, the Minnesota Board of Pharmacy sought legislation to retain patient data for five years and give more individuals access to the data. Minnesota State Representative Tina Liebling (D) opposed it, and pushed to have the data de-identified after one year, saying, "It's very personal data on basically every patient in the state who gets pain medication, and that is very intrusive." Cody Wiberg, director of the pharmacy board opposed Liebling's proposal to have the data de-identified after one year, saying, "You just can't get quite as full a picture of what is going on without having the data in a form where you can still identify people." Even with expanded retention, the bill was insufficiently prescriptive for its senate author, Republican Senator Julie Rosen. Per the *Post-Bulletin*, "As for Rosen, she said the bill does not go far enough for her. State law does not require doctors to use the database before writing a prescription. Rosen would like to make its use mandatory." Someone in the county sheriff's office had asked Liebling to change the law to let them access the data with a simple administrative subpoena rather than a search warrant. But Liebling refused. "From my point of view, this data is not being collected as a law enforcement tool. The initial collection of it is for doctors to help their patients. That is why it is being collected."[310]

Many physicians complain that accessing the PDMP is time-consuming, taking precious minutes away from interaction with patients.[311] Physicians also object to these "burdensome incursions into clinical practice."[312] As a result, at least seven states, including Indiana and Michigan have implemented a program to *integrate* the state government's PDMP into the EHR[313] and the National Governors Association has called on the ONC to "require that EHR vendors make their systems interoperable with all state PDMPs."[314] According to *Healthcare IT News*, "PDMP data and analytics are integrated into physician and pharmacist workflow through EHRs and pharmacy management systems in 32 states."[315] Congress is also considering 2018 legislation that would "require state Medicaid programs to incorporate prescription drug monitoring programs, known as PDMPs, into pharmacists' clinical workflows" and "require states to report to CMS on the status of those programs, including the number of providers using them and whether they're working," reports *Politico*.[316]

Besides the privacy intrusion, other concerns include the unintended consequences from the PDMP surveillance programs. These include, according to CSR, limiting patient access to medications for legitimate use, and prescriber hesitation to prescribe medications tracked by the PDMP for fear of coming under scrutiny from law enforcement or licensing boards. Patients may also try to avoid monitoring by the PDMP by avoiding certain useful medications. Additionally, there may be an increase in nonprescription opioids, such as heroin.[317]

Deaths from opioid addiction have fueled surveillance databases. A draft report from the Commission on Combating Drug Addiction and the Opioid Crisis released July 31, 2017, recommended "federal funding and technical support to states to enhance interstate data sharing among state-based prescription drug monitoring programs (PDMPs) to better track patient-specific prescription data and support regional law enforcement in cases of controlled substance diversion."[318] It suggests a July 1, 2018, deadline for data sharing. It also recommends that "federal health care systems, including Veterans Administration Hospitals, participate in state-based data sharing."[319] This would be the integration of state and federal PDMPs.

The draft report further recommends the inclusion of unnamed "other data to assist prescribing doctors" in the PDMP and repeal of 42 CFR Part 2, a regulatory provision that requires addiction treatment professionals to obtain patient consent before sharing substance use disorder (SUD) information. The commission wants sharing of this data permitted without consent of a patient's other health care providers, "including when the addiction treatment facility is part of a larger health care system." The report calls the patient consent requirement a "particular hindrance to comprehensive health care" that "limits the ability to use electronic health records to their full potential." The United States Congress and Senate have proposed legislation to allow data sharing of substance abuse records without consent.[320] These bills and the draft report ignore the reason the consent requirement was established in 1975—so patients would not "avoid seeking needed treatment."[321] Finally, the report calls for "[t]he possibility of a behavioral health surveillance system run through CDC that tracks prevalence rates, treatment modalities, and comorbidities with other illnesses in real-time."[322] Clearly, some think patients with substance abuse issues should have no privacy or consent rights, when in fact these patients currently have the kind of privacy and consent rights all Americans should have—the kind HIPAA eliminated—and Congress should not take it away from them.

VI

The Cost of Coercion

Prices and Penalties

False Claims of Cost Savings

Once upon a time, purveyors of electronic medical records made lofty claims about cost savings, which were used to push the EHR mandate. Less than a month before the mandate became law, HIMSS, a leader in the effort, announced the following:

> Deloitte LLP reported this month that investing in e-prescribing and electronic medical records, along with better coordination of patient care through primary-care doctors, would result in 10-year savings of $530 billion.
>
> The RAND Corporation reported in a 2005 study that widespread health IT adoption (90 percent of hospitals and physicians) could save $77 billion annually. In testimony presented before the Senate Finance Committee on July 17, 2008, RAND forecast that during the 15-year adoption period, cumulative net savings would be about $510 billion or approximately $34 billion per year.
>
> The Center for Information Technology Leadership estimated in a 2005 study that full implementation of health IT could yield annual savings of $77.8 billion.[1]

The Center for Information Technology Leadership project to assess the value of health IT claimed in 2004 and 2005 that $77.8 billion could be saved by a complete turnover from paper records to EHRs.[2] The CITL project was funded by the Foundation for the eHealth Initiative,[3] which received more than $6.8 million in federal grants to pursue HIE and came under fire by the Health Resources and Services Administration in 2005 for possible mismanagement of the program.[4]

RAND estimated health care efficiency savings of approximately $80 billion annually *after* a fifteen-year implementation period. It also estimated implementation costs of $7.6 billion per year, assuming adoption by 90 percent of hospitals and doctors over fifteen years.[5] The estimated savings were to come from various sources, including reductions in length of stay and increases in nurse productivity.[6] Frustrated nurses nationwide who feel their productivity hampered by the EHR may not agree with the assertion.

But the Congressional Budget Office (CBO) in 2008, one year before the EHR mandate was enacted, dismissed RAND's claims of $80 billion, saying it "suffers from significant flaws and is therefore not an appropriate guide to estimating the effects of legislative proposals aimed at boosting the use of health IT."[7] In particular, the CBO found that the RAND study ignored studies in peer-reviewed journals that found evidence of zero or negative net savings.

In fact, the CBO found potential financial harm because those who pay the costs may not reap the benefits:

> For providers and hospitals that are not part of integrated systems, however, the benefits of health IT are not as easy to capture, and perhaps not coincidentally, those physicians and facilities have adopted EHRs at a much slower rate. Office-based physicians in particular may see no benefit if they purchase such a product—and *may even suffer financial harm*. Even though the use of health IT could generate cost savings for the health system at large that might offset the EHR's cost, many physicians might not be able to reduce their office expenses or increase their revenue sufficiently to pay for it.[8] (Emphasis added.)

A few months later, in December 2008, the CBO predicted more detailed possibilities of harm if small practices in particular were mandated to buy an EHR system as a condition of participation in Medicare. While CBO officials predicted the mandate would lead "virtually all hospitals and physicians to adopt electronic health record systems," they warned:

> A disadvantage of this option is that it would impose a large cost on providers. In particular, many small practices would be hard-pressed to find the financial resources to purchase a health IT system. In addition, implementing this option would create a surge in demand for health IT systems, thereby bidding up the price of IT specialists and of the systems themselves. Thus, this option could create a strong incentive for providers to favor low-cost health IT systems over high-quality systems.[9]

Four years before the 2009 mandate, as directors and analysts at the Center for Information Technology Leadership pushed for a comprehensive transition to health IT and EHRs, they posed the question of who should pay for this transition and claimed patients and providers would likely benefit most:

> Although it is beyond the scope of this paper to speculate in depth about who would benefit from HIEI [healthcare information exchange and interoperability], patients and providers most likely have the most to gain. Organizations such as regulatory agencies, research institutions, and others not considered here could benefit from aggregate information about care. However, those who depend in subtle ways on redundancy and excess could find such change costly. . . .
>
> Achieving . . . interoperability will require sizable investment in HIEI systems by providers and stakeholders. Participants realize different levels of return on HIEI investments, and the conflicting financial incentives of the health care system raise complex policy questions about who should pay for development and implementation.[10]

Forced Into EHRs

Doctors and hospitals were forced to pay. Taxpayers were forced to pay. Despite the experimental nature of EHRs and the likelihood of harm, the threat of government penalties led to wholesale adoption of government EHRs. The CBO says only about 12 percent of physicians and 11 percent of hospitals had adopted health IT as of 2006.[11] However, in 2011, two years after the HITECH Act was enacted and three years before the mandate and penalties took effect, 42 percent of all physicians had an EHR system that met federal standards.[12] By October 2012, 69 percent of physicians in 950 physician groups surveyed had an EHR system.[13]

A 2013 government survey found "more than half" of all doctors and other practitioners and 80 percent of hospitals had adopted or were "meaningfully using" government-mandated EHRs as required by the law.[14] The United States has approximately 916,264 licensed physicians and 5,564 registered hospitals.[15] According to *Healthcare IT News*:

> As of the end of November [2013], more than 436,000 hospitals and health professionals have registered for the Medicaid and Medicare EHR incentive program, and the federal government has made more than $17.7 billion in payments, the Centers for Medicare and Medicaid Services told the Health IT Policy Committee in an update.
>
> Of the $17.7 billion, almost $11 billion has gone to 4,300-plus hospitals who have achieved meaningful use status, while $4 billion has gone to about 210,000 physicians and health professionals qualifying under Medicare and $2.5 billion has gone to 107,000 professionals qualifying under Medicaid.
>
> All of that has translated in a majority of American providers now using digital health record systems.[16]

In 2015, ONC issued a report stating that almost all reported hospitals (97 percent) possessed a certified EHR in 2014 (top line in chart below). The impact of the 2009 HITECH Act's EHR mandate is clear:[17]

Three out of Four Hospitals have a Basic EHR System.

Figure 1: Percent of non-Federal acute care hospitals with adoption of at least a Basic EHR with notes system and possession of a certified EHR: 2008-2014

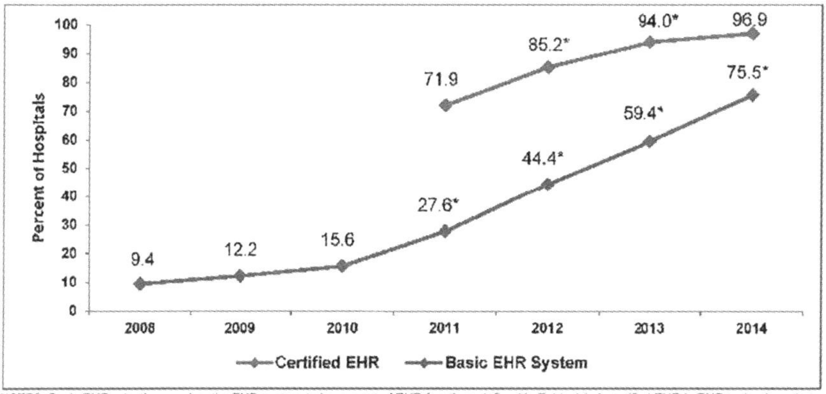

NOTES: Basic EHR adoption requires the EHR system to have a set of EHR functions defined in Table A1. A certified EHR is EHR technology that meets the technological capability, functionality, and security requirements adopted by the Department of Health and Human Services. Possession means that the hospital has a legal agreement with the EHR vendor, but is not equivalent to adoption.
*Significantly different from previous year ($p < 0.05$).
SOURCE: ONC/American Hospital Association (AHA), AHA Annual Survey Information Technology Supplement

Upfront and Hidden Costs

The cost of the EHR mandate has been staggering. Taxpayers, patients, and physicians have already felt the financial impact. Expenses include direct costs, such as buying, installing, and maintaining the systems, and indirect costs related to training, learning, and reporting compliance with Meaningful Use. These include lower productivity, reduced revenues, added costs of scribes, and more time spent with the EHR than the patient.

David Cossman, MD, a vascular surgeon in Los Angeles, writing in *General Surgery News,* shares a few clarifying comments about the mandate:

> Cost containment is clearly a joke. According to my calculations (which I will be happy to share with you upon request), implementation will cost nearly $300,000 per bed, or about

> 50% more than the cost to build the hospital from scratch (pity me, I'm still a bricks-and-mortar guy in a virtual world). There are nearly 1 million staffed hospital beds in the country; so countrywide implementation will cost $350 billion or roughly half the total expenditures of the nation's 5,700 hospitals in 2010. I know poor penmanship is a problem, but what else am I missing to justify this expense, especially when the health care business is already reeling from reduced reimbursements from a national treasury that would technically be in default of its obligations were it not for the inexplicable faith and confidence of the Chinese in our future ability to make good on our debts.[18]

At the end of 2008, the CBO estimated, "High-quality systems can cost $20,000 to $25,000 per physician, not including implementation and annual maintenance costs. Overall, startup costs can exceed $40,000 per physician."[19] Several studies say costs range between $15,000 and $70,000 per practitioner.[20] Monthly subscription fees can be as high as $2,000 a month.[21]

Annual support fees can tack on between $8,000 and $15,000 in additional expenses.[22] Cybersecurity insurance could be $300 a month.[23] Interface fees add thousands of dollars in expenses. Michael Burkey, director of operations for Braddock Medical Group in Cumberland, Maryland, said his group of six primary care physicians has "gotten killed" by these fees, reports Dark Daily, a news website for clinical laboratories. The group paid $5,000 to connect with the state's public health registry and $5,000 to create a patient portal interface, both required by Meaningful Use.[24] Citing the complexity of interfaces with laboratories, W. Campbell, PhD, MBA, commented on the Dark Daily article: "Interfaces are complex and an interface to one instance of an EMR system is not the same as an interface to another instance of the same EMR to the same reference laboratory."[25] The groups trying to convince President Bush in 2005 to build a national health information system estimated interface development costs at "$50,000 per interface for hospitals, labs, radiology centers, pharmacies, and public health departments, and $20,000 per interface in group-practice offices."[26]

There are also six hidden total-cost-of-ownership expenses, which surprise clinics that don't understand the complexity of EHRs or unwittingly trust EHR vendors:

- Hardware replacements after three to five years
- Third-party reporting system
- Ongoing customization
- Customized templates for specialty physicians
- Technical support
- Regulatory compliance[27]

For large hospital systems the costs are much higher. The price tag for Detroit's Henry Ford Health System was $356 million.[28] Geisinger Health System in Pennsylvania has spent more than $180 million.[29] Minnesota hospital systems spent between $1 million (rural hospitals) and $250 million (Allina Health System). Hennepin County Medical Center in Minneapolis, Minnesota, spent approximately $68 million.[30] Duke University Health System in Durham, North Carolina, paid approximately $700 million.[31]

EHR systems can also be short-lived. Rushed by the threat of penalties, the clinic's first EHR choice may be the wrong choice. Between 35 percent and 50 percent of EHRs are replaced after only one year of use, adding more expense to the process.[32] A 2013 survey of seventeen thousand EHR users by Black Book Market Research found as many as 17 percent of physician practices considering an upgrade or a replacement of their EHR system. Another study by KLAS, a research group, found that half of all EHR sales to physicians are replacements.[33] Data migration from one EHR to the next can be a nightmare. Some practices "literally had to print and rescan every medical record, because there wasn't an easy way to move the patient data from the old system to the new one," said Robert Tennant, director of health information policy at Medical Group Management Association.[34]

Hospitals have been forced to buy replacements as well. Phoenix-based Banner Health is getting rid of the $115 million Epic system in two Tucson hospitals in 2018, five years after purchasing it, and replacing it with a system from Cerner. In 2013 Banner experienced $32 million in unbudgeted costs, including $6.8 million due to losses in physician productivity (time spent training to use the new system and not seeing as many patients).[35] A new system means more training costs and a new round of productivity losses.

Epic is one of the nation's largest EHR companies, grossing $1.77 billion in 2014. Epic CEO Judy Faulkner donated to President Obama's 2008 campaign and was appointed to the HHS Health Information Technology Policy Committee, where she sat from 2009 until 2014.[36] She and her company have benefited from the EHR mandate. A look at the known or expected millions of dollars spent on the eight most expensive Epic EHR systems to go live in 2015 provides a snapshot of the cost of the mandate:

- Partners HealthCare: $1.2 billion
- Lehigh Valley Health Network: $200 million
- Mayo Clinic: "Hundreds of millions"
- Lahey Hospital & Medicare Center: $160 million
- Lifespan: $100 million
- Erlanger Health System: $97 million
- Wheaton Franciscan Healthcare: $54 million
- Saint Francis Medical Center: $43 million[37]

The costs of implementation have real consequences. Southcoast Health in Massachusetts announced the layoff of ninety-five employees as a result from a new $100 million Epic system. EHR training for the three-hospital system's 7,251 employees contributed to a $9.9 million operating loss.[38]

Other consequences include resignations of concerned top executives. For example, in March 2016 Charles Perry, MD, resigned in anticipation of a disaster with the pending rollout of a $764 million EHR system at NYC Health + Hospitals. He compared it to the failed and fatal launch of NASA's *Challenger*, which exploded mid-air in 1986.[39] Sources told the *New York Post* that dry runs of the system weren't complete and predicted a crash.[40]

Mandate Hits Smaller Hospitals Hard

Smaller hospitals are struggling to meet the government's EHR mandate, putting them and the patients they serve in jeopardy. A study published in *Health Affairs* concludes that "for small hospitals participating in the Medicare meaningful-use program, the inability to keep up with attestation deadlines in the penalty phase could create even greater challenges for resource-constrained hospitals by reducing payments."[41]

In September 2016 the American Hospital Association estimated that approximately two hundred hospitals had received lower reimbursements—penalties—due to failure to comply with the Medicare EHR incentive program known as Meaningful Use.[42] Many of these may have been smaller hospitals with fewer resources.

Since 2010, 80 rural hospitals have closed and 673 are at risk of closing, with 210 at "extreme risk," according to a 2017 study. Many hospitals see the shift to value-based care, including its lower reimbursements and added regulatory requirements, "as compounding their woes." A better sense of the costs associated with federal data requirements emerges from this statement by Leslie March, CEO at Lexington Regional Medical Center in south central Nebraska: "We can't afford a data analyst, but five hospitals together afford and share a data analyst."[43]

In 2017, the American Hospital Association (AHA) wrote CMS, saying the regulatory burden facing hospitals "is substantial and unsustainable." It said CMS and other agencies of HHS in 2016 "released 49 hospital and health system-related rules, comprising almost 24,000 pages."[44] In October 2017, the AHA released a report titled *Regulatory Overload*, which discussed 629 mandatory regulatory requirements and reported, "the average-sized hospital spent nearly $760,000 to meet MU [Meaningful Use] administrative requirements.

In addition, they invested $411,000 in related upgrades to systems during the year." Furthermore, the average-sized community hospital "devotes 4.6 FTEs—over half of whom are clinical staff—and spends approximately $709,000 annually on the administrative aspects of quality reporting." The report notes, "a one-size-fits-all approach may not be possible" and asked that the "unique burdens faced by rural providers . . . and small hospitals" be considered for regulatory reform aimed at reducing administrative burdens.[45]

Federal Grants Don't Cover EHR Costs

Many physicians and hospitals applied for EHR incentive payments (subsidies) to help pay for EHR installation, but Medicare-eligible professionals could only seek qualification through 2014 and Medicaid-eligible professionals could only seek qualification through 2016.[46] Costs are substantial. While the American Hospital Association reports that hospitals have been paid about $18 billion in incentive payments, it estimates that "collectively, America's hospitals spent $47.5 billion on information technology each and every year between 2010 and 2014.[47]

The maximum payment to eligible physicians and other professionals was $44,000 between 2012 and 2016 under the Medicare EHR Incentive Program (minus sequestration reductions) or $63,750 over six years between 2011 and 2021 under the Medicaid EHR Incentive Program.[48] Incentive payments were available through one program or the other, not both.[49]

However, according to a 2014 national survey, 45 percent of physicians report spending more than $100,000 on an EHR, and 77 percent of the largest practices spent nearly $200,000 on their systems. Fully 79 percent of respondents in practices with more than ten physicians said the EHR investment was not worth the effort. Other dramatic costs were associated with the need to hire more staff and a loss in physician productivity. One respondent said: "We used to see 32 patients a day with one tech, and now we struggle to see 24 patients a day with four techs. And we provide worse care."[50] Three years later, a survey of 1,100 health care professionals gave dismal ratings to the return on investment for EHRs. Nineteen percent said ROI was "terrible" and 42 percent said it was "poor." Only 1 percent said it was "superb" and 9 percent said "positive." The remaining 29 percent called it "mediocre."[51]

Incentive payments are also available for "eligible acute care inpatient hospitals," which are paid using the federal inpatient prospective payment system and can include Medicare Advantage organizations affiliated with eligible hospitals. It's a complicated three-part formula. The "total initial amount," which is the baseline for the calculation, starts at $2 million for smaller hospitals and by law cannot exceed $6,370,400 for any hospital. The final incentive payment is determined by a federal calculation that included the determined initial amount, the "Medicare Share," and a "Transition Factor." According to the examples shared by CMS, this calculation will elicit a much lower payment than $6,370,400.[52]

Payments began in 2012. By the end of October 2012, Medicare and Medicaid had paid out $8.36 billion in EHR incentive payments to eligible physicians and hospitals.[53] By the end of 2013 total incentive payments were nearing $18 billion. By September 2014 the government had paid more than $23 billion.[54] Incentive payments totaled $29.1 billion by February 2015.[55] Between May 2011 and March 2017, payments exceeded $35 billion (more than $24 billion in Medicare payments and $11.6 billion in Medicaid payments).[56] Access to incentive payments ends in 2021.[57]

Considering the cost of buying a system, what EHR-related expenses may not be covered by the incentive payments? Additional costs include conducting research to choose an EHR system, computerizing paper patient records, training staff, loss of productivity as staff learns the new system—as previously noted, Banner Health attributes losses of $6.8 million in 2013 from physicians learning the EHR system and not seeing as many patients[58]—hiring IT staff, and ongoing maintenance and updates.

Researchers studied a network of twenty-six primary care physicians in north Texas. They reported that a five-physician practice should expect overall startup costs for EHR implementation at $162,000, plus $85,000 for the first year of maintenance. In addition, 611 hours were needed on average to prepare and implement the health IT system.[59] For some clinics, it will take much longer.

Some costs never end. Drew Nietert, a certified professional in healthcare information and management systems (CPHIMS), lists twenty cost areas for EHRs and says most calculations for total-cost-of-ownership (TCO) don't exceed three to five years. "In that time frame," he writes, "almost all hardware needs to be replaced, including the servers, a multi-million dollar initiative in organizations of 200 or more." A few cost areas on his list you may not think about:

- EHR licenses
- Data center or hosted costs
- Internet bandwidth
- EHR staffing
- Staffing the "bubble"
- Data migration and system conversions
- Third-party software
- Customizations

"Customization isn't a part-time job; it requires a close relationship with your vendor throughout the life of the EHR," he wrote. He suggests putting EHR costs into four categories: Initial, Repeat, Future, and Special Projects.[60]

Then there is the cost of time. Rosemarie Nelson at MGMA Health Care Consulting Group, estimates that EHR implementation "calls for a full-timer for three to six months, plus .20 to .25 of an FTE [full time equivalent] for ongoing support and management."[61] A full 134 hours of staff time per physician is needed just to prepare for using the EHR during patient visits.[62] One physician told your author his ten-physician practice added seven office staff solely to deal with the EHR. Part or all of this cost gets passed down to the patient in higher office fees and higher premiums.

Vendors Hold Data Ransom

The Mayo Clinic is spending $1.5 billion[63] to make the switch from the Cerner EHR system to Epic Systems. The change will put Mayo's clinical and administrative data into one Epic EHR system nationwide. Epic and Mayo began collaborating in 2013[64] and full implementation is scheduled for 2018.[65] Will the switch be easy? Although there's no news of it happening, John Lynn, founder of HealthcareScene.com, wrote in February 2015 about a problem most patients aren't aware of:

> Will Cerner be nice and let Mayo and their EHR data go easily? Same for GE Centricity. I've heard of hundreds of EHR switches and many of them have a really challenging time getting their data from their previous EHR vendor. Some choose to make it expensive. Others choose to not cooperate at all. Given Mayo's stature and the switch from Pepsi to Coke (Cerner to Epic, but I'm not sure which is Pepsi and which is Coke), I'll be interested to see if Cerner lets them go without any issues.[66]

Federal Failures Cost Billions

Government health systems fare no better. The US Department of Veterans Affairs and Department of Defense began working in 1998 to create health records that could work together.[67] The effort intensified in 2009, but they gave up four years later after spending—some say *wasting*—$1.3 billion.[68] The expected price tag was $28 billion.[69] The 2014 US Department of Defense (DoD) budget listed $466.9 million for "initial outfitting" and "replacement and modernization" of its health record.[70]

In July 2015 the DoD awarded a ten-year, $4.3 billion contract to Leidos, which partnered with EHR developer Cerner and Accenture, for the Defense Healthcare Management System Modernization (DHMSM) program, which could be worth up to $10 billion over eighteen years, reports FedScoop.[71]

Continuing the attempt to achieve interoperability, the two federal departments touted a Joint Legacy Viewer in November 2015, enabling read-only access to medical records in both departments worldwide.[72] Then in April 2016 the DoD announced a new EHR system called MHS GENESIS created under the DHMSM contract that can be "easily transferred to external providers, including major medical systems and Department of Veterans Affairs hospitals and clinics."[73] Launch was expected by year end. But in June 2016, the inspector general at the defense department said the DHMSM program might not meet the December 2016 deadline.[74]

In June 2017, Secretary David Shulkin, MD, at the US Department of Veterans Affairs (VA) announced he would be handing the EHR acquisition to Cerner. With both departments using the same EHR vendor, President Trump said data sharing between the two agencies would be fixed "once and for all." Cerner claimed the work on both projects would lead to "creation of a single longitudinal health record."[75] On October 26, 2017, Shulkin told Congress it would take eighteen months to launch Cerner *after* the contract is finalized and seven to eight years to fully transition to a Cerner EHR.[76] Although DoD's EHR system was "neither operationally effective nor operationally suitable" in early May 2018, the VA inked a $10 billion contract with Cerner on May 17, 2018.[77] Thus far, the VA has lost nearly $2 billion in three pursuits to modernize its health information system—the Veterans Health Information Systems and Technology Architecture (VistA).[78]

Other military EHRs have also failed. On April 21, 2016, *Politico* reported that a deal between Epic Systems and the US Coast Guard failed, despite $34 million in contracts with Epic and others to install the system. The Coast Guard, which couldn't return to its old EHR system, went back to paper medical records.[79] The State Department, which was part of the failed Coast Guard implementation, issued a 2016 request for information as part of a plan to move to a commercial off-the-shelf, likely cloud-based EHR.[80] In April 2017, a year after terminating its contract with Epic, the Coast Guard began a new effort to acquire an EHR system by issuing a request for information (RFI).[81]

However, during a January 2018 congressional hearing, the Government Accountability Office (GAO) reported nearly $59.9 million already spent on the Coast Guard EHR project over nearly seven years.[82] Chairman Duncan Hunter (R-CA) asked the Coast Guard testifiers several times why the service wouldn't just use the DoD EHR system. At one point he asked, "Is there anything special about being in the Coast Guard that would not allow you to be in the Department of Defense's health records system?"

Despite the millions already spent, the Coast Guard had "no software, no code and no machinery," but was still making payments after cancelling the contracts. Hunter responded, "It'd be nice to be a software contractor in town here. I can do stuff for you and never give it to you, and you'll pay me. . . . I'm of the mind to make you get on DoD's thing no matter what you think. We ought to just tell you to do it. . . . You guys don't get to go off on your own and just use taxpayer dollars because it's fun, when you have the Department of Defense doing it."

Congressman John Garamendi (D-CA), asked several times for the name of the contractor but was never given a name. At one point he remarked, "I'll bet they've screwed up before and I'll bet we've hired the same folks that screwed up before to do another screw up."[83]

On April 9, 2018, the Coast Guard announced they'll join the DoD's EHR initiative. Rather than signing a contract with Cerner, their needs will be incorporated into the DoD's contract with Leidos.[84] Cerner may have won the VA and DoD contracts, but federal officials need to stay alert. Wisconsin-based Agnesian HealthCare sued Cerner in 2017 for $16 million to recoup losses caused by pervasive coding errors in the EHR vendor's software that led to the system "automatically writing off reimbursable charges for services without any notice to the hospital." Cerner admitted the billing system needed to be rebuilt.[85]

Federal and Rural Clinics in Survival Mode

Some Federally Qualified Health Centers (FQHCs), of which there are more than 1,300 in approximately 9,000 service delivery sites, aren't sure they'll survive the EHR.[86] For example, "one health center reported that the loss of productivity has resulted in $900,000 in lost revenues per year, whereas another health center estimated its loss at

$15,000," wrote the Office of Inspector General (OIG) for HHS. The OIG said EHR maintenance costs similarly varied, between $4,000 and $8,000 per year, per professional, depending on the type of EHR system.[87]

FQHCs report delaying other purchases, cutting positions, and charging patients more in order to cover the costs of the EHR system.[88] Rural clinics are also struggling under the mandate. A 2015 survey of rural health clinics found the following barriers to acquiring an EHR and implementing it. Most include a financial element:

- Cost to acquire and maintain
- Lack of capital to purchase an EHR
- Lack of physician/provider support
- Lack of resources for staff education and training
- Concerns about security/privacy
- Concerns about productivity or income loss during transition
- Lack of internal knowledge and technical resources[89]

Perpetual Threat of Penalties

As noted earlier in this book, HHS created three stages of burdensome Meaningful Use requirements, which have left physicians and hospitals struggling to comply. After HHS refused to delay Stage 3, the Senate passed a "blanket meaningful use significant hardship exception" through 2017 in an amendment to S. 1347.[90]

For some physicians the penalties are apparently preferred over participation. Of the 11,578 family physicians that claimed Meaningful Use in 2011, only 9,188 did so in 2012, a 21 percent drop in participation.[91] Another 12 percent of physicians stopped participating in 2014.[92] One survey found almost 14 percent of physicians who attested to MU in their first year did not plan on doing so in their second year.[93]

In August 2014 the Medicare administration said only 1,898 physicians and seventy-eight hospitals claimed to have reached Meaningful Use, Stage 2.[94]

Where Did the MU Money Go?

Record keeping on Meaningful Use funding is less than stellar. "The vast majority of states and the federal government have little data on how many doctors treating the nation's poorest patients are using electronic health records," *Politico* reported at the end of 2014. The news organization had asked every state Medicaid agency to disclose the EHR adoption rate of all the doctors and hospitals in its state. States have received approximately $9 billion in Medicaid MU EHR incentive payments, but only Wisconsin could provide statistics from 2014.

In contrast, Texas received $692 million in EHR incentive funds, but its Medicaid agency reported, "We do not have data for adoption rates or that show how incentives have impacted the number of providers acquiring an EHR." And a state official from Washington, which received $236 million in funds, told *Politico*, "We have the same information that CMS has and only know about providers who are seeking incentives. There is no other statewide survey or data collection effort that I am aware of that can get more specific."[95]

Federal audits have begun. Those who received the incentive payments are required to prove their Meaningful Use of EHRs. If they fail an audit, they will have to repay the entire MU grant, even if they've spent it all to buy the required EHR system.[96] This is known as a clawback—but there are also givebacks. One hospital corporation has already returned $31 million in EHR incentive payments—before the auditors came calling.[97]

Doctors Blamed for No Savings

Promised cost savings from the EHR mandate have not materialized. As noted, in 2005 RAND Corporation heralded $81 billion *per year* savings if EHRs were broadly adopted. Companies interested in health information technology, including Cerner, General Electric, Hewlett-Packard, Johnson & Johnson, and Xerox funded the study.[98]

Seven years later RAND said critics of their estimates could "claim a measure of vindication." In a January 2013 *Health Affairs* article, RAND staff note annual health care expenditures have grown by $800 billion: "Although the use of health IT has increased, *the quality and efficiency of patient care are only marginally better.* Research on the effectiveness of health IT has yielded mixed results. Worse yet, annual aggregate expenditures on health care in the United States have grown from approximately $2 trillion in 2005 to roughly $2.8 trillion today." (Emphasis added.) They take pains to say that earlier researchers had only claimed "potential savings, costs, and health and safety benefits" and that "estimates of potential savings are not predictions of what will happen but of what could happen with HIT and appropriate changes in health care."[99] However, their press release did not herald these hedging statements as loudly as they heralded the $81 billion estimate and called for federal incentives to providers who use EHRs and "embrace the technology."[100]

Claiming "theoretical benefits of health IT," RAND's researchers said, "it is remarkable how few fans it has among health care professionals."[101] But they blame physicians and other clinicians for the failure of EHRs to achieve their vastly overestimated savings, saying practitioners must change the way they practice medicine to fit the "more-standardized systems" of care that health IT was designed for:

> Providers must do their part by reengineering existing processes of care to take full advantage of the efficiencies offered by health IT. This revamping of health care delivery is unlikely to happen before payment models are realigned to favor value over volume.[102]

"They have it exactly backwards," writes Greg Scandlen on the National Center for Policy Analysis *Health Policy Blog*. "Rather than reengineering clinical practice to suit the demands of IT, IT must be developed to enhance what is happening clinically. . . . The problem with this whole top-down HIT enterprise is that they put IT engineers in charge instead of letting clinicians develop what would improve their operations."[103]

True, but that was not the point of the mandate—or the purpose of the government EHR. Certified EHRs were imposed to force physicians to practice medicine how third-party payers want it practiced. It was imposed to establish a "value over volume" payment system that lets third parties determine the value of physicians and other medical services and refuse to pay for actual services rendered. Ask your barber, plumber, or construction worker to work for "value payments" instead of hourly or service-rendered payments and see what their response is. No wonder the EHR has few fans among those who see it as an impediment to providing care and a tool for denying payment for that care.

No Evidence of Cost-Effectiveness

According to the *Journal of the American Medical Informatics Association*, researchers conducted a comprehensive review of evidence surrounding the cost-effectiveness of health information technology in the medication process. Of the 35,510 studies reviewed, only forty included some cost information—and of those, only thirty-one evaluated the costs. The researchers found that quality of economic evidence is poor, assumptions of cost savings are "speculative and are not conclusive," and "given the uncertainty that surrounds the cost and outcomes data, and limited study designs available in the literature, it is difficult to reach any definitive conclusion as to whether the additional costs and benefits represent value for money."[104]

More Charges, Higher Costs

Furthermore, government-certified EHRs can increase costs of medical care. Studies find doctors and hospitals are ordering more tests and using EHRs to capture costs for which they were not previously reimbursed. Documentation of standard services for billing is now as easy as a click of a button. One study found that clinical notes produced by scribes were coded at a higher level, bringing additional revenue of $24,257 for their physician employers.[105]

As the *New York Times* reports, "the move to electronic health records may be contributing to billions of dollars in higher costs for Medicare, private insurers and patients by making it easier for hospitals and physicians to bill more for their services, whether or not they provide additional care."[106] Hospitals say the increases reflect "more accurate billing" for services that were previously underbilled.

Furthermore, a study released in February 2018 found that EHRs do not lower administrative billing costs, which "made up as much as a quarter of professional revenue for some patient encounters," reported *Modern Healthcare*. If the cost of the EHR software was factored in, the estimated time to process a primary care visit was thirteen minutes at a cost of $32.51. The estimated time to process an inpatient surgical procedure was one hundred minutes at a cost of $319.80. "These findings suggest that significant investments in certified health information technology have not reduced high billing costs in the United States," wrote the researchers.[107]

Shortage of EHR System Experts

It's not enough to buy an EHR system. The clinics and hospitals need qualified health IT and informatics experts to implement it, maintain it, and be at the ready to fix it when it fails. However, in 2009, the year the EHR mandate became law, the US Bureau of Labor Statistics, the US Department of Education, and independent studies predicted "a shortfall of about 51,000 qualified health IT professionals over the next five years," the American Hospital Association reported.[108]

What's a doctor to do faced with a full schedule of patients and a federal mandate threatening his financial viability? Many small physician practices were forced to hire consultants to help them select an EHR vendor.[109] Thus began the often slow, expensive, and agonizing process of rolling out government-certified networked EHRs in time to meet the deadline.[110]

But selecting a consultant is just the first of many difficult barriers in the EHR obstacle course. As one headline notes, "Get in Line, No Technology Vendor Available." Due to various health IT mandates (EHRs, health information exchanges, all-payer claims databases, Obamacare exchange) there has been and continues to be a shortage of health IT professionals.[111]

Some EHR vendors have left clinics virtually stranded once the purchase and installation was complete. One physician, who was working with her third vendor in three years and had made several months of monthly payments to the company, observed that EHR vendors seem to have a "training staff of two and a sales team of 100."[112] In short, once the vendor made the sale, it focused on securing the next sale in a race to get as much of the federal money as possible before it ran out.

Leaving doctors stranded takes a second form. Now that patient records are computerized—no longer on paper—a new kind of specialist is needed: the health information management (HIM) specialist. As a result of electronic health records, employment in HIM is expected to grow 15 percent from 2014 to 2024, reports the Bureau of Labor Statistics. Because of the continuing diversification of the job, the expansion of roles and responsibilities, and specializations within the work, shortages loom.[113]

Shortages of cybersecurity professionals are already in evidence. From 2010 to 2014, job postings for cybersecurity positions increased 91 percent across all industries. The demand for experts with certified information systems security professional (CISSP) credentials has far outstripped the supply. In 2015 there were 65,362 individuals with CISSP credentials in the United States, with most of them assumed to already have a job, but employers posted jobs for nearly fifty thousand positions. An individual must have at least five years of work experience in the cybersecurity industry to even apply for CISSP, so the process is slow compared to the demand. Hospitals and health systems need cybersecurity staff to not only be CISSP-certified but to also be familiar with HIPAA and HITECH.[114] Yet 38 percent of employed cybersecurity professionals say the shortages have already led to burnout and staff attrition.[115]

ECRI ranked "ransomware and other cybersecurity threats" as the top threat for hospitals in 2018.[116] Yet 70 percent of 343 information security professionals surveyed worldwide say the cybersecurity skills shortage has had a negative impact on their organization, with 91 percent believing their organization is vulnerable to a significant cyberattack or data breach, reported *Health Data Management* in December 2017. The failure to train non-technical employees has also contributed, with an amazing 62 percent reporting inadequate training for its cybersecurity staff.[117] Given the shortage of security experts, how secure will patient data in EHRs be? And how long will it take for hospitals and clinics to recover from hacking and ransomware attacks?

EHR Vendors Sitting Pretty

While EHR purchasers are experiencing losses, the companies selling EHR systems are making out like bandits. In the second quarter of 2017, Healthcare Dive reported the following financial news:

- Cerner's second quarter bookings hit an all-time high at $1.64 billion, up 16 percent from $1.4 billion during the same period a year earlier
- Cerner expects 2017 revenue of around $5.2 billion
- eClinicalWorks added 3,000 providers to its network during the quarter (1,000 of them buying an EHR in June) and reported revenues of $120 million across its EHR, population health management and patient engagement software products
- At athenahealth, net income was $9.9 million, versus a net income loss of $1.9 million in 2016[118]

Cerner, eClinicalWorks, and athenahealth, along with Epic, McKesson, NextGen, and others, are diamond corporate members of HIMSS—the top level[119]—which, as described earlier, successfully advanced the EHR mandate.

Cutting Costs in the Cloud?

The high cost of EHRs, including many of the costs described here, have caused some doctors and hospitals to move to "the cloud," an off-premises location where data is held on servers accessible over the Internet. In short, it's a web-based EHR. Here's how *Modern Healthcare* described one small hospital's decision to enter the cloud:

> The hospital Brad Huerta leads simply didn't have enough money to pay for a traditional electronic health record system. It couldn't afford the software. And it couldn't afford hiring a single information technology employee, not to mention a complete staff. So Huerta, CEO of Lost Rivers Medical Center in Arco, Idaho, decided to put the 14-bed critical-access hospital's records and billing systems in the cloud. There, they'd be overseen and maintained by a software vendor, not by an internal employee that the hospital couldn't afford to pay anyway.[120]

"One of the things that became apparent was that the only thing harder for me to recruit than a doctor was a full-time IT guy," said Huerta. But a significant unanticipated expense was the need to upgrade hospital telecommunications wiring to support the speed and dataflow of a web-based EHR. The cloud requires a strong and fast Internet—something that may or may not be available in rural America. Therefore, struggling rural hospitals that can't afford an in-house EHR or the staff to run it, may not be able to enter the cloud if they don't have the funds necessary to upgrade their Internet connections or if available bandwidth is insufficient.

That's not all. Although costs may be cheaper up front, a cloud vendor can create long-term cost concerns because of uncertain returns on investment and "because there's always something more they can charge for," said health IT analyst Nancy Fabozzi.[121]

VII

Future Considerations

A Few More Things to Know

The End of Clicking?

EHR developers and others have begun to focus on a major cause of physician frustration. On January 4, 2018, the Vanderbilt University Medical Center announced the development of a voice assistant to help practitioners locate key information within the EHR without going on a clicking expedition.[1] It's called V-EVA for Vanderbilt EHR Voice Assistant. Doctors and nurses will use their voices to query the computer for the information, similar to Apple's Siri or Amazon's Alexa.

"There is a lot of information foraging that occurs in the EHR, although users often know the precise pieces of data they need to understand a clinical picture," said project director Yaa Kumah-Crystal, MD, MPH, assistant professor of biomedical informatics and pediatrics at the university.[2] Vanderbilt is working with Epic Systems, their EHR vendor, to build the necessary mapping to accommodate verbal requests. V-EVA is being tested by a small group of users to determine the "usability, efficiency and safety of this new workflow."[3]

In April 2018, Robert Wachter, MD, and Jeff Goldsmith suggested adoption of voice commands for documenting the patient visit and for ordering: "Typing and point and click must go." They want to "replace the time-wasting click storm presently required to unearth patient data." If the EHR becomes a "well-designed and useful partner" through AI and improved usability, they believe doctors, nurses, and other clinicians "will be converted from surly prisoners of poorly realized technology to advocates of the systems themselves."[4]

That may be true, but it will not solve the problem of the systems serving the data-collecting and data-reporting agendas of third-party payers and the big-data industry. It only improves the willingness of practitioners to participate in the collection and submission of patient data for third-party control of patient care. All without patient consent.

MyHealthEData & Blue Button 2.0

On March 6, 2018, CMS administrator Seema Verma announced a new initiative at HIMSS 2018: MyHealthEData. She said, "After hearing dozens of stories, reading thousands of letters, and experiencing the difficulty that comes from the lack of interoperability, it is important to me to speak for all patients. It's our data. It's our personal health information, and we should control it."[5] True. Patients own their data, but under HIPAA, patient ownership isn't recognized. If you own something, someone isn't allowed to take it from you without your consent. That's called theft.

CMS issued a press release stating, "The Trump administration is launching the **MyHealthEData** initiative which aims to empower patients by ensuring that they control their healthcare data and can decide how their data is going to be used, all while keeping that information safe and secure."[6] The details are vague, but the goal is laudable.

However, other parts of Verma's speech made ownership and control less certain: "MyHealthEData will unleash data to trigger innovation, and advance research to cure disease and provide more evidence-based treatment guidelines that ultimately will drive down costs and improve health outcomes . . . Imagine if our health records weren't just used by our doctors in their workflow, but rather if EHRs allowed third-party applications to access and leverage that data in innovative ways for both the patient and doctor. Imagine if patients could authorize access to their records to researchers from all over the country who could not only develop specific treatments for their needs but the researchers could also use that information to develop cures that could save millions of lives." Notice the terms. She says *authorize* rather than *give consent*. Perhaps she doesn't realize it, but these are not the same. Under HIPAA, *authorization* is only required for data sharing that HIPAA does not already permit.

Perhaps the CMS administrator doesn't understand how much data can be shared and used without patient consent under HIPAA. This would not be surprising. Few people realize that HIPAA gives patients little to no control over their medical records. Until the HIPAA problem is solved, patient control over their private medical information will be a fairy tale—unless state legislatures pass *state* medical privacy laws.

Jonathan Porter, vice president of network services at athenahealth, an EHR vendor, responded to Verma's speech by telling the news website STAT: "It's the biggest step we've seen them take so far to say, 'Look, the benefit of liberating data outweighs the privacy concerns . . . There's always been this battle between which is more valuable to the patient: to hold their data hostage, or to actually give it to the people that need it?"[7] He may be correct about Verma's position, but the premise of an ongoing battle is faulty. This is not a decision for third parties. It's a decision for patients.

CMS also plans to give Medicare recipients ready access to their health information. Administrator Verma announced Blue Button 2.0, calling it "a developer-friendly, standards-based API that enables Medicare beneficiaries to connect their claims data to secure applications, services and research programs that they trust. Beneficiaries will maintain complete control in how and when their data is used, but the potential benefits to our recipients are endless." She said the initiative "may include enabling the creation of health dashboards for Medicare beneficiaries to view their health information in a single portal, or allowing beneficiaries to share complete medication lists with their doctor to prevent dangerous drug interactions."[8] But as this book explains, under HIPAA, Meaningful Use, ACA innovation projects, quality measurement, and value-based payments, Medicare recipients will not have "complete control" over who gets their private medical information or how it's used.

A month later, on April 2, CMS suggested Blue Button 2.0 may soon be required in Medicare Advantage (MA) plans: "CMS is encouraging plans to adopt data release platforms for their enrollees that meet or exceed the capabilities of CMS's Blue Button 2.0. This would enable enrollees in MA plans to connect their claims data to the applications, services and research programs they trust. CMS is also signaling that we are contemplating future rulemaking in this area to potentially require the adoption of such platforms by MA plans in 2020."[9]

The Dark Side of "Interoperability"

The goal of Congress, government officials and the health and data industry is interoperability, which means easy connection and data transfer regardless of the equipment used to connect. Thus, a clinic with an Amazing Charts EHR could easily "talk" to a hospital with a Centricity EHR system. Or a physician using the Practice Fusion EHR could send medical information to a clinic across the country using a NextGen system, and it could be read and used.

But that's a very limited view compared to how some view interoperability. Drew Schiller, co-founder and chief technology officer of Validic, a health IT company, writes, "Clinical health records, including both primary care and hospital visits; payment information and history; patient-generated health data; pharmacy and prescription information; patient and family-health history; genomics; clinical-trial data; and so on—all of this information needs to be easily accessible digitally for providers as well as patients to realize the full potential and promise of interoperability."[10]

Interestingly, Congress did not require the HHS secretary to assure interoperability of the EHR and health information exchange systems when it enacted HITECH. Nor did it require that in the Affordable Care Act just one year later, where interoperability was only mentioned twice, but again not as a mandate for systems sold or purchased.[11] It was only after the fact—years after doctors and hospitals had purchased disparate EHRs that could not "talk" to one another—that Congress tried to force them all to work together. As you see below, the HITECH language was soft, not hard. The word *interoperability* appears only twice, in two different sections of the law:

> RESEARCH AREAS. —Research areas may include . . . (C) software that improves interoperability and connectivity among health information systems;

• • •

> The Secretary shall invest funds through the different agencies with expertise . . . to support the following: . . . (5) Promotion of the interoperability of clinical data repositories or registries.[12]

Senator Lamar Alexander (R-TN), chairman of the Health, Education, Labor & Pensions Committee declared his support for interoperability in 2015: "This committee is interested not least because the government has invested $30 billion to encourage doctors and hospitals to install these expensive systems."[13]

Is this a reasonable assertion?

First, Congress did not "encourage" installation. The penalties turned it into a mandate. Second, government invested nothing. The more than $30 billion in EHR/MU grants are dollars earned by and taken from hard-working American men and women. Third, this is a surprising argument when you consider that the EHR is a costly, unfunded mandate on physicians, hospitals, and others with online connection, interfacing, update, data storage, system maintenance, cybersecurity and other costs in perpetuity. The $30 billion doesn't come close to covering the total and ongoing costs of compliance. It's also surprising because Republicans claim to support free markets, small business, limited government, reduced costs, and personal liberty—none of which are served by the EHR mandate or interoperability requirements.

John R. Graham, a *Forbes* contributor and now a Principal Deputy Assistant Secretary for Planning and Evaluation at HHS in the Trump administration, called interoperability, "A $30 Billion Unicorn Hunt."[14] Indeed, sociologist Ross Koppel, former chair of the American Medical Informatics Association (AMIA) working group, says Meaningful Use came out of a "plan hatched by vendors 30 years ago to sell more software with the help of government subsidies and did not always have interoperability in mind," reports *Healthcare IT News*.[15] When the GAO did a 2015 study on interoperability, it described five barriers to broader data sharing:

a. Insufficiencies in health data standards

b. Variation in state privacy rules

c. Difficulty in accurately matching all the right records to the right patient

d. The costs involved in achieving the goals

e. The need for governance and trust among entities to facilitate sharing health information[16]

Variation in state privacy rules has caused no amount of angst for public health officials. The Office of the National Coordinator for Health Information Technology (ONC) laments, "Many states have laws and regulations to protect the privacy of health information that have stricter privacy protections and requirements on use and disclosure than the HIPAA Rules."[17] The agency, which supports interoperability, claims the variation in privacy laws across states "makes it difficult and expensive to harness technology to ensure privacy compliance. This, in turn, impedes interoperability."[18]

These impediments are actually a blessing. They protect patients from the full scope of HIPAA-enabled data exchange. Interoperability under HIPAA's "no privacy" rule would permit greater surveillance in the exam room, more detailed profiling of doctors and patients, and ever more control over the practice of medicine by outsiders. In short, interoperability is the final step in the creation of a national medical-records system—a step that would end what little privacy we have. Thankfully, according to the GAO, the federal government can do little to move toward interoperability and thus it has "remained limited."[19]

Interoperability is rare. At the end of 2016, only 6 percent of practitioners could access data that was held in another EHR system, according to a KLAS report.[20]

Daniel Essin, MD, thinks those "beating the interoperability drum have their heads in the clouds." He wrote an entertaining column on interoperability. Since his personal clinical needs are fairly minimal (e.g., notes, X-rays, lab reports) he's perfectly fine getting them in his hands any way they come in, but they must be readable. He concludes, "Since I can pretty much always read what I receive, I'd rather have paper in my hand than to need to go fishing for it in the computer." He questions how badly the data is needed, and reminds readers that license fees are often required for each "live" interface: "Is the benefit to patient care sufficient to justify the costs?"[21]

Who's Blocking Whom?

Congress isn't interested in cost versus benefit. It took action to facilitate interoperability by force. The US House of Representatives passed the 21st Century Cures Act in July 2015.[22] The bill encouraged interoperability, threatened to decertify EHR products that don't allow interoperability, and prohibited "information blocking"—on penalty of $10,000 for each offense.[23] The Senate's 2016 Improving Health Information Technology Act, S. 2511, authored by Senator Alexander, authorized penalties for developers, vendors, and networks, and "appropriate incentives and disincentives under applicable federal law" for health care providers engaged in information blocking.[24]

The final 21st Century Cures Act, which included $6.3 billion in funding for ten years, passed on December 7, 2016, and was signed into law by President Obama six days later.[25] It defines "interoperability" as health information technology that:

- "Enables the secure exchange of electronic health information with, and use of electronic health information from, other health information technology without special effort on the part of the user;
- Allows for complete access, exchange, and use of all electronically accessible health information for authorized use under applicable State or Federal law; and
- Does not constitute information blocking as defined in section 3022(a)."[26]

Notably, government certifications of EHRs on or after January 1, 2018, must include certification that the technology is interoperable as defined by the standard for interoperability in the Act. Beginning January 1, 2019, any products that fail to meet the standard will be decertified.[27] The law allows health care providers to get a one-year hardship waiver if the government decertifies their EHR.[28]

One year? "Hospitals may need at least three years from choosing a new system to integrating it with an existing IT system," reports the Lewin Group.[29] How much time would it take a clinic that has no IT staff and no administrative employees who can leave their other duties behind?

Unfortunately, the Senate's original "blanket exemption"[30] from penalties if the EHR was decertified did not become law. Decertification is a financial threat to health care providers who faithfully followed the law and bought government-certified EHRs on schedule. Decertification could leave clinics and hospitals stranded with previously approved systems that no longer meet requirements, resulting in Medicare penalties. The physician, clinic, or hospital that has already spent thousands, hundreds of thousands, or millions of dollars to meet the federal mandate could be forced to purchase a new system or retrofit the decertified system in just twelve months.

To achieve the elusive interoperability, Congress is determined to stop "information blocking." The Act states that health IT developers may not take any action that would constitute information blocking. As you read the following list of information-blocking actions prohibited by the legislation, remember all the disclosures and uses *permitted* by HIPAA without your consent. Impermissible under the Act are:

- Practices that restrict authorized access, exchange, or use of information for treatment and other permitted purposes

- Implementing health IT in nonstandard ways that increase the complexity or burden of accessing, exchanging or using electronic health information

- Implementing health IT in a way that restricts exports of complete information sets and transitions between health IT systems

- Implementing health IT in a way [that] leads to fraud, waste, or abuse or impedes innovations and advancements in health IT access, exchange and use, including care delivery enabled by health IT[31]

Developers must also attest that they are not engaging in any form of information blocking. Penalties for information blocking are stiff: up to $1 million *per violation*. While the no-blocking requirements apply to health care providers too, they will be "referred to the appropriate agency to be subject to appropriate disincentives" under applicable federal law, as determined by the secretary through rulemaking.[32] So, there are penalties for everyone.

Yet some in the industry don't believe information blocking exists.

Says John Halamka, chief information officer at the CareGroup Health System: "It's not IT vendors being reluctant or hospitals holding their data hostage. If the definition of information blocking is that the vendors have all hired Chief Information Blocking Officers who spend their nights thinking about ways to restrict information flow, I've never seen it. Find me one example."[33]

Perhaps it's a matter of definition. In an April 2015 report to Congress on health information blocking, the ONC writes:

> Most complaints of information blocking are directed at health IT developers. Many of these complaints allege that developers charge fees that make it cost-prohibitive for most customers to send, receive, or export electronic health information stored in EHRs, or to establish interfaces that enable such information to be exchanged with other providers, persons, or entities. Some EHR developers allegedly charge a substantial per-transaction fee each time a user sends, receives, or searches for (or "queries") a patient's electronic health information. EHR developers may also charge comparatively high prices to establish certain common types of interfaces—such as connections to local labs and hospitals. Many providers also complain about the costs of extracting data from their EHR systems for their own use or to move to a different EHR technology.[34]

So, they're not "blocking" information, per se; they're charging clinics for access to their own data. "A vice president from athenahealth says some vendors are charging $1 million to build an interface, a half million to maintain it and $2 every time a doctor uses it to send data," writes Irv Lichtenwald, president and CEO of Medsphere Systems Corporation, the solution provider for the OpenVista electronic health record, in an article about whether information blocking is a myth.[35]

Under the anti-blocking law, will the federal government be empowered to penalize physicians who refuse to pay the exorbitant costs to connect? Will that refusal be considered "information blocking"? Release of a proposed rule is expected by the summer of 2018.[36]

Epic, which has 68.2 million MyChart accounts, may have found a path out of harm's way.[37] On September 13, 2017, the company which developed Care Everywhere to allow records to travel among Epic providers, announced Share Everywhere. This new product will allow patients to give doctors access to their medical records through an Internet browser. No EHR is required. Epic Systems Corporation holds the medical records of 64 percent of Americans in Epic EHRs.[38] Epic's website says 190 million patients have a current EHR in Epic.[39] Sean Bina, Epic's vice president of access applications said, "This is really patient-driven interoperability."[40] That may be true, but it may also save Epic from charges of information blocking, litigation, and federal penalties.

Congress's insistence that physicians install government health surveillance systems in the exam room and use them for the care of patients, despite being untested and unproven—and an unfunded mandate—is disturbing at so many levels—from privacy to professional ethics to the patient-doctor relationship. But it's clear from this and other legislation that both Republican and Democrat members believe in the EHR surveillance system and want it in working order.

Comprehensive Dossiers on Americans?

"The '*E*' in 'EHR' is so last year," announced Judy Faulkner, the founder and CEO of Epic Systems at the EHR company's annual user group meeting on September 26, 2017. Festooned in a red and gold gown with a wizard's cap on her head, she added, "Electronic has to go away as a distinguisher now, because everything is electronic these days."[41]

Faulkner wants the electronic health record (EHR) to become the comprehensive health record (CHR). The small letter change would be a major shift in scope.[42] She said, "We have to look at who you are, what you eat, how much you sleep, and what your social conditions are like." Saying "We know these factors affect health," Faulker added, "We won't be able to afford to continue doing what we're doing if we don't change the way we look at social determinants and population health . . . There is information that is not in the EHR right now that has to be accessible."[43]

She suggests the CHR should go beyond the health care system. "We have to knock the walls down whether they're the walls of the hospital or the walls of the clinic."[44] She told *Healthcare IT News*, "Because healthcare is now focusing on keeping people well rather than reacting to illness, we are focusing on factors outside the traditional walls."[45]

Faulkner could be talking about ACOs, population health, and value-based payments for care. But she could also be talking about mental health. A few weeks later, on October 3, 2017, Pine Rest Christian Mental Health Services announced plans to spend millions to buy and install the Epic EHR throughout their organization by June 2018, giving its fifty thousand patients "a complete patient record that spans the care continuum." Pine Rest says it's "the first independent freestanding behavioral health system in the United States to partner directly with Epic," and claims "Epic's integrated software makes it easier for Pine Rest's patients to have their behavioral healthcare integrated with their physical health care." How comfortable will Pine Rest patients be with this integration? In particular, will they want other doctors outside Pine Rest to know about their mental health treatment? Faulker, quoted in the press release said, "The head and the body belong together."[46]

At the user group meeting she shared a poll showing Epic as the top EHR in satisfaction with 24 percent of users very satisfied. Forty-six percent are satisfied and 29 percent are dissatisfied or very dissatisfied. Christopher Lonhurst, CIO at UC San Diego Health was less sanguine about Epic being on the top. "But to be honest, that's sort of like being 'cream of the crap,'" he told journalists after the show. "One in three doctors is still dissatisfied." In the packed auditorium, however, Faulkner claimed, "Making software a joy to use is a high bar."[47] Only under an EHR mandate could this be true. No company aiming to sell a product would agree. Joy is the why of most purchases. However, Epic and other EHRs didn't have to aim for joy. Customers were required to buy an EHR whether it was good, bad, or in between.

Faulkner, with a net worth of $3.3 billion,[48] told her attendees, "If you want to keep patients well and you want to get paid, you're going to have to have a comprehensive health record. . . . You'll need to use software as your central nervous system, and that's how you standardize and manage your organization."[49] Epic holds the medical records of 64 percent of Americans. Do you want this corporation to collect and compile your medical, genetic, behavioral, and lifestyle data into a comprehensive dossier (CHR) of your life?

The call for comprehensive data on patients is often related to the "population health" initiatives detailed in section V. Epic's population health management system, called Healthy Planet was "born out of the Affordable Care Act and its related Accountable Care Organizations (ACO), which was set up to pay providers for delivering services and healthy patient outcomes."[50] Epic's system includes an enterprise data warehouse called "Caboodle," which "consists of an LPR [longitudinal patient record] populated by clinical, claims, and other local and remote data sources," reports the blog *HealthIT & mHealth*. "It use[s] Epic Care Everywhere to ingest Epic and non-Epic data from participating provider organizations."[51]

How large could a CHR be? Consider how big EHRs already are. In an August 2017 conversation, former Vice President Joe Biden told Faulkner he wants patients to have full access to their medical records. According to Greg Simon, president of the Biden Cancer Initiative, Faulkner responded, "Why do you want your medical records? They're a thousand pages of which you understand 10." As reported in Politico Morning eHealth, Biden retorted, "None of your business. . . . If I need to, I'll find someone to explain them to me and, by the way, I will understand a lot more than you think I do." Simon said, "And it went downhill from there."[52] Simon emailed *Morning eHealth* later to say that the issue is EHR companies "want to make . . . and are required to make . . . only summaries available" instead of the "complete digital record" that he and Biden want.[53]

Faulker is serious about CHR. When asked if Epic would continue using the acronym, she told *Healthcare IT News*, "Yes. . . . We think it should be the new terminology, replacing EHR."[54] It would certainly be easier to type—computers would no longer auto-correct EHR to HER—but that doesn't make it a good idea.

Facebook Wants Your Medical Records

A bombshell hit the news on April 5, 2018. CNBC published a story titled "Facebook Sent a Doctor on a Secret Mission to Ask Hospitals to Share Patient Data." Had the collaborative research project described in the article continued, it would have combined what health systems know about their patients with what Facebook knows about its users. The project was paused after the Cambridge Analytica data leak scandal came to light—87 million Facebook profiles secured to use for election purposes.[55]

Facebook had talked with Stanford Medical School and the American College of Cardiology (ACC) but no data-sharing agreement had yet been signed. Facebook planned to use the data to help determine which patients may need special care or treatment. Data would have been "anonymized."[56] More likely, it would've been "de-identified" under HIPAA and thus still be considered identifiable. See section IV.

The ACC's health databases, created by extracting computerized patient data from the EHR, make this kind of research relatively easy. The ACC has a lot of data: "More than 2,400 hospitals and over 8,500 outpatient providers worldwide participate in one or more of the ACC's ten registries."[57] For outpatient practices, the data collection page of the ACC's National Cardiovascular Data Registry (NCDR) says, "Relevant registry data fields can be extracted from your EHR" and transmitted directly to the registry's database.[58] Data in the registries can include patient demographics, procedures, provider and facility characteristics, compliance with ACC clinical guideline recommendations, cardiac status, appropriate use criteria, history/risk factors, "practice, provider and patient characteristics" and more.[59]

The NCDR is considered a qualified clinical data registry (QCDR) for the purposes of submitting quality measurement data as required by the Medicare Merit-based Incentive Payment System (MIPS). See section II. The ACC's registry sends the submitted data to CMS.[60]

The American College of Cardiology issued the following statement: "For the first time in history, people are sharing information about themselves online in ways that may help determine how to improve their health. As part of its mission to transform cardiovascular care and improve heart health, the American College of Cardiology has been engaged in discussions with Facebook around the use of anonymized Facebook data, coupled with anonymized ACC data, to further scientific research on the ways social media can aid in the prevention and treatment of heart disease—the #1 cause of death in the world. This partnership is in the very early phases as we work on both sides to ensure privacy, transparency and scientific rigor. No data has been shared between any parties."[61]

Let's assume no data's been shared. But would the story have been the same six or twelve months later? Given what you know about the free flow of data under HIPAA (see section IV), ponder this statement by Aneesh Chopra, president of CareJourney and former White House chief technology officer: "Consumers wouldn't have assumed their data would be used in this way. . . . If Facebook moves ahead (with its plans), I would be wary of efforts that repurpose user data without explicit consent." Whether he's talking about Facebook user data or patient medical data, he is correct.

So where is the outcry about the sharing and repurposing of patient data under HIPAA? In England, the privacy regulator found Google's DeepMind "artificial intelligence" operation using the data of 1.6 million National Health Service patients to be illegal because "[p]atients would not have reasonably expected their information to have been used in this way."[62] Most Americans wouldn't expect their medical data to be shared as permitted by HIPAA, but no regulator has yet risen to stop the ongoing sharing and repurposing of patient data in the US.

In a *Forbes* article with details every Facebook participant needs to know, data expert Kalev Leetaru writes, "Facebook's proposed foray into medical research is as frightening as it is predictable: users are data points to be secretly exploited, rather than human individuals whose informed consent must be gained. In turn, its hospital partners would happily hand over their patients' most sensitive medical information to Facebook—again without any notification or consent. In Facebook's world, as in the academic world from which it draws, informed consent is unnecessary when it comes to data—as long as the law says it is probably legal, there is no need to tell users about it or get their permission in any way."[63] And indeed, consent did not come up in the early discussions, reports CNBC.[64]

This privacy debacle may not be over. Facebook only "paused" the program: "Last month we decided that we should pause these discussions so we can focus on other important work, including doing a better job of protecting people's data and being clearer with them about how that data is used in our products and services."[65] They may have also paused it to prepare for Facebook founder and CEO Mark Zuckerberg's appearances before Congress for data privacy hearings on April 10 and 11, 2018.[66]

Mobile Web-Based EHRs

Five EHR developers and four health care systems—Intermountain Healthcare, the Mayo Clinic, The Advisory Board Company, and federally funded SMART Health IT, a mobile application development project at the Boston Children's Hospital Informatics Program—are working to use the Internet to bring interoperability through smartphones and tablets. The alliance is called the Argonaut Project.[67] The emphasis is on "mobile apps linked to EHRs using a standardized API"—an application programming interface for health information exchange.[68] Or to put it more clearly, an API is "a set of programming instructions and standards that software companies can release so that other software applications can be built to interface with each other using the web."[69]

This new architecture will be based on Internet development principles that JASON, a group of scientists advising the HHS secretary, would like HHS to mandate. The name of the architecture is Fast

Healthcare Interoperability Resources, or FHIR, "the best candidate API approach to data-level and document-level access to healthcare data," wrote the JASON task force.[70] FHIR was invented in 2014.[71] According to Russell Leftwich, MD, an adjunct assistant professor of biomedical informatics at Vanderbilt University School of Medicine, FHIR is "quickly becoming the foundation for the future of interoperability" because it simplifies and accelerates the sharing of patient clinical data between systems.[72]

Apple's project to put medical record information on iPhones uses "SMART on FHIR," writes Ken Mandl, MD, bioinformaticist and director of the Computational Health Informatics Program at Boston Children's Hospital, on CNBC's website. He says SMART is meant to make EHRs work like iPhones.[73] Apple plans to let you access your medical records from your iPhone Health app. To make this possible, Apple is partnering with EHR vendors and hospitals.

The vendors are key. Medical records are often housed outside the hospital. As explained by the website Elite Daily, "Hospitals and doctors' offices usually work with third-party vendors who maintain the software that allows health care providers to share electronic health records with their patients (in other words, there are companies who keep your health records to share between hospitals and doctor's offices)." Thus, medical records are often offsite in the cloud, and Apple has partnered with vendors to get that information to iPhones. Once the patient signs in, the data will be displayed in seven categories, which are subsets of the medical record: "allergies, clinical visits, conditions, immunizations, lab results, medications, and procedures." The data will not be stored in Apple's cloud and it will be encrypted.[74] On March 29, 2018, Apple announced that at total thirty-nine health systems are sharing medical records data through the iPhone.[75]

Real-Time API Access

Former employees of Epic Systems have announced an API plan using their health IT startup, Redox. Co-founder Luke Bonney says: "Redox believes that one of the biggest issues holding back innovation in the health-tech space is how to access all of the incredibly valuable data that resides in different EHR systems across the health care landscape." The company hopes to solve the issue of interoperability with an API that will help apps share patient data with almost any EHR in any health care system. At least 120 apps are already using the Redox integration platform, HIT Consultant reports.[76]

Then there's the Human API Data Platform, described on the Silicon Badia website as "next generation healthcare applications with a complete and unified view of a consumer's health."[77] Human API claims to have "created the world's largest real-time data network with coverage that is broader and deeper than anything else in the industry. Our network enables users to find their health and wellness data where it's originally stored." They have "visibility into" 230 million unique lives over 35,000 data sources. The eighteen types of data that can be retrieved include conditions, medications, test results, demographics, narratives, social history, genetic traits, sleep, meals, and healthcare claims.[78]

Government officials are moving in the same direction. The ONC interoperability plan focuses on APIs. In October 2015, a final EHR rule supported "innovative API functionality" stating, "APIs support the patient's ability to access their health information in increasingly flexible ways, including by being able to enable easier access to health data for patients via mobile devices."[79] In October 2017, the ONC announced the Secure API Server Showdown Challenge to build a secure FHIR server, in which its source code will be made publicly available through open source. The ultimate goal is to produce "'ready to use'/'turn-key' secure, FHIR server code . . . on which industry stakeholders can build."[80]

The blog *American EHR* discusses linking APIs to the Internet of Things (IoT): "On the EHR front, it can enable anytime, anywhere access to patient records from not only practitioners, but also patients and authorized devices and systems. IoT is where we'll see the transformation of smartphones and apps into genuine medical devices that can take diagnostics and integrate real-time data.[81]

Remote Patient Monitoring

Starting in 2018, hospitals and clinics can be paid by Medicare for using technology to monitor patients outside the hospital, reports MobiHealthNews. Under MIPS, a review of patient-generated data will count in the "clinical practice improvement activity" category. See section II. CMS expects about 250,000 claims to be filed under the new reimbursable improvement activity code.[82]

Devices to promote wellness, predict coming adverse events, and "ultimately, create ways to stop people from being admitted to the hospitals in the first place" are being designed, reports *Healthcare IT News*. Or as David Chou, chief information and data officer at Children's Mercy Hospital in Kansas City, told the publication, "The future of healthcare is figuring out how to keep patients out."[83]

Sensors to monitor the vital signs of patients at home are already in the works. For example, Ken Mandl, MD, writes, "Apple's hardware, including sensors in the phone and watch, will monitor patients at home."[84] This differs from telemedicine, now called telehealth, which is also covered by Medicare. Telehealth uses an interactive, two-way, real-time telecommunications system (audio and video) and is conducted by a physician or other clinician in a location different from where the patient is located.[85]

Licensure Requirement?

In 2012, Massachusetts legislators decided EHRs were so essential they'd strip the medical license from any physician who didn't install and meet Meaningful Use requirements by 2015. Chapter 224 made EHR proficiency a standard of licensure forcing doctors to use EHRs, retire, or leave the state if they wanted to practice.[86] The law required doctors to violate patient confidentiality, professional ethics, and personal autonomy—or stop practicing.

Breathtaking, really.

Physician outrage soon followed. The Massachusetts Medical Society (MMS) began to lobby against the requirements. Former MMS president Ronald Dunlap, MD, said, "Collectively, these requirements increase administrative demands, add costs to the practice of medicine, and to the health care system as a whole." He said the mandate would encourage consolidation by driving "small to midsize practices to seek alignment with larger entities" that could meet the requirements.[87] By February 2014, lawmakers were introducing bills to whittle down the draconian requirements.[88]

The Massachusetts Board of Registration in Medicine wrote rules giving physicians options that would allow them to keep their license even if they couldn't attest to Meaningful Use. Starting in January 2015, physicians renewing their license had multiple options to fulfill the EHR proficiency requirement:

- Participate in Meaningful Use as an Eligible Professional
- Have a relationship with a hospital certified as a Meaningful Use participant
- Complete at least three hours of accredited CME program on EHRs
- Participate or be an authorized user in MassHI, Massachusetts HIE[89]

For Dr. Zwerling, an endocrinology specialist practicing in Massachusetts, this is the latest encroachment, not the first. In a blog post he writes, "As we all know, the practice of medicine has become increasingly difficult as a result of external mandates. These mandates specify which medicines we may prescribe, which radiology tests we can order, how many days our patients are allowed to remain in the hospital, which CME [continuing medical education] classes we must take, etc. And now, the politicians intend to tell physicians which software they must use in their office and which EMR options must be utilized during the office visit."[90]

This "misguided obsession" to impose the EHR hasn't yet been proven to cut costs—he calls cost-reduction claims a "hypothesis"—and "places the politicians in the middle of the exam room between the patient and the physician, and seriously disrupts the physician-patient relationship." Zwerling, underscoring the importance of the patient-doctor relationship as a "prerequisite for high quality healthcare" says it's high time that "physicians reclaim control of their offices, if not the practice of medicine."[91]

This is exactly what the Illinois Pain Institute did. The clinic's seventy employees unanimously decided to go back to paper medical records. "Not one person in the practice thought we should keep the EHR," said John Prinskis, MD, founder and co-medical director.[92] In August 2017, they had been free of the EHR for two years—and had no regrets.[93]

Is There a Doctor in the House?

To minimize the administrative burdens on physicians, some health care systems are expanding the use of nonphysician workers. For example, PEW Charitable Trust reports on the "team-based" model of care, describing how patients at one Denver-based clinic spend more time with a medical assistant than a physician. The assistant gathers patient information—such as symptoms and medical history—and then the physician comes in to make the medical decisions.

Is this substitution of nonphysician workers an unintended consequence of the EHR mandate, Meaningful Use, MIPS, PQRS, pay-for-performance, value-based payments, lower reimbursements, and higher costs? What will it mean for patient care?

The use of medical assistants generates more revenue for the Denver clinic because the doctor can see more patients.[94] One physician has acquiesced to working with a medical assistant "because I don't want to be the only one here at 8 o'clock at night, typing." According to PEW, "Distributing work across team members can help keep costs down, relieve doctors of the busywork that jams up their day, and make everyone more productive."[95]

PEW notes the difficult transition to team-based care where physicians are no longer always in charge and then makes a startling statement, "To be sure, doctors won't be displaced anytime soon. But shifting tasks to other professionals may reduce the need to train so many of them." Patients may not be comfortable with the transition to workers who have less clinical training. A 2013 study by the American Academy of Family Physicians found 72 percent of Americans prefer a doctor, who is considered more knowledgeable and experienced, when it comes to their medical care.[96]

What the patient thinks may soon not matter. As noted previously, a 2016 study found 48 percent of physicians are considering dropping the number of patients they see or leaving the practice of medicine altogether.[97] A 2018 study reported in *Mayo Clinic Proceedings* also found that physicians uncomfortable with EHRs are more likely to reduce hours or leave the profession.[98] As reported by *Medical Economics*, the EHR has "created a number of unintended negative consequences including reducing efficiency, increasing clerical burden and increasing the risk of burnout for physicians."[99]

The departure of a physician costs the hospital about $250,000. Stephen Klasko, MD, president and CEO of Thomas Jefferson University and Jefferson Health, thinks one of the answers to physician burnout is an overhaul of the health care system into team-based care in non-traditional locations. He says, "We have to move beyond the hospital as the geographic center of care, and beyond the doctor as the captain of the ship."[100]

But patients prefer direct access to physicians. Ari Melmed, MD, an emergency room physician at Kaiser Permanent Colorado oversees the Chat with a Doctor program, an online chat service. He says, "One of the unusual things about this program is we put the physician up front rather than having the members go through a screening process of some sort. . . . We've found that this is very surprising and highly satisfying to the members. They're just not used to having instant access to a physician. It's just unprecedented in most people's healthcare experience. Our satisfaction is through the roof."[101]

Will Blockchain Protect Privacy?

On the horizon is blockchain, otherwise known as a "chain of trust."[102] It's also been called a "shared single source of truth."[103] Part of its allure is that "it enables 'trustless' collaboration between network participants while recording an immutable audit trail of all interactions," writes Varun Gera, founder and CEO of HealthAssure. In short, it's a way to transact with entities you don't know or trust.[104]

The technology is relatively new and most closely associated with bitcoin transactions. It's considered a decentralized approach to authorizations and edits.[105] Discussing use of blockchain for health care, the blog KLAS says it works by "spreading out the ledger (for financial transactions) across an entire network of computers. This network constantly checks the ledger against the rest of the network to verify authenticity, making it difficult for fraud and hacking to occur" but KLAS says blockchain "isn't a silver bullet."[106] *HealthITAnalytics* describes it like this:

> In essence, a blockchain is a defined series of identical copies of information held locally by every member of the chain, instead of in a single, central repository. When one entity within the community wants to make a change or addition to the data set, every other participant must agree, cryptographically or otherwise, that the change is valid.
>
> Once the action is approved by a majority of the community, every locally held copy of the data reflects that the edit took place. This ensures that everyone stays informed of all changes and has a chance to dispute an edit or block access if an unauthorized entity tries to tamper with the data.[107]

When the ONC offered a cash prize of up to $5,000 for papers describing potential uses, the agency received seventy entries, including from MIT, the Mayo Clinic, Deloitte, and IBM. They selected fifteen papers and distributed thousands of dollars in prize money to the winning organizations. Accenture addressed how blockchain may improve patient consent issues, helping institutions adhere to patient wishes. The paper by Deloitte said it could revolutionize the health information exchange, leaving the need for centralized HIEs and HIOs behind. National Quality Forum wrote about how blockchain could be used to collect and manipulate data from EHRs, smartphone apps, wearables, personal health records, and the Internet of Things.[108]

Although there have been "few real-world applications of the technology in healthcare," 70 percent of payers say they plan to begin using it by 2019, reports FierceHealthcare.[109] On April 2, 2018, five health care groups announced a seven-month blockchain pilot program in a single undisclosed market. Humana, MultiPlan, Quest Diagnostics, UnitedHealthcare, and UnitedHealth Group's Optum will test the use of blockchain to improve accuracy of information in provider directories.[110] And in January 2017, the FDA announced an agreement to work with IBM Watson to figure out how to use blockchain to share data from EHRs, clinical research, genetic sequencing, and wearable and IoT devices.[111]

Blockchain technology is already being tested. At Beth Israel Deaconess Medical Center and MIT Media Lab, a project called MedRec is a decentralized record management system that "stores a signature of the record on a blockchain and notifies the patient, who is ultimately in control of where that record can travel," write Beth Israel's CIO John D. Halamka, MD, and his MIT colleagues. It doesn't store medical records.[112]

Medicalchain is a blockchain that takes the perspective that patients are the "ultimate owners of their EHRs." It gives patients control over "who can view their records, how much they see and for what length of time," reports Medium's *Crypt Bytes Tech* blog. The system uses MedTokens to pay for costs associated with blockchain data storage. Drug companies could reward patients with these tokens for granting access to certain medical data, and doctors could be rewarded for viewing data using the blockchain.[113]

Blockchain uses time stamping to authenticate changes to data sets. Patients could authorize new members to their "private secure EHR community, approve changes, and govern sharing between their disparate providers," reports *HealthITAnalytics*.[114] Might there be turf issues? "The industry will need vendor-neutral coordinators and collaborative organizers like [open source] Hyperledger to help stakeholders transcend traditional boundaries that prioritize centralized repositories and incentivize proprietary development without eliminating all the economic rewards for creating blockchain-based technologies," reports *HealthITAnalytics*.[115] Thus, the answer is yes. Will you trust the "vendor-neutral" coordinators, the "trusted third parties"? The answer may be no.

There's at least one more possible rub for those concerned about national patient IDs and the creation of a single lifelong medical record. Although blockchain completely de-identifies users,[116] it creates a unique patient identifier through digital signatures. This assures that "all records on the chain bearing that identifier are linked to create a comprehensive EHR for that patient across his/her providers and payers."[117] Others say blockchain has its own privacy problems. "The blockchain is broken at the moment in terms of privacy. It's simply too public," says Michael Smolenski, CEO and founder of Lightstreams, which developed a blockchain protocol to support decentralized applications (DApps) and is working to fix the privacy problems.[118]

You may want to research this emerging topic in more detail, including available diagrams and videos.[119] Americans will need to look long and hard at whether blockchain will actually restore patient control or whether it could centralize control in unexpected ways.

Ownership versus "Stewardship"

Who owns your medical information? This topic can lead to high-spirited debate. As reported by *Medical Economics*, "There is no consensus on who owns medical records. The Health Insurance Portability and Accountability Act (HIPAA) does not specify ownership and state laws are inconsistent. Only New Hampshire has a law stating that the patients own their medical records. In twenty other states, providers own them. The rest of the states have no legislation addressing the matter."[120]

Legal opinions vary. One Philadelphia attorney cited in the article says, "patients own their records, or it's their interests that are ultimately paramount." However, an attorney in Michigan says, "the records belong to the provider who has the control over it."[121]

Physicians disagree as well. Ira Nash, MD, a cardiologist in Manhattan says doctors may be required to store them, but they don't own them. Especially in light of the increase of patient-generated data, he said, "It's a very narrow and a somewhat paternalistic view for a provider to tell a patient, 'I own this.'" However, medical records are often considered a valuable commodity that's part of the sale of a practice.[122]

Now consider stewardship of medical information. There are two types. The first type is simple and straightforward. Your doctors and the health care facilities you use keep and protect your medical records on your behalf. Toni Brayer, MD, an internist in San Francisco and CEO of Sutter Pacific Medical Foundation says, "My understanding is that patients have a legal right to their medical records when they request them. The physician is the caretaker and has the responsibility for maintaining those medical records."[123]

The second type is a data grab by outsiders. The American Medical Informatics Association in 2006 published a white paper focused on building a national framework for "secondary use of health data."[124] Two years later, they published another paper to advance a "robust framework for an infrastructure of policies, standards, and best practices to facilitate the collection, storage, aggregation, linkage, and transmission of health data for various uses"—for which data stewardship was considered key.[125]

In 2009, the National Committee on Vital and Health Statistics (NCVHS), which describes itself as a federal advisory committee for HHS on health information policy since 1949, issued a brief called "Health Data Stewardship: What, Why, Who, How." The brief defined health data stewardship, in part, as "a responsibility, guided by principles and practices, to ensure the knowledgeable and appropriate use of data derived from individuals' personal health information.... Health data stewardship supports the benefits to society of using individuals' personal health information to improve understanding of health and health care while at the same time respecting individuals' privacy and confidentiality."[126] Thus, stewardship prioritizes the benefits to society rather than to the individual who is the subject of the data. However, as British Prime Minister Margaret Thatcher once said, "There is no such thing as society. There is living tapestry of men and women and people ..."[127] All of them individuals.

The NCVHS brief focuses on *secondary uses* of the patient's data. When describing who should practice data stewardship, NCVHS writes, "Everyone who collects, views, stores, exchanges, aggregates, analyzes, and/or uses electronic health data should practice data stewardship. This includes health care organizations, clinicians, payers, information exchanges, vendors, the quality improvement community, health statistics agencies, researchers, and caregivers."[128]

The key component of stewardship is the presence of a data steward who has "final authority and accountability for appropriate use of health data."[129] According to a 2014 Health Catalyst slideshow, a centralized data warehouse and metadata tools that aid in creating a "self-sufficient data warehouse user community" help ensure data steward success. Health Catalyst also explains that "once the data is unlocked in the EDW [enterprise data warehouse] the best way to create long-term value is to have a thriving user base."[130]

Will most Americans believe their privacy and confidentiality is being respected if this "thriving user base" of corporations, government agencies, researchers, and individuals can share and use their information for secondary purposes? Is their privacy being respected just because each organization has a data steward (likely employed by the organization) overseeing the handling and exchange of their private information? Probably not. Notably, the NCVHS brief acknowledges that individual consent is key to patient trust but then limits the patient's right to decide who gets their data: "The degree of choice may vary with the type of information, the purpose of the exchange, applicable law, population health needs, and other factors."[131]

Estonia provides an example of data ownership rights. The 1999 Estonian Human Genes Research Act "literally codified into law that a person who contributes their genetic information has absolute ownership and control over it and has the sole authority to decide who can see it and what can be done with it. The donor decides what studies they wish to make their information available to (if any) and can log into a secure system to see which of the studies they granted permission to actually ended up using their data," reports Kalev Leetaru, senior fellow at the George Washington University Center for Cyber & Homeland Security.[132]

One final point should not be missed. "As a matter of U.S. public policy, HIPAA legislation has de facto broadened the definition of primary use [of the patient record] to include business operations and quality of care," reports the American Medical Informatics

Association. Previously, in a 1991 report on computer-based patient records, the Institute of Medicine had defined "primary use" as patient care. All other uses were considered secondary.[133] Under HIPAA's permissive use of patient data, most secondary uses are now considered "primary."

What EHRs Could Have Been

The EHR mandate forced doctors to buy and use a computerized system that wasn't ready for prime time or designed for the primary purpose of medicine: patient care. Under the mandate, doctors and hospitals had to buy or be penalized. This was a boon for the EHR industry, which raced to grab a slice of the $30 billion or more in grants before the federal funding deadlines passed.

As a result, there are "three freshly minted billionaires," reports Arthur Allen at Politico Pro.[134] Or as Greg Simon, president of the Biden Cancer Initiative, told Politico Morning eHealth about EHR vendors: "We've made billionaires of the executives of these companies. . . . They've had fun."[135]

But the race to capture the gold was counterproductive.

Discussing usability of the EHR, Rollin J. (Terry) Fairbanks, MD, MS, who directs MedStar Health National Center for Human Factors in Healthcare, said "it would have been better to give $1–$2 billion to the vendors initially and tell them to spend two years designing good products. . . . Then give the money to hospitals and doctors to buy the products."[136]

EHRs could've been innovative, but the mandate and the deadline didn't leave room for innovation. In January 2018, James Hereford, president and CEO of Minneapolis-based Fairview Health Services, called Epic an "impediment to innovation." He chastised the Wisconsin-based EHR company for using a closed platform that restricts innovation and said Epic has "architected an organization that has its belief that all good ideas are from Madison, Wisconsin. And on the off chance that one of us think of a good idea, it's still owned by Madison, Wisconsin." He called on health care leaders to get together and figure out "how we march on Madison."[137]

Thomas LaGrelius, MD, president and chairman of The American College of Private Physicians, says easy-to-use EHRs already exist.

But they aren't government-certified EHRs. He writes, "There are doctor-designed EHRs that are agnostic to billing and statistical data mining. They work very well but are only used by private Concierge and Direct Patient Care practices that concern themselves only with patient care and not with data or insurance billing."[138]

Dr. Scot Silverstein writes, "First, I believe healthcare IT can live up to all the predictions made about its benefits—but only if **done well.** There is massive complexity behind those two words 'done well,' and that is HIT's key stumbling block in 2009. I believe we are only in the adolescent stage of knowing how to 'do health IT well.'"[139] Nine years later, the government EHR is not an example of "done well."

"I used to think we could improve the electronic health record from within," Andrew Hines, an engineer at Canvas Medical, told Shawn Martin, AAFP senior vice president of advocacy, practice advancement, and policy, "but now I realize the only way to truly improve electronic health records is to start over."[140]

David Brailer, MD, national coordinator of health IT under President George W. Bush, thinks the Meaningful Use mandate stifled innovation. The incentives were a bad idea "because they encouraged purchases of tech that wasn't ready, for medical practices that weren't ready to share patients or their data."[141]

The mandate, the five-year deadline, the threat of penalties, and the billions in Meaningful Use subsidies left doctors and hospitals at a disadvantage when vendors came calling. EHR vendors had no incentive to meet their customers' unique clinical requirements. Practices were forced to buy what EHR vendors were selling, no matter how poor the product or faulty the service. Within that deadline, clinics and hospitals also had to train staff and get the system up and running "meaningfully" to avoid Medicare penalties—even if the EHR didn't match the workflow of the physician's practice or meet the clinical needs of hospitalized patients and their doctors.

Prior to the EHR experiment being foisted onto the health care system by Congress, "the records industry made hundreds of thousands of dollars of political contributions to both Democrats and Republicans," reveals the *New York Times*.[142]

Health IT lobbying continued at the regulatory level for years after the mandate passed: "The biggest players drew this incredible huddle around the rule-makers and the rules are ridiculously favorable to these companies and ridiculously unfavorable to society," said Jonathan Bush, co-founder and CEO of the cloud-based EHR company athenahealth and a first cousin to former President George W. Bush.[143]

Frustrated members of Congress now demand the interoperability never required by law. If prohibiting "information blocking" in the 2016 21st Century Cures Act is their way of telling EHR vendors the interfacing (connection) fees are exorbitant, it may be working. As the Cures Act was about to be introduced in 2015,[144] Epic CEO Judy Faulkner, whose system holds the medical information of nearly half the country, announced at the HIMSS15 conference (with a record-breaking 43,129 registered attendees[145]) that Epic would drop the fees it charges doctors to connect the Epic system with other EHR systems—until at least 2020.[146] Cerner and athenahealth have waived the fees as well.[147]

But interoperability is not the problem Congress should be trying to fix. The mandate to install and use unsafe, government surveillance systems in exam rooms and at the bedside—on pain of penalty for refusal—is the real problem patients and doctors face every day.

And for that, there are action steps everyone can take.

Steps Back to Privacy, Safety, and Freedom

HIPAA, the federal EHR mandate, Meaningful Use requirements, MIPS, data-reporting requirements, and penalties imposed by Congress created the problem doctors and patients face today. When Americans take back responsibility for their own medical bills and reassert control over dollars, data, and decisions, that's where the solutions begin.

For those who think it's impossible to send this intrusive ship back to dry dock, imagine what would happen if Congress had mandated a similar surveillance system in every attorney's office, the backrooms of every manufacturer, the front desks of hotels, the counters of mom-and-pop restaurants, or the corporate headquarters of Hewlett-Packard, the Green Bay Packers, Delta Airlines, IBM, Lockheed Martin, Whole Foods, Microsoft, Google, Target, Verizon, Facebook, Walmart, SuperAmerica, Big Lots, or Congress itself? (After all, Congress does claim to be a "small business.")[148]

Imagine if federal or state officials began telling these small and large private companies—many under federal regulations or federal contracts—that they will be penalized if they do not use the government-certified and government-imposed data system "meaningfully," including regular ongoing reporting of customer satisfaction and "quality" statistics to the government.

Now imagine business owners like Microsoft's Bill Gates, Whole Food's John Mackey, Southwest Airline's Gary Kelly, Facebook's Mark Zuckerberg, or Walmart CEO Doug McMillon being told to "attest" annually to "meaningful use" of the government-certified data-collection and data-tracking system for federal quality- and cost-control efforts. Imagine them threatened with penalties for information blocking and non-interoperable systems.

It would not happen. Nor should it.

The path back to patient safety, privacy, and physician freedom begins with moving toward direct payment and restoring patient consent rights. Below are four separate lists of action steps—for concerned citizens and patients, practitioners, state legislatures, and Congress—in no particular order. Some are big steps and some are little steps, but what's important is that the feet keep walking in the right direction. These four groups can work separately or in unison to take back the rights and freedoms that Congress used federal law to eviscerate—and too many states have not yet resisted. Also included are five steps for Congress and three steps for state legislators to move the country back to first-party payment for medical care. Feel free to add to this list as other ideas emerge.

Note: All consent requirements listed below are opt-in, written, voluntary, specific, informed consent by the individual, the parent of a child, or the guardian. In short, disclosure and use of patient data doesn't happen without a signature.

Steps for Congress

1. Repeal the federal EHR mandate (MU requirements and penalties).

2. Repeal MIPS, PQRS reporting, advanced alternative payment models (APMs), and value-based payments.

3. Repeal the HIPAA "privacy" rule.

4. Require patient consent for the twelve broad "Uses and disclosures for which an authorization or opportunity to agree or object is not required" section of the HIPAA rule (45 CFR 164.512)[149]

5. Enact legislation that restores the opt-in patient consent requirements for treatment, payment, and health care operations (TPO) that were in the Clinton administration's original final HIPAA rule—before the Bush administration stripped them out. (The American Hospital Association has estimated that only $101 million of the $22.5 billion cost of

complying with HIPAA over five years was attributable to asking for consent as previously required.[150])

6. Add "Patient consent is required for all use and sharing of medical information" to health care legislation, including health information exchange legislation.
7. Require patient consent for transferring patient data into or through the eHealth Exchange.
8. Change the name of the Notice of Privacy Practices (NPP) to "Notice of Disclosure Practices" to end misperception of HIPAA as a privacy rule.
9. Require all Notice of Privacy Practices (NPP) documents to incorporate state laws that are more protective of confidentiality, consent, and privacy rights in the text of the NPP. (The Mayo Clinic NPP provides a good example of how it should be done.)
10. Require clinics and hospitals to inform patients that they are not required to sign the HIPAA form or NPP acknowledgement of receipt and cannot be refused care if they refuse to sign.
11. Prohibit single-signature, consolidated consent forms that force patients to sign away their right to privacy to secure medical treatment.
12. Require an audit trail and an accounting of all disclosures (including to federal, state, and local governments) to patients that request such an accounting, including the name of the person accessing the data, the corporate entity receiving the data, the specific information shared, the intended use, contact information of the recipient, and the authority under which the patient's data was shared.
13. Require a written warning be given to patients if the federal government requests access to medical data. The warning should inform patients whether they have an option to

refuse and what their legal rights are regarding the data requested. The Minnesota-required Tennessen warning provides a good example to follow.[151]

14. Require patient consent requirements for bedside research, including CMS Innovation Center experiments.

15. Require patient consent for federally funded research projects, including use and analysis of biospecimens.

16. Mandate parent consent requirements for storage, use, sequencing, and dissemination of newborn DNA by withholding federal funds from state health departments that refuse to secure parent consent.

17. Repeal REAL ID, disassemble the "national identity registry,"[152] and repeal the language that allows the Secretary of Homeland Security to unilaterally expand the official purposes for which REAL ID is required, for example, to health care.

18. Repeal and defund the national patient-matching strategy (national patient ID).

19. Require physicians to disclose to patients if their medical decisions are restricted by federal mandates, funding, or initiatives (e.g., EHRs; CMMI programs; CER research; treatment protocols; financial risk-sharing arrangements [e.g., ACOs]); or value, performance, quality, outcomes, or patient-satisfaction measurements.

20. Use financial penalties and withholding of state funding wherever necessary to enforce patient-consent requirements.

21. Repeal the CMS Innovation Center, the Agency for Healthcare Research and Quality (AHRQ), and the Patient-Centered Outcomes Research Institute (PCORI), and rescind all related research and data-sharing rules.

22. Repeal section 1311(h) of the Affordable Care Act.

23. Prohibit assignment of Medicare recipients to ACOs without their consent and require separate, written patient consent for sharing the data of Medicare patients with ACO.

24. Prohibit hospitals and clinics from forcing senior citizens to submit to an annual inspection called the Annual Wellness Visit (AWV).

25. Delink Medicare enrollment from Social Security retirement benefits so senior citizens can choose to retain private coverage without losing benefits. Repeal the executive instructions in the SSA Program Operations Manual System (POMS) that force seniors to enroll in Medicare Part A (hospitalization) or lose their Social Security benefits.[153]

26. Do not require states to set up state health surveillance programs and do not provide federal funds for state surveillance programs, including the PDMP and APCD.

27. Repeal the requirement that forces physicians to file unassigned Medicare claims,[154] allowing patients to file claims if they so choose.

28. Let the affordable free market grow by protecting cash-based medical practices and health-sharing organizations from federal mandates and regulations.

29. Equalize tax treatment for health insurance to discourage employer-sponsored coverage and encourage personal lifelong ownership of private health insurance.

30. Repeal the ACA prohibition against catastrophic indemnity (non-managed care) health insurance policies.

31. Repeal the HMO Act of 1973, which allowed the merger of the delivery and financing of medical care and established HMOs (now health plans) nationwide.

Steps for State Legislators

1. Counter federal mandates with states' rights under the Tenth Amendment.
2. Refuse to mandate the EHR.
3. Write and enact laws that honor states' rights by protecting physicians and others from federal data-sharing mandates.
4. Legally recognize patient ownership of patient data, which is "central to a lot of the things that need to be accomplished," says ONC head Don Rucker.[155]
5. Impose no monetary or other penalties for doctors and hospitals that go EHR-free.
6. Refuse to make EHR use or proficiency a requirement of licensure.
7. Repeal laws that conform state medical privacy laws to HIPAA.
8. Use state preemption authority to enact state medical privacy laws that protect patients *from* HIPAA.
9. Enact a state law providing patients a private right of action, permitting lawsuits for breach of privacy and violation of privacy and consent requirements.[156]
10. Require patient consent for treatment, payment, and health care operations.
11. Require all Notices of Privacy Practices (NPP) to incorporate more protective state laws on confidentiality, consent, and privacy rights in the text of the NPP and enforce it with penalties. (The Mayo Clinic NPP provides a good example of how it should be done.)
12. Inform the public that HIPAA does not protect patients' privacy.

13. Require written voluntary patient consent for transfer of patient data to or through a health information exchange.

14. Prohibit state participation in the eHealth Exchange (formerly, National Health Information Network).

15. Require an audit trail and an accounting of all disclosures (including to federal, state, and local governments) to patients that request such an accounting, including the name of the person accessing the data, the corporate entity receiving the data, the specific information shared, the intended use, contact information of the recipient, and the authority under which the patient's data was shared.

16. Require consent forms to be single subject or have *yes* and *no* checkboxes by each item for which the health care provider is seeking patient consent.

17. Repeal state All-Payer Claims Database (APCD).

18. Notify self-insured companies of their right to refuse APCD data reporting (2016 Supreme Court ruling).

19. Repeal e-prescribing mandate.

20. Repeal state prescription drug monitoring program.

21. Repeal state health surveillance systems.

22. Require opt-in patient consent for sharing patient data with state health surveillance systems, including immunization and cancer registries.

23. Repeal quality-reporting requirements.

24. Repeal creation of and mandated use of unique patient IDs, national provider identifiers (NPI), employer identification numbers (EIN) and Health Plan Identification Numbers (HPID) for health care transactions—and refuse state patient-matching strategies.

25. Repeal pay-for-performance and pay-for-value initiatives.

26. Require informed, written patient consent prior to all clinical or health-data research initiatives, including CMS Innovation Center treatment and payment experiments.

27. Destroy the newborn dried blood spots (Baby DNA) stored without parent consent, and prohibit state storage, use, sequencing, and dissemination of newborn DNA.

28. Switch all statutory and regulatory opt-out (dissent) options to opt-in (consent) requirements.

29. Until Congress changes the name of the Notice of Privacy Practices to "Notice of Disclosure Practices," require clinics and hospitals to clearly warn patients in a separate document that their data will be freely shared under HIPAA unless there's a stronger state privacy law or the patient objects in writing and the provider agrees to the restriction.

30. Require physicians and other practitioners to issue verbal and written warnings to patients about their use of standardized treatment protocols, conflicts of interests, and research conducted at the bedside.

31. Prohibit reduced payments to physicians based on so-called value equations and quality, health disparity, performance, or outcomes scores.

32. Require health care providers to notify patients that they aren't required to fill out, digitally or otherwise, information about habits, homes, hobbies, families, and more to receive medical care.

33. Require consent for all outside access to patients' data, except with voluntary fully informed patient consent or a valid search warrant.

34. Prohibit direct and real-time government access to patient data.

35. Require written, separate, and informed patient consent for health profiling, risk-scoring, predictive analysis, familial

profiling, genomic sequencing, population-health initiatives, and outside assessments.

36. Prohibit linking of EHR with patients' social media or personal fitness data without fully informed, voluntary patient consent.

37. Permit all providers to use paper medical records or electronic medical records with no reporting functionality.

38. Prohibit storage of identified or de-identified patient data in government and corporate data repositories or registries without patient consent.

39. Authorize patients to be the holder of their own medical records, if they so choose.

40. Provide incentives for medical charity to reduce claims that government has a right to the private medical information of the poor and disadvantaged.

41. Provide protection for EHR whistleblowers.

42. Let the affordable free market grow by protecting cash-based medical practices and health-sharing organizations from federal mandates and regulations.

43. Restore access to affordable coverage, such as the "health benefit plans" enacted by the Iowa legislature and signed into law April 2, 2018.[157]

44. Enact a state law that encourages indemnity insurers to offer parents health insurance for each pre-born child, thus building a nation of citizens who have lifelong, private indemnity insurance and pay doctors and hospitals directly.

Steps for Physicians and Clinicians

1. Refuse the government EHR.

2. Offer patients the option of a paper chart.

3. Transition back to paper charts for clinical care.[158]
4. Offer patients who travel a thumb-drive option for their medical records.
5. Refuse to report patient data or share patient data with a data registry without patient or parent consent.
6. Request written consent from patients for health plan or government reporting requirements and refuse to report if consent is not given.
7. Warn patients about the use of standardized treatment protocols, conflicts of interests, and research conducted at the bedside.
8. Inform patients that the HIPAA privacy form does not protect their privacy.
9. Inform patients that signing the HIPAA form or Notice of Privacy Practices acknowledgement statement isn't required by law and isn't a prerequisite for care.
10. Inform patients that they aren't required to fill out questionnaires or patient-satisfaction surveys or disclose anything about family members, lifestyle, habits, hobbies, and home environment as a prerequisite for care.
11. Do not hand patients a coercive iPad questionnaire that requires them to divulge information they don't want to divulge, such as "are there guns in the house?" before they can move to the next question.[159]
12. Do not use a consolidated consent form (many consent provisions; one signature) unless it includes a *yes* and *no* checkbox by each consent provision.
13. Ask patients if they're comfortable having a scribe (virtual or live) transcribe the interaction and warn patients that virtual scribes (e.g. Alexa) are always on.

14. Refuse to sign contracts with health plans, Medicaid, or Medicare.

15. Do not engage in activities that make your patients serve you or the system.

16. Do not force your patients to use a portal to communicate with your office, learn about test results, or schedule appointments.

17. Do not use a consent form that consists of an electronic pad. Patients must be able to see what they're signing and only sign what they see.

18. Tell your staff to expect people to refuse to sign forms, including the HIPAA acknowledgment statement.

19. Be your patient's best advocate against the corporate and government powers that seek to intrude and exert control when they are the most vulnerable and the least able to say no.

20. Transition to a cash-based, third-party-free practice, as described on The Wedge of Health Freedom website and join the direct-pay practices nationwide listed on its "Find a Practice" map (JoinTheWedge.com).

Steps for Citizens and Patients

1. Don't trust the EHR for accuracy or confidentiality.

2. Verify accuracy of treatments ordered and information recorded.

3. Keep notes of clinic visits, hospital stays, and treatments ordered.

4. Stay with hospitalized family members to reduce errors and omissions.

5. Ask your physician to certify that your treatment plan is not part of a research program.
6. Tell the pediatrician, the hospital, and the health plan not to share your child's data with the American Academy of Pediatric's national CHILD registry.
7. Ask hospitals and clinics for an "accounting of disclosures" for disclosures of your data made in the past six years—a right patients have under HIPAA to information on certain disclosures, including for research and other "nonroutine purposes."[160]
8. Ask if your treatment options are being limited or influenced by the computer, standardized treatment protocols, value-based payment programs, or quality measurement requirements for reimbursement.
9. Ask for a paper prescription.
10. Ask for a detailing of your information held by the state government in any health surveillance system (e.g., immunization, birth defect, cancer, prescription monitoring, APCD, newborn screening, chronic disease registry, and many more)
11. If you're an employer with a self-insured company, refuse to allow your third-party administrator to send employee data to the state All-Payer Claims Database.
12. Refuse to sign the HIPAA Notice of Privacy Practices acknowledgement statement.
13. Ask for a separate consent for treatment and payment only.
14. Refuse to sign consolidated, multi-consent, single-signature consent forms.
15. Refuse to sign electronic pads; ask for the physical document and then make a signing decision on paper.

16. Refuse to fill out patient-satisfaction surveys.

17. Refuse to fill out family history, social history, or other data-gathering questionnaires.

18. Only provide information pertinent to the purpose of your visit with the doctor.

19. Be kind, calm, and firm when you refuse to sign or complete objectionable forms.

20. Inform your doctor about whether you do or don't want a virtual or live scribe in the room.

21. Ask for the credentials of workers in the exam room and at the bedside (MD, RN, NP, PA, CMA, etc.).

22. Refuse hospital, clinic, or government offers to send a home visitor to your house.

23. Send a copy of coercive patient consent forms to Citizens' Council for Health Freedom (cchfreedom.org).

24. Ask state legislators to pass state privacy-protection laws that protect you *from* HIPAA.

25. Ask state legislators to *repeal* state laws that conform to HIPAA's data-sharing rule.

26. Ask state legislators to enact a law giving you absolute control and property rights over your DNA and data, similar to the Estonian Human Genes Research Act.[161]

27. Ask state legislators to enact a law giving you a private right of action, allowing you to sue for breach of privacy or violation of privacy and consent requirements.

28. Share your HIPAA refusal stories at hipaahurtme.com.

29. Check CCHF's state-by-state list of newborn DNA retention and take steps to require the state to destroy your child's DNA (go to itsmydna.org).

30. If your state stores newborn DNA, ask state legislators to dismantle the state's Baby DNA warehouse and to enact a law prohibiting the state from storing, using, sequencing, or sharing newborn dried blood spots (DNA) taken at birth to conduct newborn genetic screening.

31. Sue the state health department if it stores, uses, sequences, or shares newborn DNA without consent.[162]

32. Search out direct-pay, privacy-protecting, third-party-free cash practices, such as those listed at The Wedge of Health Freedom (JoinTheWedge.com).

33. Search for a doctor that does not have a shared EHR system and is not "hooked up to the grid"—does not participate in an HIE or HIO.

34. Consider refusing to disclose that you have insurance and pay cash instead.

35. Do not disclose your Social Security number.

36. Restrict disclosures to your health insurer, by paying-in-full out of pocket. (*Note*: The clinic can still share your data elsewhere if required by state or federal law.)[163]

37. Consider health sharing, a cash-based, confidential affordable option for coverage.

38. Ask Congress to equalize tax treatment for health insurance to encourage personal lifelong ownership of affordable private indemnity health insurance.

39. Ask Congress to repeal the ACA prohibition against catastrophic indemnity (non-managed care) health insurance policies.

40. Ask for a state law that encourages indemnity insurers to offer parents health insurance for each pre-born child, thus building a nation of citizens who have lifelong, private indemnity insurance and pay doctors and hospitals directly.

41. Ask Congress to delink Medicare enrollment from Social Security retirement benefits so seniors can voluntarily keep private coverage without losing Social Security benefits.

Conclusion

The government EHR has been imposed to give government agencies and other third parties control of medical decisions. This computerized surveillance system in the exam room threatens the lives of America's patients and violates their privacy rights. Left to market forces, the computerized medical record would have evolved to meet the efficiency, recording, accuracy, completeness, confidentiality, workflow, care coordination, and time-sensitive needs of physicians and patients. It would have been patient-centric, physician-approved, and free from government control.

But politicians on both sides of the aisle imposed the government-certified EHR on doctors and patients and mandated how it must be used. As a completely unproven methodology, its primary purpose has less to do with caring for patients than with data mining, unconsented research, and control over the practice of medicine. The federal laws that facilitate this intrusion—HIPAA, ARRA, HITECH, ACA, MACRA—violate patient rights, privacy rights, constitutional rights, professional obligations, private contracts, and ethical integrity.

The EHR mandate was a dream come true for those whose only goal was to force doctors and hospitals to buy their product, not just once, but repeatedly into the future. And not just a product, but all the updates, leasing costs, extraction fees, and interfacing fees for the life of the contract and the life of the practice.

If Congress had refused to commandeer America's doctors, this book wouldn't have been written. If Congress had refused to establish third parties as the primary payers of medical care, patients and doctors would still be in control and care would be more affordable. If Congress had refused to unilaterally end patient privacy rights, no one would know the term *HIPAA*. Patient consent would still be a legal requirement for data sharing. The word *scribes* would rarely surface outside of church. Three American EHR CEOs wouldn't be freshly minted billionaires. And 48 percent of our nation's physicians wouldn't be dreaming up ways to leave patient care behind.

Americans can end the surveillance, restore professional autonomy and patient safety to the exam room, and stop the drive to a government-controlled health care system.

This book is a call for action, not acquiescence.

Now that you know the dangerous truth about the government EHR, take action to protect the lives of patients, the excellence and integrity of American medicine, and the individual freedom of all Americans.

Afterword

Let me speak for a moment as the registered nurse that I am.

The government electronic health record is a clinical disaster.

Everything required for medical excellence is impeded by the technology Congress thrust between the patient and the clinician. Eye contact, comforting touch, penetrating clinical evaluation as the patient talks about what's wrong, critical thinking, probing questions, caring expression, listening ear, life-saving swiftness, and complete attention to words, appearance, and body language.

The heart and soul of medicine—and its patients—are in danger.

The EHR is everything care is not. It steals time, interrupts flow, creates a barrier, constricts thought processes, and forces eyes and hands to turn away from the patient. It controls the interaction, limits the questions, restricts the choices, destroys confidentiality, forces patients to become data subjects, and allows outsiders to interfere.

The government EHR is also an ethical catastrophe.

No doubt an entire book could be written about the duty to protect the patient. The patient is the point. If there wasn't a patient, there wouldn't be a physician. There wouldn't be a nurse. There wouldn't be a health care system. There wouldn't be a medical record.

There are principles here, all the way back to the Great Physician in the scriptures, of beneficence and charity and care; of being a servant to those in need; of not exploiting the one whose life is in your hands. The patient should never serve the physician. The patient should never serve "the system."

Congress forgot the patient. When policy makers enacted HIPAA to force the patient-doctor interaction onto a computer screen for outside monitoring and data reporting, they set a course to break Hippocrates' inviolable rule of medicine: to "abstain from all intentional wrong-doing and harm."

Hippocrates wrote, "And whatsoever I shall see or hear in the course of my profession, as well as outside my profession in my intercourse with men, if it be what should not be published abroad, I will never divulge, holding such things to be holy secrets."

The protection of "holy secrets" is critical to medical excellence. Confidentiality gives patients the trust they need to speak freely and frankly—to tell the whole truth and nothing but the truth—even in the most embarrassing or self-incriminating situations. The interaction between the patient and the doctor is a holy moment in a sanctuary of security. The patient must feel safe. The patient's sole purpose for being in the exam room—bereft of all but a flimsy gown and a pounding heart or lying alone in a hospital bed hooked up to life-sustaining IVs and a hissing respirator—is to receive care, not to be the subject of a government experiment, a research project, or a profiteering venture.

In their vulnerability, today's patients are being exploited. Their doctors are being used for corporate and big-government purposes that reach far beyond the bedside, deep into home and hearth. At a time when they cannot say no, individuals are stripped of their privacy and their inherent human dignity.

It's dangerous to be a patient today.

The practice of medicine is a mission. It's a calling. It's a profession. It is not a business. And patients are not "customers." That's the intrusion of corporate language into the caring practice of medicine. The last person a patient needs as a physician is someone for whom medicine has become just a job, or for whom the outside forces intruding upon medicine have turned him or her into an employee of the system.

Patients need critically thinking physicians who are dedicated to medical excellence, personally interested in their well-being, and motivated to solve difficult and sometimes mysterious problems. Patients need nurses who can spend time with them, calm their fears, hold their hands, not back out of the room because the chart needs their continued attention.

Lives are saved by critical attention to detail. How many lives have been lost because the doctor's or the nurse's time and attention were diverted by the computer screen?

The government EHR is a barrier to care. It puts thinking in a box, focuses the doctor's and nurse's concentration on computer clicks and performance metrics, introduces a new realm of dangerous medical errors, and in the process, threatens the very fabric of American medicine.

Big Brother's intrusion in the exam room forces doctors and patients to serve a new master: the government EHR. It puts clinical care under computer control. It hides critical information. It delays and distracts.

Patients' lives hang in the balance. Call on Congress to repeal the EHR mandate and the HIPAA no-privacy rule. All it takes is political will. I look forward to a future where physicians have their joy restored, patients come first, affordability and personal control are restored by the exodus of third-party payment, privacy is reclaimed—and Big Brother has been banished once and for all.

How Patients Lost Control to Third-Party Payers

Before the Affordable Care Act (ACA) was enacted, third parties—government, employers, and corporate managed-care health plans—were in charge of paying for most medical services. Since the ACA, most health plans in and outside of government and employment, offer plans with high deductibles and high premiums, forcing enrollees to pay most medical expenses out of pocket. Nevertheless, most of the expenses are run through the health plan to determine whether the enrollee's payment for care will be counted toward the deductible. The third-party payer is in charge.

Third-party payment was not always the rule. In 1940, only 9 percent (12.3 million) of the American population had any form of coverage for medical expenses. The majority of Americans paid their bills directly out of pocket. By 2006, 161.7 million people, approximately 62.2 percent of the nonelderly population, had employer-sponsored coverage, and 17.5 percent were in government programs. Only 6.8 percent had individually purchased policies, leaving 18 percent without a third party paying their medical bills.[1]

By 2026, federal, state, and local governments are expected to pay for 47 percent of total national health expenditures, up from 45 percent in 2016.[2] And much of that spending will run through the hands of government collaborators, the managed care health plans. Already 33 percent of Medicare recipients are in health plans (Medicare Advantage) and 50.9 million people are in managed-care Medicaid (see below). In addition, everyone enrolled in Obamacare coverage through the exchanges is enrolled in a federally-qualified health plan. That's the only option. The ACA all but prohibited indemnity (major medical, catastrophic) policies.

As this book demonstrates, most of today's patients have no control over their data and little control over health care dollars as a result of third-party payment. The government agencies and their health-plan collaborators who hold the dollars are making the rules and using the EHR to impose control. It doesn't have to stay this way. The following dates give a brief timeline of how we got here, starting with employer-sponsored coverage in 1942—and thus a sense of the way back to freedom and privacy. That which has been done can be undone, and the time to start is now.

Timeline: How Congress Advanced Third-Party Control

1942: In the midst of Congress-imposed wage and price controls, employers were allowed by the War Labor Board to provide benefits to employees without the employer or the employee paying taxes. One year later the IRS issued a special ruling confirming "employees were not required to pay tax on the dollar value of group health-insurance premiums paid on their behalf by their corporate employers."[3]

1954: Congress made this generous tax exclusion permanent under the Internal Revenue Code of 1954. Thus, today's group health benefits are excluded from employees' taxable wages.[4] However, employees are limited to the employer's choice, face the possibility of becoming uninsured through unemployment, may be left with an uninsurable (preexisting) condition with loss of employment, may face medical bankruptcy if they lose employment and insurance due to a medical condition, and experience lower wage increases as more income is diverted to cover the cost of the employer's health plan.[5] Premiums for employer-sponsored family coverage have risen 213 percent since 1999, while wages have risen only 60 percent, the Associated Press reported in late 2016.[6]

1965: Medicare and Medicaid were enacted by Congress to provide government health care to the poor, the disabled, and to everyone age sixty-five and older. Medicare began on July 1, 1966, making nineteen million senior citizens eligible to enter Medicare Part A at no cost and Medicare Part B for $3.00 per month.[7] Spending on Medicare is expected to reach $1.4 trillion by 2027.[8]

1971: Over a period of three months, US Senator Edward M. Kennedy (D-MA) held hearings on the "Health Care Crisis in America." Following those hearings, he held a series of hearings "on the whole question of HMOs."[9]

1973: The HMO Act of 1973 was authored by Senator Kennedy, enacted by Congress, and signed into law by Republican President Richard Nixon to merge the financing and delivery of health care. It provided $375 million to establish HMOs nationwide.[10]

1982: Medicare HMOs (later called Medicare+Choice) were established as a result of the enactment of the Tax Equity and Fiscal Responsibility Act (TEFRA). Also, the federal government granted Arizona a waiver, allowing the state to enroll their Medicaid recipients into HMOs (managed care/health plans) and not offer a fee-for-service alternative.[11] More states sought waivers to limit enrollee choices through HMOs. By 2011, 42.2 million individuals in Medicaid (74% of all Medicaid enrollees) were in HMOs.[12] By 2015, 50.9 million of 77.8 million Medicaid recipients were enrolled in comprehensive managed care organizations.[13]

1993: The Clinton Health Security Act was introduced. Although it failed in 1994, it included a national health information system, electronic data network, unique identifier numbers, health security cards, regional alliances, state single-payer systems, managed care organizations (HMOs), government-issued clinical practice guidelines (protocols), national guideline clearinghouse, health service utilization protocols, quality of care monitoring, National Quality Management Program, research on "quality, appropriateness and effectiveness of health care," and more. Some provisions became law later. Had the entire act become law, the federal government would have issued "treatment-specific or condition-specific practice guidelines for clinical treatments and conditions . . . for use in reviewing quality and appropriateness of medical care."[14]

1996: Congress passed the bipartisan (Kennedy-Kassebaum) Health Insurance Portability and Accountability Act of 1996 on August 21, 1996. The Administrative Simplification section of the law established the foundation for a national health information network, requiring unique identification numbers and national standards for the electronic exchange of health information. It also required the Secretary of Health & Human Services to promulgate a health privacy rule if Congress failed to do so within three years after enactment.[15] The proposed rule released November 3, 1999, eliminated consent requirements for data sharing. After receiving more than fifty-two thousand comments, many in support of retaining patient consent, the final rule was published December 28, 2000 with consent requirements for treatment, payment, and health care operations.[16] The consent requirements were stripped out by the Bush administration in 2002 in response to industry complaints.[17]

1997: The Balanced Budget Act of 1997 led to lower payments for Medicare managed care plans, causing the plans to reduce benefits, which led to reduced enrollment.[18] By 2003, Medicare HMO enrollment had slipped to 4.6 million from 6.4 million in 1999.

1999: The Healthcare Research and Quality Act of 1999 established the Agency for Healthcare Research and Quality (AHRQ), which is required to promote health care quality improvement through research that develops "scientific evidence regarding all aspects of health care." This includes research and dissemination of information on the quality, effectiveness, efficiency, appropriateness, and value of health care service; quality measurement and improvement; and outcomes, cost effectiveness, clinical practice, health care costs, database development, productivity, and more. It began data collection and reporting on performance and "quality" measures.[19] Notably, AHRQ's National Guideline Clearinghouse (Guideline.gov), which reviews and posts treatment guidelines, will close on July 16, 2018, at the end of the five-year, $19 million contract with the ECRI Institute due to discontinued congressional funding.[20]

2003: Congress enacted the Medicare Prescription Drug, Improvement, and Modernization Act of 2003 (called the Medicare Modernization Act (MMA)), which switched the name of the Medicare HMO program from Medicare+Choice to Medicare Advantage (Medicare Part C),[21] added Private Fee-For-Service (PFFS) Plans, and paid the PFFS plans significantly more per recipient than traditional Medicare fee-for-service plans (16.6 percent in one report[22]). In 2004, Medicare Advantage had 5.3 million enrollees (13 percent). By 2017, 19 million Medicare recipients (33 percent) were enrolled in a Medicare Advantage plan.[23]

2006: The Tax Relief and Health Care Act of 2006 created a voluntary reporting program, which CMS labeled the Physician Quality Reporting Initiative (PQRI). Reporting began July 1, 2007. A 1.5 percent bonus was available to physicians who successfully participated.[24] In 2010, the PQRI program was made mandatory by the PPACA and renamed the Physician Quality Reporting System (PQRS).

2008: The Medicare Improvements for Patients and Providers Act of 2008 mandated electronic prescribing and required HHS to establish an "integrated national strategy and priorities for health care performance measurement in all applicable settings."[25]

2009: The American Recovery and Reinvestment Act of 2009 was signed into law less than a month after the inauguration of President Obama.[26] The law's Health Information Technology for Economic and Clinical Health Act (HITECH) mandated Meaningful Use of electronic health records (EHRs) and provided upwards of $30 billion to hospitals and clinics to buy and install the computer systems.

2010: The Patient Protection and Affordable Care Act (PPACA)[27] passed on March 23, 2010 and was amended one week later by the Health Care and Education Reconciliation Act (HCERA)[28] on March 30, 2010. The 2,700-page[29] Affordable Care Act (ACA), the name for the combined laws,[30] prohibits the sale of affordable catastrophic (major medical) indemnity insurance to anyone over the age of twenty-nine (unless the person qualifies for an exemption), mandated creation of a government exchange system, required individuals and employers to buy insurance or be penalized, forced most Americans into a managed-care corporation (health plan) or government program, such as Medicaid and Obamacare, created 159 new bureaucratic structures,[31] established surveillance systems, and much more.

2015: The GOP-led Congress passed the Medicare Access and CHIP Reauthorization Act of 2015 (MACRA)[32] creating a pay-for-performance system based on data reporting and federally-defined quality and value metrics. Requirements include use of EHRs for activities specified by the federal government. Physicians and hospitals will increasingly be paid for government-defined "value" (including electronic data collection and reporting) instead of their time, expertise and actual services provided to patients.[33]

2016: The 21st Century Cures Act, which was signed into law on December 13, 2016, requires researchers to share scientific data (some have called it the establishment of an "information commons"[34]), authorizes a Global Pediatric Clinical Study Network, prohibits "information blocking" and authorizes penalties for information blocking of up to $1 million per violation for EHR developers, networks, and exchanges as well as "appropriate disincentives" for providers.[35]

2017: The Consolidated Appropriations Act, 2017,[36] and its explanatory report,[37] permits HHS to provide technical support for establishing a national "patient-matching" strategy, an alternative strategy to establish a national patient ID, the controversial Unique Patient Identifier (UPI), which was enacted into law as part of HIPAA in 1996, but later halted by annual prohibitions on development and funding.

Acronyms

ACA—Patient Protection and Affordable Care Act of 2010; Affordable Care Act; Obamacare

ACC—American College of Cardiology

ACI—Advancing Care Information

ACO—Accountable Care Organization

ADT—Admission, Discharge and Transfer

AHA—American Hospital Association

AHIC—American Health Information Community

AHIMA—American Health Information Management Association

AHIP—America's Health Insurance Plans

AHRQ—Agency for Healthcare Research and Quality

AI—Artificial Intelligence

AMA—American Medical Association

AMBA—American Medical Billing Association

AMIA—American Medical Informatics Association

API—Application Programming Interface; for HIE

APCD—All-Payer Claims Database

APM—Alternative Payment Models

ARRA—American Recovery and Reinvestment Act of 2009

BMI—Body Mass Index

BMJ—formerly British Medical Journal

CBO—Congressional Budget Office

C-CDA—Consolidated Clinical Document Architecture (clinical data)

CCHF—Citizens' Council for Health Freedom

CCHIT—Certification Commission for Healthcare Information Technology

CDC—Centers for Disease Control and Prevention

CDRN—Clinical Data Research Networks

CDS—Clinical Decision Support

CEHRT—Certified EHR Technology

CEO—Chief Executive Officer

CER—Comparative Effectiveness Research

CFR—Code of Federal Regulations

CHIME—College of Healthcare Information Management Executives

CHIP—Children's Health Insurance Program

CHR—Comprehensive Health Record

CIO—Chief Information Officer

CISSP—Certified Information Systems Security Professional

CITL—Center for Information Technology Leadership

CJR—Comprehensive Care for Joint Replacement Model

CMA—Certified Medical Assistant

CMIO—Chief Medical Information Officer

CMMI—Center for Medicare & Medicaid Innovation; "Innovation Center"

CMS—Centers for Medicare & Medicaid Services

COPD—Chronic Obstructive Pulmonary Disease

CPC+—Comprehensive Primary Care Plus

CPOE—Computerized Physician Order Entry

CPT—Current Procedural Terminology

CQM—Clinical Quality Measures

CRM—Customer Relationship Management

CRS—Congressional Research Service

CT—Computed Tomography Scan

D.C.—District of Columbia

DBS—Dried Blood Spots from Newborn Screening

DHMSM—Defense Healthcare Management System Modernization

DHS—US Department of Homeland Security

DNA—Deoxyribonucleic Acid

DNS—Domain Name System

DoD—US Department of Defense

DOJ—US Department of Justice

DOL—US Department of Labor

DUA—Data Use Agreement

DURSA—Data Use and Reciprocal Support Agreement

EBM—Evidence-Based Medicine

eCR—Electronic Case Reporting

ED—Emergency Department

EDGE—Enhanced Data GSM Environment; server

EHR—Electronic Health Record

EHRA—HIMSS EHR Association

EIN—Employer Identification Number

EKG—Electrocardiogram

EMPI—Enterprise Master Patient Index

e-MAR—Electronic Medication Administration Record

EMR—Electronic Medical Record

EP—Eligible Professional

ER—Emergency Room

ERISA—Employee Retirement Income Security Act

eRx—Electronic Prescribing

FAAFP—Fellow of the American Academy of Family Physicians

FCC—Federal Communications Commission

FDA—Food and Drug Administration

FHIR—Fast Healthcare Interoperability Resources

FQHC—Federally Qualified Health Center

FTE—Full-Time Equivalent

GAO—Government Accountability Office

GOP—Grand Old Party, aka Republican

GPRO—Group Practice Reporting Option

H.R.—US House of Representatives Bill

HANYS—Healthcare Association of New York State

HCA—Hospital Corporation of America

HCAHPS—Hospital Consumer Assessment of Healthcare Providers and Systems survey

HCO—Health Care Operations

HELP Committee—US Senate Committee on Health, Education, Labor & Pensions

HFMA—Healthcare Financial Management Association

HGRI—Human Genome Research Institute

HHS—US Department of Health & Human Services

HIE—Health Information Exchange

HIM—Health Information Management

HIMSS—Health Information Management Systems Society

HIO—Health Information Organization

HIPAA—Health Insurance Portability and Accountability Act of 1996

HIT—Health Information Technology

HITECH—Health Information Technology for Economic and Clinical Health Act (part of ARRA)

HMO—Health Maintenance Organization

IBM—International Business Machines

ICD-9—International Classification of Diseases, 9th Revision

ICD-10—International Classification of Diseases, 10th Revision

ICD-10-CM—International Classification of Diseases, 10th Revision, Clinical Modification

ICD-10-PCS—International Classification of Diseases, 10th Revision, Procedural Code Set

ICU—Intensive Care Unit

ID—Identification; Identifier

IMPACT—Improving Medicare Post-Acute Care Transformation Act of 2014

IOM—Institute of Medicine

IoT—Internet of Things

IRB—Institutional Review Board

IRS—Internal Revenue Service

IT—Information Technology

ITIN—Individual Taxpayer Identification Number
KHN—Kaiser Health News
LDS—Limited Data Set
LIS—Laboratory Information System
LPR—Longitudinal Patient Record
MA—Master of Arts
MA—Medicare Advantage
MACRA—Medicare Access and CHIP Reauthorization Act of 2015
MassHI—Massachusetts Health Information Exchange
MAUDE—Manufacturer and User Facility Device Experience
MBA—Masters of Business Administration
MD—Medical Doctor
MDH—Minnesota Department of Health
MDMA—Medical Device Manufacturers Association
MDR—Medical Device Reporting
MGMA—Medical Group Management Association
MIPPA—Medicare Improvements for Patients and Providers Act of 2008
MMA—Medicare Prescription Drug, Improvement, and Modernization Act of 2003
MPH—Masters of Public Health
MRI—Magnetic Resonance Imaging
MU—Meaningful Use
NBS—Newborn Screening; government genetic testing program
NCDR— National Cardiovascular Data Registry
NCVHS—National Committee on Vital Health Statistics
NHIN—National Health Information Network
NICE—National Institute for Health and Clinical Excellence
NIH—National Institutes of Health
NIST—National Institute of Standards and Technology
NP—Nurse Practitioner
NPI—National Provider Identifier
NPP—Notice of Privacy Practices
NPRM—Notice of Proposed Rulemaking
NwHIN—Nationwide Health Information Network
OCM—Oncology Care Model
OCR—Office for Civil Rights; HHS
OHRP—Office for Human Research Protections
OIG—Office of Inspector General; HHS
ONC/ONCHIT—Office of the National Coordinator for Health Information Technology
OPM—Office of Personnel Management
PA—Physician Assistant
PACS—Picture Archiving and Communication System (X-rays)

PCDH—Patient Centered Data Home
PCORI—Patient-Centered Outcomes Research Institute
PCORTF—Patient-Centered Outcomes Research Trust Fund
PCP—Primary Care Physician
PDMP—Prescription Drug Monitoring Program
PECOS—Provider Enrollment, Chain and Ownership System
PET—Positron Emission Tomography Scan
PHI—Protected Health Information
PHM—Population Health Management
PHR—Personal Health Record
PPACA—Patient Protection and Affordable Care Act, aka "Obamacare"
PPO—Preferred Provider Organization
PPRN—Patient-Powered Research Networks
PQRI—Physician Quality Reporting Initiative
PQRS—Physician Quality Reporting System
QCDR—Qualified Clinical Data Registry
QPP—Quality Payment Program
RA—Risk Adjustment
REAL ID—Public Law 109-13, enacted May 11, 2005 as part of H.R.1268
RFI—Request for Information
RHIO—Regional Health Information Organization
RN—Registered Nurse
ROI—Return on Investment
RTS—Return to Stock
S.—US Senate bill
SGR—Sustainable Growth Rate
SHIEC— Strategic Health Information Exchange Collaborative
SSN—Social Security Number
TBD—To Be Determined
TEFCA— Trusted Exchange Framework and Common Agreement
TPO—Treatment, Payment and Health Care Operations
UPI—Unique Patient Identifier
VA—US Department of Veterans Affairs
VM—Value-based Payment Modifier
WEDI—Workgroup for Electronic Data Interchange
WHO—World Health Organization

Endnotes

Preface

1. Joshua Rubenstein, "Stalin's Children," *New York Times*, November 25, 2007, http://www.nytimes.com/2007/11/25/books/review/Rubenstein-t.html.
2. Justin Huggler, "East German Stasi Files Open to Public Online for First Time," *The Telegraph*, January 9, 2015, http://www.telegraph.co.uk/news/worldnews/europe/germany/11336288/East-German-Stasi-files-open-to-public-online-for-first-time.html.
3. Edwin Black, "IBM and the Holocaust," *New York Times*, October 2000, http://www.nytimes.com/books/first/b/black-ibm.html.
4. Andrei Soldatov and Irina Borogan, "Inside the Red Web: Russia's Back Door onto the Internet—Extract," *The Guardian*, September 8, 2015, https://www.theguardian.com/world/2015/sep/08/red-web-book-russia-internet.
5. The Wedge of Health Freedom was launched by Citizens' Council for Health Freedom on June 28, 2016. More than two hundred and fifty practitioners in forty-six states have already joined The Wedge. They can be located on the "Find a Practice" page at http://www.JoinTheWedge.com.
6. Ralph Grams, "The Obama EHR Experiment," *Journal of Medical Systems* vol. 36, no. 2 (April 2012): 951–6, https://link.springer.com/article/10.1007/s10916-010-9559-z.
7. "144.295 Disclosure of Health Records for External Research," 2017 Minnesota Statutes, https://www.revisor.mn.gov/statutes/?id=144.295.
8. Sheryl Gay Stolberg, "Health Identifier for All Americans Runs Into Hurdles," *New York Times*, July 20, 1998, http://www.nytimes.com/1998/07/20/us/health-identifier-for-all-americans-runs-into-hurdles.html.
9. Gary Hamilton, "Patient Portals: More Than Meets the Eye," *Healthcare IT News*, July 16, 2013, http://www.healthcareitnews.com/blog/patient-portals-more-meets-eye.
10. Jessica Kim Cohen, "Paper Records Are Here to Stay: 4 Questions with Illinois Pain Institute's Dr. John Prunskis," Becker's Health IT & CIO Report, August 9, 2017, http://www.beckershospitalreview.com/healthcare-information-technology/paper-records-are-here-to-stay-4-questions-with-illinois-pain-institute-s-dr-john-prunskis.html.

I. The History of the EHR Mandate

1. Ralph Grams, "The Obama EHR Experiment," *Journal of Medical Systems* vol. 36, no. 2 (April 2012): 951–6, https://link.springer.com/article/10.1007/s10916-010-9559-z.
2. Ibid.
3. Richard Morris, MD, "Electronic Health Records Could Hurt Small Clinics," *StarTribune*, March 26, 2015, http://www.startribune.com/electronic-health-records-could-hurt-small-clinics/297724711/.
4. Stephen T. Parente and Jeffrey S. McCullough, "Health Information Technology and Patient Safety: Evidence from Panel Data," *Health Affairs* vol. 28, no. 2 (March/April 2009): 357-360, https://www.healthaffairs.org/doi/pdf/10.1377/hlthaff.28.2.357.
5. Senthil Selvaraj et al., "Association of Electronic Health Record Use with Quality of Care and Outcomes in Heart Failure: An Analysis of Get with the Guidelines—Heart Failure," *Journal of*

the American Heart Association vol. 7, no. 7 (April 3, 2018), http://jaha.ahajournals.org/content/7/7/e008158.long.

6. "Medicare Program; Merit-Based Incentive Payment System (MIPS) and Alternative Payment Model (APM) Incentive under the Physician Fee Schedule, and Criteria for Physician-Focused Payment Models, Final Rule with Comment Period," Centers for Medicare & Medicaid Services, *Federal Register* vol. 81, no. 214 (November 4, 2016): 77532, https://www.federalregister.gov/documents/2016/11/04/2016-25240/medicare-program-merit-based-incentive-payment-system-mips-and-alternative-payment-model-apm.

7. Jennifer Bresnick, "EHR Adoption, Health IT Use Improve Patient Safety, ONC Says," *HealthITAnalytics* (blog), April 28, 2015, http://healthitanalytics.com/news/ehr-adoption-health-it-use-improve-patient-safety-onc-says.

8. Ibid.

9. Fred Schulte and Emma Schwartz, "FDA, Obama Digital Medical Records Team at Odds Over Safety Oversight," *HuffPost* (blog), last updated December 26, 2017, http://www.huffingtonpost.com/2010/08/04/fda-obama-digital-medical_n_670036.html.

10. Bresnick.

11. Hayward K. Zwerling, MD, "A Time Out for Health IT?" *The Health Care Blog*, March 17, 2013, http://thehealthcareblog.com/blog/2013/03/17/commentology-a-time-out-for-the-federal-promotion-of-health-information-technology/.

12. Richard I. Cook, MD, "Dissenting Statement: Health IT Is a Class III Medical Device," in *Health IT and Patient Safety: Building Safer Systems for Better Care* (prepublication copy), (Washington, D.C.: National Academies Press, 2012), E-3, http://www.ischool.drexel.edu/faculty/ssilverstein/Patient%20Safety%20and%20Health%20IT%20prepub.pdf.

13. "Testimony of Jeffrey Shuren, Director of FDA's Center for Devices and Radiological Health," Health Information Technology (HIT) Policy Committee Adoption/Certification Workgroup, February 25, 2010, http://www.cchfreedom.org/cchf.php/597.

14. Bernie Monegain, "New CMS Rules May Spur EHR Uptake," *Healthcare IT News*, July 22, 2015, http://www.healthcareitnews.com/news/long-term-cares-digital-moment.

15. "2017 Medicare Electronic Health Record (EHR) Incentive Program Payment Adjustment Fact Sheet for Eligible Professionals," Centers for Medicare & Medicaid Services, last updated October 2017, https://www.cms.gov/Regulations-and-Guidance/Legislation/EHRIncentivePrograms/Downloads/PaymentAdj_EPTipsheet.pdf.

16. Chun-Ju Hsiao, PhD, MHS, et al., "Trends in Electronic Health Record System Use Among Office-Based Physicians: United States, 2007–2012," National Health Statistics Reports, Centers for Disease Control and Prevention, US Department of Health & Human Services, no. 75, May 20, 2014, 5, https://www.cdc.gov/nchs/data/nhsr/nhsr075.pdf.

17. Evan Sweeney, "Researchers: Meaningful Use Legislation Led to a 'Substantial Change' in EHR Adoption," FierceHealthcare, August 8, 2017, http://www.fiercehealthcare.com/ehr/researchers-hitech-act-was-a-driving-force-behind-ehr-adoption.

18. Arthur Allen, "Why Health Care IT Is Still on Life Support," *Politico*, June 11, 2015, http://www.politico.com/magazine/story/2015/06/electronic-medical-records-doctors-118881.html#.VZwZ7-vhLhN.

19. Kenneth D. Mandl, MD, MPH, and Isaac S. Kohane, MD, PhD, "Escaping the EHR Trap—The Future of Health IT," *New England Journal of Medicine* vol. 366 (June 14, 2012): 2240–2, http://www.nejm.org/doi/full/10.1056/NEJMp1203102#t=article.

20. Anthony Brino, "Briefs: TriCare Awards EHR Contract, Peak 10 HIPAA Cloud, EHR Patient Safety," *Healthcare IT News*, November 8, 2012, http://www.healthcareitnews.com/news/news-brief-tricare-awards-ehr-contract-peak-10-hipaa-compliant-cloud-ehr-patient-safety.

21. Margalit Gur-Arie, "How to Put EHRs Back on the Right Track," *KevinMD* (blog), December 24, 2015, http://www.kevinmd.com/blog/2015/12/put-ehrs-back-right-track.html?utm_content=bufferf01fc&utm_

medium=social&utm_source=twitter.com&utm_campaign=buffer.

22. Neil Versel, "Podcast: Scot Silverstein Talks Health IT Safety Risks," Meaningful HIT News, October 20, 2014, http://www.meaningfulhitnews.com/2014/10/20/podcast-scot-silverstein-talks-health-it-safety-risks/.

23. "2016 Survey of America's Physicians Practice Patterns & Perspectives," The Physicians Foundation, 2016, 8, https://physiciansfoundation.org/wp-content/uploads/2018/01/Biennial_Physician_Survey_2016.pdf.

24. "Healthcare IT Delirium," *Health Care Renewal* (blog), January 20, 2011, http://hcrenewal.blogspot.com/2011/01/healthcare-it-delirium.html.

25. Kevin James Shay, "Contractors Hungry for Stimulus," *The Gazette*, July 24, 2009, http://ww2.gazette.net/stories/07242009/businew181942_32521.shtml.

26. Adrian Gropper, MD, "Why and How Secretary Sebelius Should Avoid a Network Monopoly," *The Health Care Blog*, March 5, 2009, http://thehealthcareblog.com/blog/2009/03/05/why-and-how-secretary-sebelius-should-avoid-a-network-monopoly/.

27. Robert O'Harrow Jr., "The Machinery Behind Health-Care Reform," *Washington Post*, May 16, 2009, http://www.washingtonpost.com/wp-dyn/content/article/2009/05/15/AR2009051503667.html.

28. Sreedhar Potarazu, "What Obamacare Is Missing," CNN, August 18, 2016, http://www.cnn.com/2016/08/18/opinions/reforming-obamacare-potarazu/index.html.

29. O'Harrow.

30. Donna Marbury, "Are EHRs Delivering on Expectations," *Managed Healthcare Executive*, March 30, 2016, http://managedhealthcareexecutive.modernmedicine.com/managed-healthcare-executive/news/are-ehrs-delivering-expectations?cfcache=true.

31. Chris Mazzolini, "Tips on How to Put Patients before Electronic Paperwork," *Medical Economics*, October 25, 2017, http://medicaleconomics.modernmedicine.com/medical-economics/news/tips-put-patients-electronic-paperwork.

32. Arthur Allen, "Rucker Suggests ONC Policy," Politico Morning eHealth, June 12, 2017, http://www.politico.com/tipsheets/morning-ehealth/2017/06/12/rucker-suggests-onc-policy-220790.

33. Howard Green, MD, "EMR and EHR Buyers Beware Deceptive Sales," LinkedIn, December 9, 2016, https://www.linkedin.com/pulse/emr-buyer-beware-howard-green-md/.

34. Hal Scherz, MD, "Romney's Healthcare Land Mines," *Townhall*, July 3, 2012, https://townhall.com/columnists/halscherz/2012/07/03/romneys-healthcare-land-mines-n1112733.

35. Robert A. Heverly, "Technology Raises Risk of Tyranny," *Los Angeles Times*, December 5, 2002, http://articles.latimes.com/2002/dec/05/opinion/oe-heverly5.

36. Kathryn M. McDonald, MM, et al., "Chapter 4, Emerging Trends in Care Coordination Measurement," in "Care Coordination Measures Atlas Update," Agency for Healthcare Research and Quality, US Department of Health & Human Services, last updated June 2014, http://www.ahrq.gov/professionals/prevention-chronic-care/improve/coordination/atlas2014/chapter4.html.

37. Adam Tanner, "How Data Brokers Make Money off Your Medical Records," *Scientific American*, February 1, 2016, http://www.scientificamerican.com/article/how-data-brokers-make-money-off-your-medical-records/.

38. Nicholas Terry, "Protecting Patient Privacy in the Age of Big Data," Indiana University Robert H. McKinney School of Law Research Paper No. 2013-04; *University of Missouri-Kansas City Law Review* vol. 81, no. 2 (September 27 2012), https://papers.ssrn.com/sol3/papers.cfm?abstract_id=2153269.

39. Richard Sobel, "The HIPAA Paradox: The Privacy Rule That's Not," *Hastings Center Report* 37, no. 4 (July/August 2007), http://pipatl.org/data/library/HIPAAparadox.pdf.

40. "What Is the Difference between a Personal Health Record, an Electronic Health Record, and an Electronic Medical Record?" The Office of the National

Coordinator of Health Information Technology, n.d., http://www.healthit.gov/patients-families/faqs/what-difference-between-personal-health-record-and-electronic-health-record-a.

41. "Health IT Terms," The Office of the National Coordinator of Health Information Technology, last updated January 15, 2013, https://www.healthit.gov/policy-researchers-implementers/glossary.

42. "Trend Watch: The Road to Meaningful Use: What It Takes to Implement Electronic Health Record Systems," American Hospital Association, April 2010, 4. Former access to 16-page document: http://webcache.googleusercontent.com/search?client=safari&rls=en&q=cache:zGVLhKG5f_IJ:http://www.aha.org/research/reports/tw/10apr-tw-HITmeanuse.pdf%2Btrendwatch+sample+workflow+order+before&oe=UTF-8&hl=en&&ct=clnk.

43. "Health Information Exchange (HIE): What is HIE?" Healthcare Information and Management Systems Society (HIMSS), n.d., http://www.himss.org/health-information-exchange.

44. "Health Information Exchange (HIE): Meaningful Use and Health Information Exchange," Healthcare Information and Management Systems Society (HIMSS), n.d., http://www.himss.org/library/health-information-exchange/toolkit%3FnavItemNumber%3D16137.

45. Chanley T. Howell et al., "Stimulus Package Contains $19 Billion for Health Care Technology Spending and Adoption of Electronic Health Records," Foley & Lardner LLP, February 18, 2009, https://www.foley.com/stimulus-package-contains-19-billion-for-health-care-technology-spending-and-adoption-of-electronic-health-records-02-18-2009/.

46. "Defining Key Health Information Technology Terms: The National Alliance for Health Information Technology Report to the Office of the National Coordinator for Health Information Technology," National Alliance for Health Information Technology and US Department of Health & Human Services, April 28, 2008, 6, http://www.hitechanswers.net/wp-content/uploads/2013/05/NAHIT-Definitions2008.pdf.

47. Gary Brown et al., "Final Project—Health Information Exchange: Technology, Challenges & Opportunities," (PowerPoint presentation, MMI 402, Fall 2013, 6), http://kazirussell.weebly.com/uploads/5/2/8/9/52894915/russell_group_final.pptx.

48. "Defining Key Health Information Technology Terms," 5.

49. "Health IT Terms."

50. Gerard Castro, PhD, MPH, et al., "Investigations of Health IT-Related Deaths, Serious Injuries or Unsafe Conditions: Final Report," The Joint Commission, March 30, 2015, 10, https://www.healthit.gov/sites/default/files/safer/pdfs/Investigations_HealthIT_related_SE_Report_033015.pdf.

51. "Personal Health Records: What Health Care Providers Need to Know," Office of the National Coordinator for Health Information Technology, n.d., https://www.healthit.gov/sites/default/files/about-phrs-for-providers-011311.pdf.

52. Marla Durben Hirsch, "Should the DoD Be Entitled to Its Own Definition of Interoperability?" FierceHealthcare, November 24, 2015, http://www.fierceemr.com/story/should-dod-be-entitled-its-own-definition-interoperability/2015-11-24.

53. Vangie Beal, "Cloud Computing," Webopedia, n.d., https://www.webopedia.com/TERM/C/cloud_computing.html.

54. "What is the Cloud?—Definition" SDxCentral, n.d., https://www.sdxcentral.com/cloud/definitions/what-is-cloud/.

55. Kenneth D. Mandl, MD, MPH, and Isaac S. Kohane, MD, PhD, "Escaping the EHR Trap—The Future of Health IT," *New England Journal of Medicine* vol. 366 (June 14, 2012): 2240-2, http://www.nejm.org/doi/full/10.1056/NEJMp1203102#t=article.

56. Stephen Goundrey-Smith, "What Every Pharmacist Needs to Know about Using Electronic Health Records," *The Pharmaceutical Journal* vol. 289 (November 7, 2012): 533, http://www.pharmaceutical-journal.com/news-and-analysis/news/what-every-

pharmacist-needs-to-know-about-using-electronic-health-records/11110907.article.

57. Christopher Snowbeck, "Mayo Rolls Out Big Health Record Project," *Star Tribune*, September 15, 2007, http://m.startribune.com/mayo-rolls-out-big-health-record-project/444757193/.

58. Prince K. Zachariah, MD, "Automation of the Clinical Practice: Cost-Effective and Efficient Health Care," National Center for Biotechnology Information, in *Building a Better Delivery System: A New Engineering/Health Care Partnership* (Washington, D.C.: National Academies Press, 2005), http://www.ncbi.nlm.nih.gov/books/NBK22856/.

59. Lawrence R. Huntoon, MD, PhD, "The Disaster of Electronic Health Records," *Journal of American Physicians and Surgeons* vol. 21, no. 2 (2016): 35–7, http://www.jpands.org/vol21no2/huntoon.pdf.

60. H.R. 3600, Health Security Act, Congressman Richard Gephardt, November 20, 1993, US Government Publishing Office, http://www.gpo.gov/fdsys/pkg/BILLS-103hr3600ih/pdf/BILLS-103hr3600ih.pdf.

61. Paul Starr, "The Signing of the Kennedy-Kassebaum Bill," Princeton University, August 22, 1996, https://www.princeton.edu/~starr/articles/signing.html.

62. Akanksha Jayanthi, "10 Things to Know about WEDI," Becker's Health IT & CIO Report, September 15, 2015, https://www.beckershospitalreview.com/healthcare-information-technology/10-things-to-know-about-wedi.html.

63. "WEDI Presents Testimony to HHS National Committee on Vital and Health Statistics," Workgroup for Electronic Data Interchange, June 1, 2017, https://www.wedi.org/news/press-releases/2017/06/01/wedi-presents-testimony-to-hhs-national-committee-on-vital-and-health-statistics.

64. Jim Daley, Chairman, WEDI, "WEDI Update" (presented to the National Committee on Vital and Health Statistics Subcommittee on Standards, June 17, 2013), The National Committee on Vital and Health Statistics, May 2015, https://www.ncvhs.hhs.gov/wp-content/uploads/2014/05/130617p1.pdf.

65. Ibid.

66. Laura Levit et al., "HIPAA, the Privacy Rule, and Its Application to Health Research," National Center for Biotechnology Information, in *Beyond the HIPAA Privacy Rule: Enhancing Privacy, Improving Health Through Research* (Washington, D.C.: National Academies Press, 2009), chap. 4, https://www.ncbi.nlm.nih.gov/books/NBK9573/.

67. "Administrative Simplification," Section 262, Health Insurance Portability and Accountability Act of 1996, Public Law No. 104-191, 110 Stat. 1936 (August 21, 1996), https://www.gpo.gov/fdsys/pkg/PLAW-104publ191/pdf/PLAW-104publ191.pdf.

68. Goundrey-Smith.

69. Levit et al.

70. "Confidentiality of Individually Identifiable Health Information: Recommendations of the Secretary of Health and Human Services, pursuant to section 264 of the Health Insurance Portability and Accountability Act of 1996," Office of the Assistant Secretary for Planning and Evaluation, US Department of Health & Human Services, September 11, 1997, https://aspe.hhs.gov/report/confidentiality-individually-identifiable-health-information.

71. "Standards for Privacy of Individually Identifiable Health Information; Final Rule," Part V, US Department of Health & Human Services, *Federal Register* vol. 67, no. 157 (August 14, 2002): 53182–3, https://www.gpo.gov/fdsys/pkg/FR-2002-08-14/pdf/02-20554.pdf.

72. "Summary of the HIPAA Privacy Rule," US Department of Health & Human Services, last reviewed July 26, 2013, https://www.hhs.gov/hipaa/for-professionals/privacy/laws-regulations/index.html.

73. "Summary of the HIPAA Privacy Rule," OCR Privacy Brief, US Department of Health & Human Services, last revised May 2003, https://www.hhs.gov/sites/default/files/privacysummary.pdf.

74. "Standards for Privacy of Individually Identifiable Health Information; Final Rule," Part II, (45 CFR Parts 160 and 164), US Department of Health & Human Services, *Federal Register* vol. 65, no. 250 (December 28, 2000): 82463, http://www.

hhs.gov/sites/default/files/ocr/privacy/hipaa/administrative/privacyrule/prdecember2000all8parts.pdf.

75. "§1711-C. Confidentiality of Health Care Information," Title 22, Subtitle 2, Part 4, Chapter 401, Maine Revised Statutes, revised 2013 (c 289, §2), http://legislature.maine.gov/legis/statutes/22/title22sec1711-C.html.

76. "Professions, Occupations, and Business Operations: (225 ILCS 60/) Medical Practice Act of 1987," Illinois General Assembly, n.d., http://www.ilga.gov/legislation/ILCS/ilcs3.asp?ActID=1309&ChapterID=24.

77. "Hippocratic Oath," *Encyclopaedia Britannica*, last updated November 15, 2017, http://www.britannica.com/topic/Hippocratic-oath.

78. "Text of President Bush's 2004 State of the Union Address," *Washington Post*, January 20, 2004, http://www.washingtonpost.com/wp-srv/politics/transcripts/bushtext_012004.html.

79. O'Harrow.

80. Blackford Middleton, MD, MPH, "Assessing Value/Calculating ROI," The Health Information Technology Summit (PowerPoint presentation, The PreConference II Symposium, Washington D.C., October 20, 2004), 15-46, http://www.hitsummit.com/past1/agenda/index.html.

81. George W. Bush, President of the United States of America, "Executive Order 13335—Incentives for the Use of Health Information Technology and Establishing the Position of the National Health Information Technology Coordinator," The American Presidency Project, April 27, 2004, http://www.presidency.ucsb.edu/ws/?pid=61429.

82. Carolyn Clancy, MD, "Accelerating the Adoption of Health Information Technology: Testimony Before the Senate Committee on Commerce, Science, and Transportation Subcommittee on Technology, Innovation, and Competitiveness," Agency for Healthcare Research and Quality, US Department of Health & Human Services, June 21, 2006, https://archive.ahrq.gov/news/test062106.htm; see also C. Stephen Redhead, "The Health Information Technology for Economic and Clinical Health (HITECH) Act," Congressional Research Service, February 23, 2009, https://digital.library.unt.edu/ark:/67531/metadc743451/m1/1/high_res_d/R40161_2009Feb23.pdf.

83. Margaret Rouse, "CCHIT—Certification Commission for Healthcare Information Technology," SearchHealthIT, last updated January 2010, http://searchhealthit.techtarget.com/definition/CCHIT; see also Micky Tripathi, "EHR Evolution: Policy and Legislation Forces Changing the EHR," *Journal of AHIMA* vol. 83, no. 10 (October 2010): 24-29, http://library.ahima.org/doc?oid=105689#.WprtiGaZPGZ.

84. "Leading Health Care and Information Technology Groups Endorse Common Framework for Health Information Exchange to Support Improvements in Health and Healthcare." The Markle Foundation, January 18, 2005, http://www.markle.org/sites/default/files/press_release_11805.pdf.

85. O'Harrow.

86. Jeffrey Rideout, "The Impact of Healthcare Costs for American Companies," Competitive Financial Operations: The CFO Project, n.d., 124–7, http://www.mthink.com/legacy/www.cfoproject.com/content/pdf/cfo3_4_124_wp_cisco_rideout.pdf.

87. Steve Lohr, "Road Map to a Digital System of Health Records," *New York Times*, January 19, 2005, https://www.nytimes.com/2005/01/19/technology/road-map-to-a-digital-system-of-health-records.html.

88. Jan Walker et al., "The Value of Health Care Information Exchange and Interoperability," *Health Affairs*, January 2005, http://www.providersedge.com/ehdocs/ehr_articles/The_Value_Of_Health_Care_Information_Exchange_And_Interoperability.pdf.

89. "Secretary Leavitt Takes New Steps to Advance Health IT," US Department of Health & Human Services, June 6, 2005, https://archive.hhs.gov/news/press/2005pres/20050606.html.

90. "HIMSS Summit: HHS Secretary Michael Leavitt Announces Formation of American Health Information Community (AHIC)," Healthcare

Information and Management Systems Society (HIMSS), June 6, 2005, http://www.himss.org/news/himss-summit-hhs-secretary-michael-leavitt-announces-formation-american-health-information-community.

91. "Secretary Leavitt Takes New Steps to Advance Health IT."

92. "RAND Study Says Computerizing Medical Records Could Save $81 Billion Annually and Improve the Quality of Medical Care," RAND Corporation, September 14, 2005, http://www.rand.org/news/press/2005/09/14.html.

93. Arthur L. Kellermann and Spencer S. Jones, "What It Will Take to Achieve the As-Yet-Unfulfilled Promises of Health Information Technology," *Health Affairs* vol. 32, no. 1 (2013): 63–8, http://content.healthaffairs.org/content/32/1/63.full.pdf+html.

94. C. Stephen Redhead, "The Health Information Technology for Economic and Clinical Health (HITECH) Act," Congressional Research Service, February 23, 2009, 7, https://digital.library.unt.edu/ark:/67531/metadc743451/m1/1/high_res_d/R40161_2009Feb23.pdf.

95. "What Is EHR Interoperability and Why Is It Important?" The Office of the National Coordinator of Health Information Technology, US Department of Health & Human Services, last updated January 15, 2013, https://www.healthit.gov/providers-professionals/faqs/what-ehr-interoperability-and-why-it-important; see also "Connecting Health and Care for the Nation, A Shared Nationwide Interoperability Roadmap," Supplemental Materials, Version 1.0, The Office of the National Coordinator for Health Information Technology, US Department of Health & Human Services, n.d., 23, https://www.healthit.gov/sites/default/files/hie-interoperability/Interoperibility-Road-Map-Supplemental.pdf.

96. "Physician Quality Reporting Initiative: 2007 Reporting Experience," Centers for Medicare & Medicaid Services, December 3, 2008, https://www.cms.gov/Medicare/Quality-Initiatives-Patient-Assessment-Instruments/PQRS/downloads/pqri2007reportfinal12032008csg.pdf.

97. Medicare Improvements for Patients and Providers Act of 2008, Public Law No. 110-275, 122 Stat. 2494 (July 15, 2008), http://www.gpo.gov/fdsys/pkg/PLAW-110publ275/pdf/PLAW-110publ275.pdf.

98. "What's a Medicare Advantage Plan?" Centers for Medicare & Medicaid Services, revised April 2015, https://www.medicare.gov/Pubs/pdf/11474.pdf.

99. David Stout, "Congress Overrides Bush's Veto on Medicare," *New York Times*, July 16, 2008, http://www.nytimes.com/2008/07/16/washington/16medic.html.

100. "HHS Performance Measurement," National Quality Forum, n.d., http://www.qualityforum.org/About_NQF/HHS_Performance_Measurement.aspx.

101. "Medicare Improvements for Patients and Providers Act of 2008."

102. Redhead, 8.

103. "What Is the Physician Quality Reporting System?" APA Practice Organization, n.d., http://www.apapracticecentral.org/medicare/pqrs/faqs/index.aspx.

104. "Electronic Prescribing: CMS Should Address Inconsistencies in its Two Incentive Programs that Encourage the Use of Health Information Technology," US Government Accountability Office, GAO-11-159, February 17, 2011, 13, http://www.gao.gov/assets/320/315816.html.

105. "The ONC-Coordinated Federal Health Information Technology Strategic Plan: 2008–2012: Synopsis," Office of the National Coordinator for Health Information Technology, US Department of Health & Human Services, June 3, 2008, https://www.healthit.gov/sites/default/files/hit-strategic-plan-summary-508-2.pdf.

106. Tom Daschle, *Critical: What We Can Do About the Health-Care Crisis* (New York: Thomas Dunn Books, St. Martin's Press: 2008), 163.

107. "Obama and McCain Support Health IT Adoption," HIPAA and Health Information Technology, Fox Rothchild LLP, September 30, 2008, https://hipaahealthlaw.foxrothschild.com/2008/09/articles/hit-health-information-technol/obama-and-mccain-support-health-it-adoption/.

108. O'Harrow.

109. O'Harrow.

110. "Medicare EHR Incentive Program Payment Adjustments: What Providers Need to Know," Centers for Medicare & Medicaid Services, last updated May 2013, https://www.cms.gov/Regulations-and-Guidance/Legislation/EHRIncentivePrograms/Downloads/How_Payment_Adj_Affect_ProvidersTipsheet.pdf.

111. American Recovery and Reinvestment Act of 2009, Public Law No. 111-5, 123 Stat. 115 (February 17, 2009), https://www.gpo.gov/fdsys/pkg/PLAW-111publ5/pdf/PLAW-111publ5.pdf.

112. "A 21st Century Roadmap for Advancing America's Health: The Path from Peril to Progress," The Commission on U.S. Federal Leadership in Health and Medicine: Charting Future Directions, Center for the Study of the Presidency and Congress, May 2010, 10, http://susan-blumenthal.org/wp-content/uploads/2015/07/Health-Report-Presidential-commission.pdf.

113. O'Harrow.

114. Dustin Charles, MPH, et al., "Adoption of Electronic Health Record Systems Among US Non-Federal Acute Care Hospitals, 2008-2014," ONC Data Brief, Office of the National Coordinator for Health Information Technology, US Department of Health & Human Services, April 2015, https://www.healthit.gov/sites/default/files/data-brief/2014HospitalAdoptionDataBrief.pdf.

115. Stephen Soumerai and Tony Avery, "Don't Repeat the UK's Electronic Health Records Failure," *HuffPost* (blog), December 1, 2010, updated May 25, 2011, https://www.huffingtonpost.com/stephen-soumerai/dont-repeat-the-uks-elect_b_790470.html.

116. Ibid.

117. Margaret Rouse, "CCHIT—Certification Commission for Healthcare Information Technology," SearchHealthIT, last updated January 2010, http://searchhealthit.techtarget.com/definition/CCHIT.

118. Darrell K. Prutt, DDS, "An Open Letter on EMRs from Hayward Zwerling, MD," Medical Executive Post, January 25, 2009, https://medicalexecutivepost.com/2009/01/25/an-open-letter-on-emrs-from-hayward-zwerling-md/.

119. Kevin James Shay, "Contractors Hungry for Stimulus," *Gazette*, July 24, 2009, http://ww2.gazette.net/stories/07242009/businew181942_32521.shtml.

120. O'Harrow.

121. These ideas are further discussed by O'Harrow and Shay—and also in: Adrian Gropper, MD, "Why and How Secretary Sebelius Should Avoid a Network Monopoly," *The Health Care Blog*, March 5, 2009, http://thehealthcareblog.com/blog/2009/03/05/why-and-how-secretary-sebelius-should-avoid-a-network-monopoly/.

122. American Recovery and Reinvestment Act of 2009, Sections 3002, 228, and 234.

123. "Health Information Technology for Economic and Clinical Health Act," Section 3002, The American Recovery and Reinvestment Act of 2009 Public Law 111-5, 123 Stat. 115 (February 17, 2009): 240, https://www.gpo.gov/fdsys/pkg/PLAW-111publ5/pdf/PLAW-111publ5.pdf

124. Ibid., 228.

125. "Electronic Health Record Adoption and Utilization: 2012 Highlights and Accomplishments," Office of the National Coordinator for Health Information Technology, September 2012, https://www.healthit.gov/sites/default/files/highlights_accomplishments_ehr_adoptionsummer2012_2.pdf.

126. American Recovery and Reinvestment Act of 2009, 470.

127. "Modifications to the HIPAA Privacy, Security, and Enforcement Rules under the Health Information Technology for Economic and Clinical Health Act," US Department of Health & Human Services, *Federal Register* vol. 75, no. 134 (July 14, 2010): 40869, https://www.gpo.gov/fdsys/pkg/FR-2010-07-14/pdf/2010-16718.pdf.

128. Kate Goodrich, MD, MHS, "Electronic Health Records Incentive Programs," *The CMS Blog*, December 30, 2015, http://blog.cms.gov/2015/12/.

129. Ibid.

130. "What Is the Physician Quality Reporting System?" APA Practice Organization, n.d., http://www.apapracticecentral.org/medicare/pqrs/faqs/index.aspx.

131. "Changes for Calendar Year 2014 Physician Quality Programs and the Value-Based Payment Modifier," Centers for Medicare & Medicaid Services, November 27, 2013, https://www.cms.gov/Newsroom/MediaReleaseDatabase/Fact-sheets/2013-Fact-sheets-items/2013-11-27.html.

132. "2016 Physician Quality Reporting System (PQRS): Registry Reporting Made Simple." Centers for Medicare & Medicaid Services, June 2016, https://www.cms.gov/Medicare/Quality-Initiatives-Patient-Assessment-Instruments/PQRS/Downloads/2016PQRS_Registry_MadeSimple.pdf.

133. "Changes for Calendar Year 2014 Physician Quality Programs and the Value-Based Payment Modifier."

134. "Proposed Policy, Payment, And Quality Provisions Changes to the Medicare Physician Fee Schedule for Calendar Year 2016," Centers for Medicare & Medicaid Services, July 8, 2015, https://www.cms.gov/newsroom/mediareleasedatabase/fact-sheets/2015-fact-sheets-items/2015-07-08.html.

135. "2013 Physician Quality Reporting System (PQRS): 2015 PQRS Payment Adjustment," Centers for Medicare & Medicaid Services, August 2013, https://www.cms.gov/Medicare/Quality-Initiatives-Patient-Assessment-Instruments/PQRS/Downloads/2013MLNSE13_AvoidingPQRSPaymentAdjustment_083013.pdf.

136. "Proposals for the Physician Value-Based Payment Modifier Under the Medicare Physician Fee Schedule: CMS National Provider Call," Centers for Medicare & Medicaid Services, August 1, 2012, https://www.cms.gov/Outreach-and-Education/Outreach/NPC/Downloads/8-1-12-VBPM-NPC-Presentation.pdf.

137. "Value-based Payment Modifier," American Academy of Family Physicians, n.d., http://www.aafp.org/practice-management/regulatory/vbpm.html.

138. "Value-based Payment Modifier"; see also "Value-Based Payment Modifier Resource Center," MGMA, n.d., https://www.mgma.com/government-affairs/issues-overview/federal-quality-reporting-programs/value-based-payment-modifer-resource-center.

139. "2018 Value Modifier Results," Centers for Medicare & Medicaid Services, January 12, 2018, https://www.cms.gov/Medicare/Medicare-Fee-for-Service-Payment/PhysicianFeedbackProgram/Downloads/2018-Value-Based-Payment-Modifier-Factsheet.pdf.

140. "Proposed Policy, Payment, and Quality Provisions Changes to the Medicare Physician Fee Schedule for Calendar Year 2016"; see also "Value-Based Payment Modifier Resource Center."

141. Harold Gibson, "PQRS vs. Meaningful Use, What's the Difference?" M-Scribe, October 8, 2013, http://www.m-scribe.com/blog/bid/316297/PQRS-vs-Meaningful-Use-What-s-The-Difference.

142. "Medicare Program: Revisions to Payment Policies Under the Physician Fee Schedule, DME Face-to-Face Encounters, Elimination of the Requirement for Termination of Non-Random Prepayment Complex Medical Review and Other Revisions to Part B for CY 2013; Final Rule," Part II, Centers for Medicare & Medicaid Services, *Federal Register* vol. 77, No. 222 (November 16, 2012): 69339, https://www.gpo.gov/fdsys/pkg/FR-2012-11-16/pdf/2012-26900.pdf.

143. "Value-Based Payment Modifier," Centers for Medicare & Medicaid Services, last modified September 2017, https://www.cms.gov/Medicare/Medicare-Fee-for-Service-Payment/PhysicianFeedbackProgram/ValueBasedPaymentModifier.html.

144. "Medicare Program: Revisions to Payment Policies Under the Physician Fee Schedule, DME Face-to-Face Encounters," 69185.

145. "Medicare Program; Revisions to Payment Policies Under the Physician Fee Schedule, Clinical Laboratory Fee Schedule, Access to Identifiable Data for the Center for Medicare and Medicaid Innovation Models & Other Revisions to Part B for CY 2015, Final Rule with Comment Period," Centers for Medicare & Medicaid Services, *Federal Register* vol. 79, no. 219 (November 13, 2014): 67553, https://www.federalregister.gov/articles/2014/11/13/2014-26183/medicare-program-revisions-to-payment-policies-under-the-physician-fee-schedule-clinical-laboratory.

146. John Commins, "Processing Quality Measures Cost $40K Per Physician Per Year," *HealthLeaders* Media, March 9, 2016, http://www.healthleadersmedia.com/physician-leaders/processing-quality-measures-costs-40k-physician-year.

147. Dennis Whalen, "Focusing on the Measures that Matter to Advance Quality Improvement in Healthcare," Healthcare Association of New York State, January 14, 2016, http://www.hanys.org/news/?date=2016-01-14.

148. "Measures That Matter," Healthcare Association of New York State, n.d., http://www.hanys.org/quality/clinical_operational_oversight/measures_that_matter/docs/mtm_report.pdf.

149. Commins.

150. Ken Terry, "CMS to Stress Outcomes Over Process in Quality Reporting," Medscape, November 1, 2017, https://www.medscape.com/viewarticle/887917.

151. Commins.

152. Ibid.

153. Lynn Bentson, MD, November 6, 2013, comment on Robert A. Berenson, MD, and Deborah R. Kaye, MD, "Grading a Physician's Value—The Misapplication of Performance Measurement," *New England Journal of Medicine*, November 28, 2013, https://www.nejm.org/doi/full/10.1056/NEJMp1312287?activeTab=comments&page=6#article_comments.

154. Scott Jensen, MD, *Relationship Matters: The Foundation of Medical Care Is Fracturing* (Amazon Digital Services, 2015), 206.

155. The Patient Protection and Affordable Care Act of 2010, Section 1311(h)(1)(b).

156. US Rep. Phil Gringrey (R-GA), "SCOPE Act: Protecting the Physician-Patient Relationship," *National Review*, October 24, 2012, http://www.nationalreview.com/critical-condition/331574/scope-act-protecting-physician-patient-relationship-phil-gingrey#.

157. Commins.

158. TAMMM News, "Optum, Inc. Makes Big Moves Since Rising from the Ashes of UnitedHealth Group's Infamous Ingenix," The American Medical Money Machine, June 23, 2015, http://www.theamericanmedicalmoneymachine.com/optum-inc-makes-big-moves-since-rising-from-the-ashes-of-unitedhealth-groups-infamous-ingenix/.

159. Avery Johnson, "Reforms Prod Insurers to Diversify," *Wall Street Journal*, May 12, 2011, https://www.wsj.com/articles/SB10001424052748703643104576291022457851278.

160. O'Harrow.

161. "HIMSS Membership," Healthcare Information and Management Systems Society, n.d., http://www.himss.org/membership; see also "Corporate Member Directory," Healthcare Information and Management Systems Society, n.d., http://marketplace.himss.org/CompanyDirectory/Corporate/.

162. O'Harrow.

II. Congress Seizes Control of the Exam Room

1. "State Breakdown of Payments to Medicare and Medicaid Providers through March 31, 2017," Data and Program Reports, EHR Incentive Program, Centers for Medicare & Medicaid Services, http://www.cms.gov/Regulations-and-Guidance/Legislation/EHRIncentivePrograms/DataAndReports.html.

2. Heather Landi, "Report: Meaningful Use Payments Total $34.7 Billion," Healthcare Informatics, June 27, 2016, https://www.healthcare-informatics.com/news-item/report-meaningful-use-payments-total-347-billion.

3. "Medicare Advantage Electronic Health Record (EHR) Incentive Program," EHR Incentive Program, Centers for Medicare & Medicaid, n.d., https://www.cms.gov/Regulations-and-Guidance/Legislation/EHRIncentivePrograms/Downloads/MedicareAdvantageFAQSheet.pdf.

4. "Medicare & Medicaid EHR Incentive Program: Meaningful Use Stage 1 Requirements Overview" (PowerPoint presentation, Centers for Medicare & Medicaid Services, 2010), https://www.cms.gov/Regulations-and-Guidance/Legislation/EHRIncentivePrograms/downloads/MU_Stage1_ReqOverview.pdf.

5. "EHR Incentive Program for Medicare Hospitals: Calculating Payments," Centers for Medicare & Medicaid Services, last updated May 2013, http://www.cms.gov/Regulations-and-Guidance/Legislation/EHRIncentivePrograms/Downloads/MLN_TipSheet_MedicareHospitals.pdf.

6. "Incentive Payments," The American Recovery and Reinvestment Act of 2009, Subtitle A—Medicare Incentives, Section 4101(a), Public Law No. 111-5, 123 Stat. 115 (February 17, 2009): 467, https://www.gpo.gov/fdsys/pkg/PLAW-111publ5/pdf/PLAW-111publ5.pdf.

7. "Medicare and Medicaid EHR Incentive Program Basics," Centers for Medicare & Medicaid Services, last modified February 6, 2018, https://www.cms.gov/regulations-and-guidance/legislation/ehrincentiveprograms/basics.html.

8. Arthur Allen, "High Noon for Federal Health Records Program?" Politico Pro, December 28, 2014, http://www.politico.com/story/2014/12/federal-health-records-program-113787.

9. Joel Dziengielewski and Margaret J. Davino, "Mergers and Acquisitions in Healthcare on the Rise: Legal and Compliance Issues," The American Health Lawyers, n.d., https://webcache.googleusercontent.com/search?q=cache:pKbNsCTBIjgJ:https://www.healthlawyers.org/find-a-resource/HealthLawHub/Documents/Compliance/FC15_davino_dziengielewski.docx+&cd=6&hl=en&ct=clnk&gl=us&client=safari.

10. Donna Marbury, "Are EHRs Delivering on Expectations," *Managed Healthcare Executive*, March 30, 2016, http://managedhealthcareexecutive.modernmedicine.com/managed-healthcare-executive/news/are-ehrs-delivering-expectations?cfcache=true.

11. Ben-Tzion Karsh et al., "Health Information Technology: Fallacies and Sober Realities," *Journal of the American Medical Informatics Association* vol. 17, no. 6 (Nov-Dec 2010): 617–23, https://www.ncbi.nlm.nih.gov/pmc/articles/PMC3000760/.

12. Marbury.

13. American Recovery and Reinvestment Act of 2009, Public Law No. 111-5, 123 Stat. 115 (February 17, 2009), https://www.gpo.gov/fdsys/pkg/PLAW-111publ5/pdf/PLAW-111publ5.pdf.

14. "Electronic Health Records (EHR) Incentive Programs," Centers for Medicare & Medicaid Services, last modified Februrary 28, 2018, https://www.cms.gov/Regulations-and-Guidance/Legislation/EHRIncentivePrograms/index.html?redirect=/EHRIncentivePrograms.

15. "Medicare & Medicaid EHR Incentive Program: Meaningful Use Stage 1 Requirements Overview."

16. Ralph Grams, "The Obama EHR Experiment," *Journal of Medical Systems* vol. 36, no. 2 (April 2012): 951–6, http://link.springer.com/article/10.1007%2Fs10916-010-9559-z/fulltext.html.

17. "Medicare & Medicaid EHR Incentive Program: Meaningful Use Stage 1 Requirements Overview."

18. "What Are Clinical Quality Measures," The Office of the National Coordinator of Health Information Technology, last updated January 15, 2013, https://www.healthit.gov/providers-professionals/faqs/what-are-clinical-quality-measures.

19. "Medicare and Medicaid Programs; Electronic Health Record Incentive Program—Stage 3 and Modifications to Meaningful Use in 2015 Through 2017; Final Rule," Part III, Centers for Medicare & Medicaid Services," *Federal Register* vol. 80, No. 200 (October 16, 2015): 62762, https://www.gpo.gov/fdsys/pkg/FR-2015-10-16/pdf/2015-25595.pdf.

20. Amendments were issued on March 4, 2016, and on June 1, 2016.

21. Erin McCann, "CMS Drops Final EHR Meaningful Use Rule," *Healthcare IT News*, October 6, 2015, http://www.healthcareitnews.com/news/cms-onc-release-final-ehr-meaningful-use-rules.

22. "EHR Meaningful Use Doomed Unless Congress Steps In," AMA Wire, November 3, 2015, http://www.ama-assn.org/ama/ama-wire/post/ehr-meaningful-use-doomed-unless-congress-steps.

23. "Alexander: Committee Working to Identify Immediate Solutions to Electronic Health Records Program that Has Physicians 'Terrified,'" US

Senate Committee on Health, Education, Labor & Pensions, June 10, 2015, http://www.help.senate.gov/chair/newsroom/press/alexander-committee-working-to-identify-immediate-solutions-to-electronic-health-records-program-that-has-physicians-terrified.

24. Steve Lohr, "The Agenda Behind Electronic Health Records," *Bits* (blog), *New York Times*, May 9, 2010, http://bits.blogs.nytimes.com/2010/05/09/the-agenda-behind-electronic-health-records/?_php=true&_type=blogs&_r=0.

25. "Improvements to the Physician Quality Reporting System," Section 3002(b), Patient Protection and Affordable Care Act, Public Law No. 111-148 (March 23, 2010), as amended through Public Law No. 115-123 (February 9, 2018), https://legcounsel.house.gov/Comps/Patient%20Protection%20And%20Affordable%20Care%20Act.pdf.

26. "Health Information Technology: Initial Set of Standards, Implementation Specifications, and Certification Criteria for Electronic Health Record Technology; Final Rule" (45 CFR Part 170), The Office of the National Coordinator for Health Information Technology, US Department of Health and Human Services, *Federal Register* vol. 75, no. 144 (July 28, 2010): 44590, https://www.gpo.gov/fdsys/pkg/FR-2010-07-28/pdf/2010-17210.pdf.

27. Steven E. Larson, MD, MPH, letter to Andrew Slavitt, Acting Administrator of Centers for Medicare & Medicaid Services, California Medical Association, June 27, 2016, http://www.cmanet.org/files/assets/news/2016/07/macra-cma-letter.pdf.

28. "Medicare & Medicaid EHR Incentive Program: Meaningful Use Stage 1 Requirements Overview."

29. Ibid.

30. John Barnett, "Beyond Meaningful Use: The Value of Patient Portals," Health IT Outcomes, January 25, 2017, https://www.healthitoutcomes.com/doc/beyond-meaningful-use-the-value-of-patient-portals-0001.

31. "Medicare & Medicaid EHR Incentive Program: Meaningful Use Stage 1 Requirements Overview."

32. "Stage 2 Eligible Professional (EP) Meaningful Use Core and Menu Measures Table of Contents," Centers for Medicare & Medicaid Services, October 2012, https://www.cms.gov/Regulations-and-Guidance/Legislation/EHRIncentivePrograms/Downloads/Stage2_MeaningfulUseSpecSheet_TableContents_EPs.pdf.

33. "Record Demographics," The Office of the National Coordinator for Health Information Technology, last updated February 24, 2014, https://www.healthit.gov/providers-professionals/achieve-meaningful-use/core-measures-2/record-demographics. Ibid.

34. Ibid.

35. "Use Secure Electronic Messaging," The Office of the National Coordinator of Health Information Technology, last updated February 24, 2014, https://www.healthit.gov/providers-professionals/achieve-meaningful-use/core-measures-2/use-secure-electronic-messaging.

36. "Stage 2 Eligible Professional Meaningful Use Menu Set Measures Measure 6 of 6," Centers for Medicare & Medicaid Services, October 2012, https://www.cms.gov/Regulations-and-Guidance/Legislation/EHRIncentivePrograms/downloads/Stage2_EPMenu_6_ReportSpecificCases.pdf.

37. "Step 5: Achieve Meaningful Use Stage 2," The Office of the National Coordinator for Health Information Technology, last updated April 21, 2014, https://www.healthit.gov/providers-professionals/step-5-achieve-meaningful-use-stage-2.

38. Joseph Conn, "Final Stage 3 EHR Rule Is Out, but HHS Signals More Changes Ahead," *Modern Healthcare*, October 6, 2015, http://www.modernhealthcare.com/article/20151006/NEWS/151009952.

39. "Medicare and Medicaid Programs; Electronic Health Record Incentive Program—Stage 3 and Modifications to Meaningful Use in 2015 Through 2017; Final Rule," Centers for Medicare & Medicaid Services," *Federal Register* vol. 80, No. 200 (October 16, 2015): 62762, https://www.gpo.gov/fdsys/pkg/FR-2015-10-16/pdf/2015-25595.pdf.

40. Bill Siwicki, "CMS Finalizes 90-Day Reporting for Meaningful Use,"

Healthcare IT News, August 3, 2017, http://www.healthcareitnews.com/news/cms-finalizes-90-day-reporting-meaningful-use.

41. Conn, "Final Stage 3 EHR Rule Is Out, But HHS Signals More Changes Ahead."

42. Charles Fiegl, "Proposed Meaningful Use Stage 3 Criticized as Hasty and Too Strict," *American Medical News*, January 28, 2013, http://amednews.com/article/20130128/government/130129950/1/.

43. Dan Bowman, "CMS to Hit 257,000 Docs with Meaningful Use Penalties," FierceHealthcare, December 17, 2014, http://www.fiercehealthcare.com/ehr/cms-to-hit-257-000-docs-meaningful-use-penalties.

44. David Pittman, "209,000 Doctors Hit with Meaningful Use Penalty This Year," Politico Morning eHealth, January 12, 2016, http://www.politico.com/tipsheets/morning-ehealth/2016/01/politicos-morning-ehealth-209-000-doctors-hit-with-meaningful-use-penalty-this-year-212129.

45. Jessica Davis, "209,000 Organizations to Pay Medicaid Penalties for Missing Meaningful Use Requirements," *Healthcare IT News*, January 13, 2016, http://www.healthcareitnews.com/news/209000-organizations-pay-medicaid-penalties-missing-meaningful-use-requirements; NOTE: The article discusses Medicaid penalties. It's actually Medicare penalties.

46. Rajiv Leventhal, "CMS: 209K Docs to be Hit with MU Penalties in 2016," Healthcare Informatics, January 13, 2016, https://www.healthcare-informatics.com/news-item/cms-209000-docs-be-hit-mu-penalties-2016.

47. Ken Terry, "CMS Releases Details on Meaningful Use Hardship Exceptions," Medscape, January 22, 2016, http://www.medscape.com/viewarticle/857688.

48. Henry Powderly, "What CMS Chief Andy Slavitt Said at J.P. Morgan," *Healthcare IT News*, January 13, 2016, http://www.healthcareitnews.com/news/what-cms-chief-andy-slavitt-jp-morgan.

49. Jordan Cohen and Thomas S. Crane, "CMS Releases Proposed Rule for MACRA Implementation—Overview and Merit-Based Incentive Payment Systems (MIPS)," *Health Law & Policy Matters* (blog), May 3, 2016, https://www.healthlawpolicymatters.com/2016/05/03/cms-releases-proposed-rule-for-macra-implementation-background-and-overview-and-merit-based-incentive-payment-systems-mips/.

50. "Answering Your FAQs About MIPS, MACRA and APMS," Mingle Analytics, n.d., https://mingleanalytics.com/confused-macra-mips-apms-explained-plain-english/.

51. "Quality Payment Program," Centers for Medicare & Medicaid Services, n.d., https://www.cms.gov/Medicare/Quality-Initiatives-Patient-Assessment-Instruments/Value-Based-Programs/MACRA-MIPS-and-APMs/Quality-Payment-Program-Long-Version-Executive-Deck.pdf.

52. Margalit Gur-Arie, "Meaningful Use Is Dead, Long Live Something Better!" HIT Consultant, January 14, 2016, http://hitconsultant.net/2016/01/14/meaningful-use-is-dead/.

53. Ibid.

54. Mike Miliard, "Meaningful Use Will Likely End in 2016, CMS Chief Andy Slavitt Says," *Healthcare IT News*, January 12, 2016, http://www.healthcareitnews.com/news/meaningful-use-will-likely-end-2016-cms-chief-andy-slavitt-says.

55. Gur-Arie, "Meaningful Use is Dead, Long Live Something Better!"

56. Twila Brase, "About," The Wedge of Health Freedom (Initiative of Citizens' Council for Health Freedom), n.d., https://JoinTheWedge.com/about/.

57. "CMS Proposes Changes to Empower Patients and Reduce Administative Burden," Centers for Medicare and Medicaid Services, April 24, 2018, https://www.cms.gov/Newsroom/MediaReleaseDatabase/Press-releases/2018-Press-releases-items/2018-04-24.html.

58. Amber Porterfield et al., "Electronic Prescribing: Improving the Efficiency and Accuracy of Prescribing in the Ambulatory Setting," *Perspectives in Health Information Management*, (Spring 2014): 1-13, http://perspectives.ahima.org/

electronic-prescribing-improving-the-efficiency-and-accuracy-of-prescribing-in-the-ambulatory-care-setting-2/#.VployRFeKvM.

59. Joy Pritts, JD, et al., "Privacy and Security Solutions for Interoperable Health Information Exchange," The Office of the National Coordinator for Health Information Technology, August 2009, https://www.healthit.gov/sites/default/files/290-05-0015-state-rx-law-report-2.pdf.

60. Meghan Hufstader Gabriel, PhD, and Matthew Swain, MPH, "E-Prescribing Trends in the United States," ONC Data Brief (no. 18), Office of the National Coordinator for Health Information Technology, July 2014, https://www.healthit.gov/sites/default/files/oncdatabriefe-prescribingincreases2014.pdf.

61. C. Stephen Redhead, "The Health Information Technology for Economic and Clinical Health (HITECH) Act," Congressional Research Service, February 23, 2009, https://digital.library.unt.edu/ark:/67531/metadc743451/m1/1/high_res_d/R40161_2009Feb23.pdf.

62. "Medicare EHR Incentive Program Physician Quality Reporting System and Electronic Prescribing Incentive Program Comparison," Centers for Medicare & Medicaid Services, last updated May 2013, http://www.cms.gov/Regulations-and-Guidance/Legislation/EHRIncentivePrograms/Downloads/MLN_MedicareEHRProgram_PQRS_eRXComparison.pdf.

63. "Participating in Medicare's E-Prescribing Incentive Program," *Journal of Oncology Practice* vol. 5, no. 4 (July 2009): 200–1, http://ascopubs.org/doi/full/10.1200/jop.0942502.

64. "Electronic Prescribing (eRx) Incentive Program," Centers for Medicare & Medicaid Services, last modified January 31, 2018, https://www.cms.gov/Medicare/Quality-Initiatives-Patient-Assessment-Instruments/ERxIncentive/index.html?redirect=/erxincentive/.

65. "Electronic Prescribing: CMS Should Address Inconsistencies in Its Two Incentive Programs that Encourage the Use of Health Information Technology," US Government Accountability Office, GAO-11-159, February 2011, http://www.gao.gov/assets/320/315816.html.

66. "June 30 Deadline to ePrescribe & Avoid 2013 Penalty," Maine Academy of Family Physicians, June 22, 2012, http://archive.constantcontact.com/fs062/1103624069953/archive/1110307443352.html.

67. Jeremy Rodriguez, "Health Information Technology - American Medical Association," November 19, 2014, Getget.org, http://getgetnet.biz/information_technology_medicine_309/2/

68. Porterfield et al.

69. Lauren Clason, "Consumer Choice for Health Care Lags Behind Rhetoric," *Roll Call,* December 4, 2017, http://www.rollcall.com/news/policy/health-care-hsa-obamacare-deductible.

70. Brian Bamberger, "The Future of ePrescribing: Leveraging HIT to Manage Medications," Point-of-Care Partners, Elsevier, Gold Standard Drug Information Summit, 2012, http://docplayer.net/5695329-The-future-of-eprescribing-leveraging-hit-to-manage-medications-brian-bamberger-point-of-care-partners.html.

71. Joseph Goedert, "As Times Change, a Group Practice Enters the Modern EHR Era," *Health Data Management*, October 10, 2017, https://www.healthdatamanagement.com/news/as-times-change-a-group-practice-enters-the-modern-ehr-era.

72. "Electronic Prescribing in Minnesota," Minnesota Department of Health, June 2015, http://www.health.state.mn.us/e-health/eprescribing/docs/facterx.pdf.

73. "Electronic Prescription Drug Program," 2017 Minnesota Statutes 62J.497, Revisor of Statutes, State of Minnesota, https://www.revisor.mn.gov/statutes/?id=62J.497.

74. "Understanding the 2011 e-Prescribing Mandate," Minnesota Department of Health, March 2011, formerly access at http://www.health.state.mn.us/e-health/eprescribing/docs/erx032011guidance.pdf.

75. "E-Prescribing Requirement Effective March 27, 2015," Medical Society of the State of New York, May 14, 2013, http://mssny.org/App_Themes/MSSNY/pdf/

March%2027%20%202015%20E%20Prescribing%20Requirements%20All%20Prescription.pdf.

76. "Electronic Prescribing, Dispensing and Recordkeeping of Controlled Substances" (Adopted Regulation: Part 80 [10 NYCRR]), New York State Department of Health, Effective Date, March 27, 2013, https://regs.health.ny.gov/sites/default/files/pdf/recently_adopted_regulations/2013-02-13_electronic_prescribing_dispensing_and_recordkeeping_of_controlled_substances.pdf.

77. Nina Flanagan, "More Than 4,000 NY Providers Request E-Prescribing Waivers," Healthcare Dive, April 19, 2016, http://www.healthcaredive.com/news/more-than-4000-ny-providers-request-e-prescribing-waivers/417724/.

78. "NYSDOH Issues Letter on Expiration of Waivers for Electronic Prescribing," New York State Dental Association, November 18, 2016, https://www.nysdental.org/blog/nysdoh-issues-letter-expiration-waivers-electronic-prescribing.

79. "The Dreaded RTS," *The Angry Pharmacist* (blog), August 2, 2011, http://www.theangrypharmacist.com/archives/2011/08/the-dreaded-rts.html.

80. Bamberger.

81. Eric Poon, MD, MPH, "Errors Associated with the Use of E-Prescribing," (PowerPoint presentation, n.d.), http://www.ehcca.com/presentations/qualitycolloquium6/poon_1b.pdf.

82. Bamberger.

83. Poon.

84. "H.R.2—Medicare Access and CHIP Reauthorization Act of 2015," Public Law 114-10, 129 Stats 87 (April 16, 2015), https://www.congress.gov/114/plaws/publ10/PLAW-114publ10.pdf,

85. Keith Fontenot et al., "A Primer on Medicare Physician Payment Reform and the SGR," Brookings Institution, February 2, 2015, http://www.brookings.edu/blogs/health360/posts/2015/02/sgr-medicare-physician-payment-primer-fontenot.

86. "The Merit-based Incentive Payment System (MIPS) & Alternative Payment Models (APMs)," Centers for Medicare & Medicaid Services, n.d., https://www.cms.gov/Medicare/Quality-Initiatives-Patient-Assessment-Instruments/Value-Based-Programs/MACRA-MIPS-and-APMs/MACRA-MIPS-and-APMs.html.

87. "Advanced APMs," Practice Fusion, n.d., https://www.practicefusion.com/quality-payment-program/what-are-apms/.

88. "Scores for Improvement Activities in MIPS APMs in the 2017 Performance Period," Quality Payment Program, Centers for Medicare & Medicaid Services, n.d., 5, https://www.cms.gov/Medicare/Quality-Payment-Program/Resource-Library/Learn-more-about-improvement-activities-and-APMs.pdf.

89. Robert M. Wolin et al., "Five Things to Know about the Medicare SGR Fix," *Health Law Update* (blog), BakerHostetler, April 27, 2015, http://www.healthlawupdate.com/2015/04/five-things-to-know-about-the-medicare-sgr-fix/.

90. Dan Diamond, "10,000 People Are Now Enrolling in Medicare—Every Day," *Forbes,* July 13, 2015, https://www.forbes.com/sites/dandiamond/2015/07/13/aging-in-america-10000-people-enroll-in-medicare-every-day/#2a1f48ce3657.

91. "2016 Physician Quality Reporting System (PQRS): Implementation Guide," Centers for Medicare & Medicaid Services, February 18, 2016; Revised March 11, 2016, https://www.acponline.org/system/files/documents/practice-resources/business-resources/payment/medicare/pqrs/2016-pqrs-implementation-guide.pdf.

92. "2016 Physician Quality Reporting System (PQRS): Understanding 2018 Medicare Quality Program Payment Adjustments," Centers for Medicare & Medicaid Services, March 2016, https://www.cms.gov/Medicare/Quality-Initiatives-Patient-Assessment-Instruments/PQRS/Downloads/Understand2018MedicarePayAdjs.pdf.

93. "Value-Based Payment Modifier," Centers for Medicare & Medicaid Services, last modified September 21, 2017, https://www.cms.gov/Medicare/Medicare-Fee-for-Service-Payment/PhysicianFeedbackProgram/ValueBasedPaymentModifier.html.

94. "CMS Quality Measure Development Plan: Supporting the Transition to the Merit-based Incentive Payment System (MIPS) and Alternative Payment Models (APMs) (DRAFT)," Center for Clinical Standards and Quality, Centers for Medicare & Medicaid Services, December 18, 2015, 4, https://www.cms.gov/Medicare/Quality-Initiatives-Patient-Assessment-Instruments/Value-Based-Programs/MACRA-MIPS-and-APMs/Draft-CMS-Quality-Measure-Development-Plan-MDP.pdf.

95. Ibid., 4.

96. "2016 Survey of America's Physicians Practice Patterns & Perspectives," The Physicians Foundation, September 2016, https://physiciansfoundation.org/wp-content/uploads/2018/01/Biennial_Physician_Survey_2016.pdf.

97. "Medicare Program: Merit-based Incentive Payment System (MIPS) and Alternative Payment Model (APM) Incentive Under the Physician Fee Schedule, and Criteria for Physician-Focused Payment Models, Final Rule with Comment Period," Centers for Medicare & Medicaid Services, Federal Register vol. 81, no. 214 (November 4, 2016): 77120, https://www.gpo.gov/fdsys/pkg/FR-2016-11-04/pdf/2016-25240.pdf.

98. "Medicare Program; Merit-Based Incentive Payment System (MIPS) and Alternative Payment Model (APM) Incentive under the Physician Fee Schedule and Criteria for Physician-Focused Payment Models, Proposed Rule," Centers for Medicare & Medicaid Services, *Federal Register* vol. 81, No. 89 (May 9, 2016): 28184 and 28188, https://www.gpo.gov/fdsys/pkg/FR-2016-05-09/pdf/2016-10032.pdf.

99. "Quality Payment Program," Centers for Medicare & Medicaid Services, n.d., 7. http://docplayer.net/34555039-Quality-payment-program.html.

100. Ibid.

101. "MIPS: Advancing Care Information Deep Dive," Centers for Medicare & Medicaid Services, April 4, 2017, 25, https://www.cms.gov/Medicare/Quality-Initiatives-Patient-Assessment-Instruments/Value-Based-Programs/MACRA-MIPS-and-APMs/MIPS-ACI-Deep-Dive-Webinar-Slides.pdf.

102. "What Is the Difference between the Two Advancing Care Information Measure Sets Available in 2017?" Practice Fusion, n.d., https://knowledgebase.practicefusion.com/knowledgebase/articles/1159114-what-is-the-difference-between-the-two-advancing-c.

103. "MIPS: Advancing Care Information Deep Dive," 22.

104. Cohen and Crane.

105. "Medicare Program; Merit-based Incentive Payment System (MIPS) and Alternative Payment Model (APM) Incentive under the Physician Fee Schedule and Criteria for Physician-Focused Payment Models, Proposed Rule," 28375.

106. "Comments," Medicare Program; Merit-Based Incentive Payment System (MIPS) and Alternative Payment Model (APM) Incentive under the Physician Fee Schedule and Criteria for Physician-Focused Payment Models, Proposed Rule," Centers for Medicare & Medicaid Services, *Federal Register*, comment period closed June 27, 2016, https://www.regulations.gov/docket?D=CMS-2016-0060.

107. "MGMA Regulatory Burden Survey," MGMA, August 2017, http://www.mgma.com/getattachment/Government-Affairs/Advocacy/Advocacy-(1)/MGMA-2017-Regulatory-Relief-Survey/MGMA-Regulatory-Relief-Survey-Results.pdf.

108. Beth Jones Sanborn, "Providers Still Largely in the Dark about MACRA as Reporting Deadline Nears, NueMD Survey Says," *Healthcare Finance*, August 25, 2017, http://www.healthcarefinancenews.com/news/providers-still-largely-dark-about-macra-reporting-deadline-nears-nuemd-survey-says.

109. Beth Jones Sanborn, "Specialty Practices Way Behind on MACRA Readiness, Survey Shows," *Healthcare IT News*, September 6, 2017, http://www.healthcareitnews.com/news/specialty-practices-way-behind-macra-readiness-survey-shows.

110. Sanborn, "Providers Still Largely in the Dark about MACRA as Reporting Deadline Nears, NueMD Survey Says."

111. "Jason Furman," Peterson Institute for International Economics, n.d., https://piie.com/experts/senior-research-staff/jason-furman.

112. Aaron Klein, "Soros-Funded Activist: 'I Helped Write Obamacare,'" (Quote begins at 00:19, video from HBO's "Real Time with Bill Maher), WorldNetDaily, June 2, 2013, http://www.wnd.com/2013/06/soros-funded-activist-i-helped-write-obamacare/.

113. Jason Furman, "The Economic Benefits of the Affordable Care Act," Remarks to the Center for American Progress, April 2, 2015, https://obamawhitehouse.archives.gov/sites/default/files/docs/20150402_aca_economic_impacts_5th_anniversary_cap.pdf.

114. Sarah Ferris, "White House Scoffs at Obamacare 'Doomsday Prophecies,'" *The Hill*, April 2, 2015, http://thehill.com/policy/healthcare/237732-obamas-chief-economist-healthcare-law-didnt-create-doomsday.

115. "CMS Quality Measure Development Plan: Supporting the Transition to the Merit-based Incentive Payment System (MIPS) and Alternative Payment Models (APMs) (DRAFT)," Health Services Advisory Group, Centers for Medicare & Medicaid Services, December 18, 2015, 3, https://www.cms.gov/Medicare/Quality-Initiatives-Patient-Assessment-Instruments/Value-Based-Programs/MACRA-MIPS-and-APMs/Draft-CMS-Quality-Measure-Development-Plan-MDP.pdf.

116. Ibid., 8.

117. Ibid., 21.

118. "Medicare Program: Merit-based Incentive Payment System (MIPS) and Alternative Payment Model (APM) Incentive Under the Physician Fee Schedule, and Criteria for Physician-Focused Payment Models, Final Rule with Comment Period," Centers for Medicare & Medicaid Services, *Federal Register* vol. 81, no. 214 (November 4, 2016): 77101, https://www.gpo.gov/fdsys/pkg/FR-2016-11-04/pdf/2016-25240.pdf.

119. The number is 19.7 percent. For example, using $100, a 9 percent penalty means a payment of $91 and a 9 percent bonus means a payment of $109. The difference of $18 is 19.7 percent.

120. "What's the Quality Payment Program?" Quality Payment Program, Centers for Medicare & Medicaid Services, n.d., https://qpp.cms.gov.

121. Shannon Firth, "CMS to Ease Physician Burden, Give More Patient Time," MedPage Today, October 26, 2017, https://www.medpagetoday.com/publichealthpolicy/medicare/68824.

122. "Speech: Remarks by Administrator Seema Verma at the Health Care Payment Learning and Action Network (LAN) Fall Summit (As prepared for delivery - October 30, 2017)," Centers for Medicare & Medicaid Services, October 30, 2017, https://www.cms.gov/Newsroom/MediaReleaseDatabase/Fact-sheets/2017-Fact-Sheet-items/2017-10-30.html.

123. "Medicare Program; CY 2018 Updates to the Quality Payment Program; Quality Payment Program: Extreme and Uncontrollable Circumstances Policy for the Transition Year, Final Rule with Comment Period and Interim Final Rule with Comment Period," Centers for Medicare & Medicaid Services, *Federal Register* vol. 82, no. 220 (November 16, 2017): 53587, https://www.federalregister.gov/documents/2017/11/16/2017-24067/medicare-program-cy-2018-updates-to-the-quality-payment-program-and-quality-payment-program-extreme.

124. Lynn Barr, "Physicians Exempt from Medicare Incentive Payment System Will Do More Harm than Good," *The Hill,* October 17, 2017, http://thehill.com/opinion/healthcare/355886-physicians-exempt-from-medicare-incentive-payment-system-will-do-more-harm?amp.

125. Shannon Firth, "MIPS Takes a Beating at MedPAC," MedPage Today, October 5, 2017, https://www.medpagetoday.com/publichealthpolicy/medicare/68362.

126. John Gregory, "MedPAC Votes to Recommend Repealing MIPS," HealthExec, January 11, 2018, http://www.healthexec.com/topics/policy/medpac-votes-recommend-repealing-mips.

127. "Reducing the Volume of Future EHR-Related Significant Hardship Requests," Section 50413, Bipartisan Budget Act of

2018, Public Law No. 115-123, 132 Stat. 64 (February 9, 2018), https://budgetcounsel.com/§030-laws-public-statutes/x§068-pub-l-115-123-bipartisan-budget-act-of-2018/.

128. Jon Reid, "HHS May Nix Reporting Requirements for Value-Based Care Program, Azar Says," Morning Consult, February 15, 2018, https://morningconsult.com/2018/02/15/hhs-may-nix-reporting-requirements-for-value-based-care-program-azar-says/.

129. "CMS Proposes Changes to Empower Patients and Reduce Administative Burden," Centers for Medicare and Medicaid Services, April 24, 2018, https://www.cms.gov/Newsroom/MediaReleaseDatabase/Press-releases/2018-Press-releases-items/2018-04-24.html; see also "CMS Changes Name of EHR Incentive Programs and Advancing Care Information to 'Promoting Interoperability,'" DAShealth, April 24, 2018, https://dashealth.com/dr-news-item/cms-changes-name-ehr-incentive-programs-advancing-care-information-promoting-interoperability.

III. Clinical Chaos

1. Marla Durben Hirsch, "EHR Adoption Up, but Doc Satisfaction Lags," FierceHealthcare, May 31, 2013, https://www.fiercehealthcare.com/ehr/ehr-adoption-up-but-doc-satisfaction-lags.

2. Marla Durben Hirsch, "Study: Physician EHR-Users Not Seeing Return on Investment," FierceHealthcare, March 7, 2013, https://www.fiercehealthcare.com/ehr/study-physician-ehr-users-not-seeing-return-investment.

3. "New IDC Health Insights Survey of Ambulatory Providers Reveals Dissatisfaction with Ambulatory EHR," Business Wire, November 13, 2013, http://www.businesswire.com/news/home/20131113006395/en/IDC-Health-Insights-Survey-Ambulatory-Providers-Reveals#.UuF2zuB6hcw.

4. Mike Miliard, "Docs Blame EHRs for Lost Productivity," *Healthcare IT News*, November 14, 2013, http://www.healthcareitnews.com/news/docs-blame-ehrs-lost-productivity.

5. Darius Tahir, "Docs Dissatisfied with their EHR Systems: New Surveys," *Modern Healthcare*, April 14, 2015, http://www.modernhealthcare.com/article/20150414/NEWS/150419963.

6. "EHR Satisfaction According to Physicians: The Under-Reported Story," Reaction Data, n.d., https://www.reactiondata.com/wp-content/uploads/2018/01/EHR-Satisfaction-According-To-Physicians-Reaction-Data.pdf.

7. Brian Schilling, "The Federal Government Has Put Billions into Promoting Electronic Health Record Use: How Is It Going?" *Quality Matters*, The Commonwealth Fund, June/July 2011, http://www.commonwealthfund.org/publications/newsletters/quality-matters/2011/june-july-2011/in-focus.

8. Arthur Allen, "Why Health Care IT Is Still on Life Support," *Politico*, June 11, 2015, http://www.politico.com/magazine/story/2015/06/electronic-medical-records-doctors-118881.html#.VZwZ7-vhLhN.

9. Michael McBride, "Measuring EHR Pain Points: High Cost, Poor Functionality Outweigh Benefits, Ease of Access," *Medical Economics*, February 10, 2014, http://medicaleconomics.modernmedicine.com/medical-economics/content/tags/ehr/measuring-ehr-pain-points-high-cost-poor-functionality-outweigh-b?page=full.

10. Ibid.

11. Margaret Polaneczky, MD, "Restoring Office Workflows to the EMR: Or How I Restored Patient Face Time and Got Back the Joy in Medicine," *The Health Care Blog*, January 17, 2012, http://thehealthcareblog.com/blog/2012/01/17/how-i-restored-patient-face-time-got-back-the-joy-in-medicine/.

12. Allen.

13. John Noseworthy et al., "Physician Burnout is a Public Health Crisis: A Message to Our Fellow Health Care CEOs" (Comments Section), *Health Affairs Blog*, March 28, 2017, http://healthaffairs.org/blog/2017/03/28/physician-burnout-is-a-public-health-crisis-a-message-to-our-fellow-health-care-ceos/.

14. Scott Jensen, MD, *Relationship Matters: The Foundation of Medical Care Is*

Fracturing (Amazon Digital Services, 2015), 208.

15. Matthias Gafni, "County Health Doctors Air Complaints about County's New $45 Million Computer System," *Mercury News*, September 18, 2012, http://www.mercurynews.com/2012/09/18/county-health-doctors-air-complaints-about-countys-new-45-million-computer-system/.
16. Ibid.
17. Ann Scheck McAlearney, MS, ScD, et al., "High Touch and High Tech (HT2) Proposal: Transforming Patient Engagement Throughout the Continuum of Care by Engaging Patients with Portal Technology at the Bedside," *JMIR Research Protocols* vol. 5, no. 4 (Oct-Dec, 2016), https://www.ncbi.nlm.nih.gov/pmc/articles/PMC5172441/.
18. "Analysis of Health IT," RAND Corporation, n.d., http://www.rand.org/pubs/technical_reports/TR562z5/analysis-of-health-it.html.
19. Stephen Soumerai and Ross Koppel, "A Major Glitch for Digitized Health-Care Records," *Wall Street Journal*, September 17, 2012, http://www.wsj.com/articles/SB10000872396390443847404577627041964831020.
20. Milt Freudenheim, "The Ups and Downs of Electronic Health Records," *New York Times*, October 8, 2012, http://www.nytimes.com/2012/10/09/health/the-ups-and-downs-of-electronic-medical-records-the-digital-doctor.html?_r=0.
21. Greg Gillespie, "HIT Think: Damn Damn Damn," *Health Data Management*, November 16, 2012, https://www.healthdatamanagement.com/opinion/damn-damn-damn.
22. Suzanne Koven, MD, "As Hospitals Go Digital, Human Stories Get Left Behind," *STAT*, April 6, 2016, https://www.statnews.com/2016/04/06/electronic-medical-records-patients/.
23. Health Day, "Quality Issues for Both Paper-, Electronic-Based Health Records," *Medical Xpress*, October 13, 2017, https://medicalxpress.com/news/2017-10-quality-issues-paper-electronic-based-health.html.
24. Jeanne M. Madden et al., "Missing Clinical and Behavioral Health Data in a Large Electronic Health Record (EHR) system," *Journal of the American Medical Informatics Association* vol. 23, no. 6 (April 14, 2016): 1143-1149, http://jamia.oxfordjournals.org/content/early/2016/04/12/jamia.ocw021.
25. Gillespie.
26. Miliard, "Docs Blame EHRs for Lost Productivity."
27. Ross Koppel, "The Health Information Technology Safety Framework: Building Great Structures on Vast Voids," *BMJ Quality & Safety* vol. 25, no. 4 (November 19, 2015), http://qualitysafety.bmj.com/content/early/2015/11/19/bmjqs-2015-004746.
28. Jennifer Dennard, "One Student's Perspective on Electronic Medical Records," *EMR and EHR* (blog), December 7, 2011, http://www.emrandehr.com/2011/12/07/one-students-perspective-on-electronic-medical-records/.
29. Joseph H. Schneider, MD, MBA, "The Missing Link: Patient Responsibility for Health Records," Hayes Management Consulting, July 26, 2017, http://meetings.hayesmanagement.com/blog/the-missing-link-patient-responsibility-for-health-records.
30. Email to author, 2017.
31. Michael D. Wang, MD, et al., "Characterizing the Source of Text in Electronic Health Record Progress Notes," *JAMA Internal Medicine* vol. 177, No. 8 (August 2017), https://jamanetwork.com/journals/jamainternalmedicine/article-abstract/2629493.
32. Robert Hirschtick, MD, "Sloppy and Paste," Patient Safety Network, Agency for Healthcare Research and Quality, US Department of Health & Human Services, July 2012, https://psnet.ahrq.gov/webmm/case/274/sloppy-and-paste.
33. Mark W. Friedberg et al., "Factors Affecting Physician Professional Satisfaction and the Implications for Patient Care, Health Systems, and Health Policy," RAND Corporation. 2013, 43, http://www.rand.org/content/dam/rand/pubs/research_reports/RR400/RR439/RAND_RR439.pdf.

34. Robert E. Hirschtick, MD, "John Lennon's Elbow," *Journal of the American Medical Association* vol. 308, no. 5 (August 1, 2012): 463–4, https://depts.washington.edu/medhmc/wordpress/wp-content/uploads/JohnLennonsElbow.pdf.

35. Ibid., 464; see also "Customizing Health IT to Support Physician Workflow and Reduce Burden," Agency for Healthcare Research and Quality, US Department of Health & Human Services, last reviewed October 2017, https://www.ahrq.gov/funding/grantee-profiles/grtprofile-payne.html.

36. Marla Durben Hirsch, "RAND: EHRs 'Significantly Worsened' Doc Satisfaction," FierceHealthcare, March 18, 2014, http://www.fiercehealthcare.com/ehr/rand-ehrs-significantly-worsened-doc-satisfaction.

37. Jason Acevedo, MD, letter to the editor, *Wall Street Journal*, July 14, 2017, https://www.wsj.com/articles/smart-medicine-can-help-but-more-is-needed-1500054850?mg=prod/accounts-wsj.

38. Jessica Kim Cohen, "Paper Records Are Here to Stay: 4 Questions With Illinois Pain Institute's Dr. John Prunskis," Becker's Health IT & CIO Review, August 9, 2017, http://www.beckershospitalreview.com/healthcare-information-technology/paper-records-are-here-to-stay-4-questions-with-illinois-pain-institute-s-dr-john-prunskis.html.

39. Susan D. Hall, "Do EMRs Make It Too Easy to Fudge Documentation?" FierceHealthcare, March 10, 2014, http://www.fierceemr.com/story/do-emrs-make-it-too-easy-fudge-documentation/2014-03-10.

40. John Dubas, "Quote of the Day," *Medicare Is Simple* (blog), January 23, 2014, http://medicareissimple.blogspot.com/2014/01/.

41. Kevin Pho, MD, "Electronic Medical Records No Cure-All Yet: Column," *USA TODAY*, January 19, 2014, http://www.usatoday.com/story/opinion/2014/01/19/kevin-pho-electronic-medical-records/4649043/.

42. Bill Graveland, "Excessive Computer Use by Doctors Has Negative Impact on Patient Care: Study," *Toronto Star*, February 24, 2017, https://www.thestar.com/amp/news/canada/2017/02/23/excessive-computer-use-by-doctors-has-negative-impact-on-patient-care-study.html.

43. Anne Marie Valinoti, "Physician, Steel Thyself for Electronic Records," *Wall Street Journal*, October 22, 2012, http://online.wsj.com/article/SB10000872396390443675404578058480752741280.html.

44. John Lynn, "An Interview with Dr. Nan Nuessle (@DrNanN)—#HITsm Spotlight," *EMR and EHR* (blog), October 31, 2012, http://www.emrandehr.com/2012/10/31/an-interview-with-dr-nan-nuessle-drnann-hitsm-spotlight.

45. Stewart Segal, MD, "Click, Click, Click: How Can I Help You Today?" *KevinMD* (blog), November 26, 2012, http://www.kevinmd.com/blog/2012/11/click-click-click-today.html.

46. Valinoti.

47. Lynn, "An Interview with Dr. Nan Nuessle (@DrNanN)—#HITsm Spotlight."

48. Alexi Mostrous, "Electronic Medical Records Draw Frequent Criticisms," *Washington Post*, October 25, 2009, http://www.washingtonpost.com/wp-dyn/content/article/2009/10/24/AR2009102400967.html.

49. Margalit Gur-Arie, "Why Everything You Know About EHR Design Is Probably Wrong," *The Health Care Blog*, November 1, 2012, http://thehealthcareblog.com/blog/2012/11/01/why-everything-you-know-about-ehr-design-is-probably-wrong/; see also "The EHR Non-User Interface," *On Health Care Technology* (blog), October 29, 2012: http://onhealthtech.blogspot.com/2012/10/the-ehr-non-user-interface.html.

50. Ben-Tzion Karsh et al., "Health Information Technology: Fallacies and Sober Realities," *Journal of the American Medical Informatics Association* vol. 17, no. 6 (November/December 2010): 617–23, https://www.ncbi.nlm.nih.gov/pmc/articles/PMC3000760/.

51. John Lynn, "New Open Source (Free) EHR Offering Developed by a Doctor," *EMR and HIPAA* (blog), October 25, 2012, http://www.emrandhipaa.com/emr-and-hipaa/2012/10/25/new-open-source-free-ehr-offering-developed-by-a-doctor-2/.

52. "Interoperability for Texas: Powering Health 2016," Texas Health and Human Services Commission, December 2016, 52, https://hhs.texas.gov/file/55576/download?token=yMO99FoT.

53. Kenneth D. Mandl, MD, MPH, and Isaac S. Kohane, MD, PhD, "Escaping the EHR Trap—The Future of Health IT," *New England Journal of Medicine* vol 366, no. 24 (June 14, 2012), http://www.nejm.org/doi/full/10.1056/NEJMp1203102#t=article.

54. Gur-Arie, "Why Everything You Know about EHR Design Is Probably Wrong."

55. Lynn, "New Open Source (Free) EHR Offering Developed by A Doctor."

56. John Lynn, "Challenges and Risks Associated with Disclosure of Health Information in an EHR World," *EMR and EHR* (blog), October 22, 2012, http://www.emrandehr.com/2012/10/22/challenges-and-risks-associated-with-disclosure-of-health-information-in-an-ehr-world/; see also Healthcare Scene, "Rita Bowen Discusses Challenges & Risks with Disclosure of Health Information," YouTube, October 22, 2012, from 1:20, http://youtu.be/1V5MOOe6VlI.

57. Bill Siwicki, "Fighting Physician Burnout: How Tech Can Undo the Damage Done by EHRs," *Healthcare IT News*, October 16, 2017, http://www.healthcareitnews.com/news/fighting-physician-burnout-how-tech-can-undo-damage-done-ehrs.

58. Laura Lovett, "Health 2.0 Sees the Future of Healthcare Innovation in Collaboration," MobiHealthNews, March 6, 2018, http://www.mobihealthnews.com/content/health-20-sees-future-healthcare-innovation-collaboration.

59. Linda Girgis, MD, "Has the Joy of Medicine Been Lost?" *Physicians Practice*, March 28, 2018, http://www.physicianspractice.com/worklife-balance/has-joy-medicine-been-lost.

60. Diana Swift, "Physician Burnout Climbs 10% in 3 Years, Hits 55%," Medscape, December 1, 2015, http://www.medscape.com/viewarticle/855233?src=wnl_edit_newsal&uac=236428HY&impID=917539&faf=1.

61. Ibid.

62. "Hospital Nurses Forced to Develop Creative Workarounds to Deal with EHR System Flaws; Outdated Technologies and Lack of Interoperability, Reveals Black Book," PRWeb, October 17, 2014, http://www.prweb.com/releases/2014/09/prweb12182208.htm.

63. "Hospital Nurses Forced to Develop Creative Workarounds to Deal with HER System Flaws; Outdated Technologies and Lack of Interoperability, Reveals Black Book, PRWeb, October 17, 2014, http://www.prweb.com/releases/2014/09/prweb12182208.htm.

64. Erin McCann, "Nurses Demand Delay of EHR Rollout," *Healthcare IT News*, June 20, 2013, http://www.healthcareitnews.com/news/nurses-demand-delay-ehr-rollout.

65. "Hospital Nurses Forced to Develop Creative Workarounds to Deal with EHR System Flaws; Outdated Technologies and Lack of Interoperability, Reveals Black Book."

66. Bill Toland, "Complaints about Electronic Medical Records Increase," *Pittsburgh Post-Gazette*, August 4, 2014, http://www.post-gazette.com/business/2014/08/03/Complaints-about-electronic-medical-records-increase/stories/201407250006.

67. Letter to Andrew Schlafly from Michael S. Marquis, director of the Division of Freedom of Information in the Office of Strategic Operations and Regulatory Affairs, Centers for Medicare & Medicaid Services, March 14, 2014, http://aapsonline.org/foia/cms-foia-ehr-aaps.pdf.

68. "EHR Impact on Nurse Workflow: Increased Patient Safety, Reduced Efficiency," Allscripts, 2015, http://landing.allscripts.com/rs/allscriptshealthcare/images/Whitepaper_Allscripts_White%20Paper_NursesSurvey_FINAL.pdf.

69. Personal comment made to author.

70. David Do, MD, "Why EMR Companies Don't Care about Usability," *KevinMD* (blog), June 26, 2013, http://www.kevinmd.com/blog/2013/06/emr-companies-dont-care-usability.html.

71. Freudenheim.

72. James Richard, December 9, 2016, comment on Howard Green MD, "EMR and EHR Buyers Beware Deceptive

Sales," Linked In, December 8, 2016, https://www.linkedin.com/pulse/emr-buyer-beware-howard-green-md/.

73. Ibid.

74. S. Silverstein (InformaticsMD), "Are Health IT Designers, Testers and Purchasers Trying to Harm Patients? Part 1 of a Series," *Health Care Renewal* (blog), February 18, 2009, http://hcrenewal.blogspot.com/2009/02/are-health-it-designers-idiots-part-1.html.

75. "Breaking Up with Your EHR," Physicians Practice (January 6, 2016, webinar), email with subject line "Your Achy, Breaky EHR" sent to author December 17, 2015.

76. Sidney L. Smith and Jane N. Mosier, "Guidelines for Designing User Interface Software," The MITRE Corporation, Bedford, MA, Prepared for Deputy Commander for Development Plans and Support Systems, Electronic Systems Division, AFSC, United States Air Force, Hanscom Air Force Base, Massachusetts, August 1986, http://hcibib.org/sam/.

77. Gerard J. Gianoli, MD, "Electronic Medical Records: The Potemkin Village of Healthcare," Association of American Physicians and Surgeons, March 1, 2016, http://aapsonline.org/electronic-medical-records-the-potemkin-village-of-healthcare/.

78. Ishaan Tharoor, "Potemkin Villages," TIME, August 6, 2010, http://content.time.com/time/specials/packages/article/0,28804,2008962_2008964_2009010,00.html.

79. Gianoli.

80. Ibid.

81. Ibid.

82. Private conversation with author.

83. Jeffrey A. Singer, MD, "How Government Killed the Medical Profession," *Reason*, May 2013, http://www.cato.org/publications/commentary/how-government-killed-medical-profession.

84. Margalit Gur-Arie, "How to Put EHRs Back on the Right Track," *KevinMD* (blog), December 24, 2015, https://www.kevinmd.com/blog/2015/12/put-ehrs-back-right-track.html.

85. "Trend Watch: The Road to Meaningful Use: What it Takes to Implement Electronic Health Record Systems in Hospitals," American Hospital Association, April 2010, 9, Former access to 16-page document: http://webcache.googleusercontent.com/search?client=safari&rls=en&q=cache:zGVLhKG5f_IJ:http://www.aha.org/research/reports/tw/10apr-tw-HITmeanuse.pdf%2Btrendwatch+sample+workflow+order+before&oe=UTF-8&hl=en&&ct=clnk.

86. Ibid.

87. Ibid.

88. James Dias, "6 Big Benefits of Applying Automation to Healthcare," HIT Consultant, July 21, 2014, http://hitconsultant.net/2014/07/21/6-big-benefits-of-applying-automation-to-healthcare/.

89. Olga Khazan, "For Some Doctors, Electronic Records Aren't a Miracle Cure," *Washington Post*, November 5, 2012, https://www.washingtonpost.com/national/health-science/for-some-doctors-electronic-records-arent-a-miracle-cure/2012/11/05/f12c3400-f1fb-11e1-a612-3cfc842a6d89_story.html.

90. Dias.

91. Jeff Byers, "Driving Better Decision-Making: Clinical Knowledge Support Integrated into the EMR," CMIO, August 2011, http://www.uptodate.com/sites/default/files/cms-files/pdf/research/CMIO_Aug2011_Integration.pdf.

92. Philip Betbeze, "Automation and the Healthcare Cost Curve," *HealthLeaders Media*, April 30, 2012, http://healthleadersmedia.com/page-5/LED-279485/Automation-and-the-Healthcare-Cost-Curve.

93. Ray Costantini, "This is Why Health Care Will Finally Be Forced to Automate," Venture Beat, October 18, 2014, http://venturebeat.com/2014/10/18/this-is-why-health-care-will-finally-be-forced-to-automate/.

94. Ibid.; see also Kaiser Permanente Share, "Innovative Web-Based Tool Helps Doctors Improve Care," October 1, 2010, http://share.kaiserpermanente.org/article/innovative-web-based-tool-helps-doctors-improve-care/.

95. "Electronic Medical Records Can Compromise Physician-Patient Engagement, Study Suggests," *Psychiatric News* (blog), January 31, 2014, http://alert.psychnews.org/2014/01/electronic-medical-records-can.html.

96. Marla Durben Hirsch, "Docs Must Follow 'POISED' Best Practices When Using EHRs in the Exam Room," FierceHealthcare, December 1, 2015, http://www.fiercehealthcare.com/ehr/docs-must-follow-poised-best-practices-when-using-ehrs-exam-room.

97. Angela Laguipo, "Exam Room Computer Detrimental to Doctor-Patient Relationship," Tech Times, December 4, 2015, http://www.techtimes.com/articles/112271/20151204/exam-room-computer-detrimental-to-doctor-patient-relationship.htm.

98. Christine Sinsky, MD, et al., "Allocation of Physician Time in Ambulatory Practice: A Time and Motion Study in 4 Specialties," *Annals of Internal Medicine* vol.165, no. 11 (December 6, 2016): 753-760, http://annals.org/aim/article-abstract/2546704/allocation-physician-time-ambulatory-practice-time-motion-study-4-specialties.

99. Marla Durben Hirsch, "Researchers: Medical Interns Spent Up to 7 Hours a Day Using EHRs," FierceHealthcare, February 15, 2016, http://www.fiercehealthcare.com/ehr/researchers-medical-interns-spent-up-to-7-hours-a-day-using-ehrs.

100. Akanksha Jayanthi, "Medical Residents Spend 30% of Time Working in EHRs: 6 Things to Know," *Beckers Hospital Review*, December 9, 2015, http://www.beckershospitalreview.com/healthcare-information-technology/medical-residents-spend-30-of-time-working-in-ehrs-6-things-to-know.html.

101. Vabren Watts, "Electronic Health Records Affect Physician-Patient Interactions," *Psychiatric News* vol. 49, no. 6 (March 19, 2014), http://psychnews.psychiatryonline.org/doi/full/10.1176%2Fappi.pn.2014.3a13.

102. David Cossman, MD, "HAL," *General Surgery News*, May 8, 2012, http://www.generalsurgerynews.com/Opinions-Letters/Article/05-12/HAL/20816/ses=ogst.

103. Dan Diamond, "Pulse Check: Confessions of an Ex-Regulator on How Government Should Work," *Politico*, May 6, 2016, http://www.politico.com/story/2016/05/confessions-of-an-ex-regulator-farzad-mostashari-on-how-government-should-work-222901.

104. Bill Frist, "What My Doctor Thinks of ObamaCare," *The Week*, August 29, 2012, http://theweek.com/article/index/232510/what-my-doctor-thinks-of-obamacare.

105. Gur-Arie, "Why Everything You Know about EHR Design Is Probably Wrong."

106. "Richard M. Frankel, PhD," Center for Health Services and Outcomes Research, Indiana University, n.d., http://iuchsor.medicine.iu.edu/people/faculty/rich-frankel/.

107. Durben Hirsch, "Docs Must Follow 'POISED' Best Practices."

108. "Inserting Computers into Heart and Soul of Medicine, The Doctor-Patient Relationship," USM Newsroom, Indiana University, November 30, 2015, http://news.medicine.iu.edu/releases/2015/11/frankel-exam-room-computing.shtml.

109. "2017 EHR Report Card," *Medical Economics,* October 25, 2017, 12 and 14, http://medicaleconomics.modernmedicine.com/medical-economics/news/2017-ehr-report-card.

110. Douglas Perednia, MD, "Doctors Hiring Scribes Because of Electronic Medical Records," *KevinMD* (blog), August 2, 2010, http://www.kevinmd.com/blog/2010/08/doctors-hiring-scribes-electronic-medical-records.html.

111. Joel Sherman, MD, "Do Medical Scribes Threaten Patient Privacy?" *KevinMD* (blog), April 27, 2014, http://www.kevinmd.com/blog/2014/04/medical-scribes-threaten-patient-privacy.html.

112. Katie Hafner, "A Busy Doctor's Right Hand, Ever Ready to Type," *New York Times*, January 12, 2014, https://www.nytimes.com/2014/01/14/health/a-busy-doctors-right-hand-ever-ready-to-type.html.

113. Sherman.

114. Hafner.

115. Joseph Conn, "Docs Weigh In on Use of Scribes in Primary Care," *Modern*

Healthcare, February 9, 2010, http://www.modernhealthcare.com/article/20100209/NEWS/302099984/1153.

116. Rajiv Leventhal, "How a Virtual Scribe Can Enhance the Doctor-Patient Relationship," Healthcare Informatics, February 2, 2017, https://www.healthcare-informatics.com/article/ehr/how-virtual-scribe-enhancing-doctor-patient-relationship.

117. Kristen Andrews Wilson, "Alexa....... What is HIPAA?" *National Law Review*, April 5, 2018, https://www.natlawreview.com/article/alexawhat-hipaa.

118. Marla Durben Hirsch, "Embrace of Scribes for EHRs Not Universal," FierceHealthcare, March 24, 2014, http://www.fiercehealthcare.com/ehr/embrace-scribes-for-ehrs-not-universal.

119. Hall.

120. Arthur L. Caplan, PhD, "Would a Scribe Repair or Destroy the Doctor-Patient Bond?" Medscape, March 17, 2014, http://www.medscape.com/viewarticle/821584.

121. Hafner.

122. Perednia, MD, "Doctors Hiring Scribes Because of Electronic Medical Records."

123. Kelly Gooch, "17 Things to Know about Medical Scribes," *Becker's Hospital Review*, January 26, 2016, https://www.beckershospitalreview.com/hospital-physician-relationships/17-things-to-know-about-medical-scribes.html.

124. Sherman.

125. George Gellert, MD and Luke Webster, MD, "The Rise of the Medical Scribe Industry: Implications for Advancement of EHRs" (PowerPoint presentation, HIMSS 16 Conference & Exhibition, March 2, 2016), http://www.himssconference.org/sites/himssconference/files/pdf/129.pdf.

126. "21st Century Cures Act—Provisions Relating to Digital Health," Ropes & Gray LLP, December 13, 2016, https://www.ropesgray.com/newsroom/alerts/2016/December/21st-Century-Cures-Act-Provisions-Relating-to-Digital-Health.aspx.

127. Conn, "Docs Weigh In on Use of Scribes in Primary Care."

128. Jeanne Whalen, "Hospitals Cut Costs by Getting Doctors to Stick to Guidelines," *Wall Street Journal*, September 22, 2014, https://www.wsj.com/articles/hospitals-cut-costs-by-getting-doctors-to-stick-to-guidelines-1411416051.

129. Jonathan D. Rockoff, "As Doctors Lose Clout, Drug Firms Redirect the Sales Call," *Wall Street Journal*, September 24, 2014, https://www.wsj.com/articles/as-doctors-lose-clout-drug-firms-redirect-the-sales-call-1411612207.

130. "Clinical Decision Support (CDS)," The Office of the National Coordinator for Health Information Technology, n.d., http://www.healthit.gov/policy-researchers-implementers/clinical-decision-support-cds.

131. Amit X. Garg, MD, et al., "Effects of Computerized Clinical Decision Support Systems on Practitioner Performance and Patient Outcomes," *Journal of the American Medical Association* vol. 293, no. 10 (March 9, 2005): 1223, http://www2.eerp.usp.br/Nepien/DisponibilizarArquivos/tomada_de_decisão.pdf.

132. Lisa Rosenbaum, MD, "Leaping without Looking—Duty Hours, Autonomy, and the Risks of Research and Practice," *New England Journal of Medicine* vol 374 (February 25, 2016): 701-703, http://www.nejm.org/doi/full/10.1056/NEJMp1600233.

133. Bethany Wheeler, "Overview of the Hospital Value-Based Purchasing (VBP) Fiscal Year (FY) 2017," Centers for Medicare & Medicaid Services, February 17, 2015, http://www.qualityreportingcenter.com/wp-content/uploads/2015/02/HVBP_021715_Overview-FY2017.pdf.

134. Jordan Rau, "First Look at Medicare Quality Incentive Program Finds Little Benefit," Kaiser Health News, August 6, 2014, http://capsules.kaiserhealthnews.org/index.php/2014/08/first-look-at-medicare-quality-incentive-program-finds-little-benefit/.

135. Juliette Mullin, "What to Know about Value-Based Penalties in the New Fiscal Year," Advisory Board, October 1, 2014, https://www.advisory.com/daily-briefing/blog/2014/10/what-to-know-about-the-care-quality-penalties-in-the-new-fiscal-year.

136. Jordan Rau, "Medicare Penalizes Nearly 1,500 Hospitals for Poor Quality Scores," National Public Radio, November 15, 2013, http://www.npr.org/sections/health-shots/2013/11/15/245254951/medicare-penalizes-nearly-1-500-hospitals-for-poor-quality-scores.

137. Bobbi Brown, "Why You Need to Understand Value-Based Reimbursement and How to Survive It," Health Catalyst, n.d., https://www.healthcatalyst.com/understand-value-based-reimbursement.

138. Rau, "First Look at Medicare Quality Incentive Program Finds Little Benefit."

139. Jordan Rau, "Nearly 1,500 Hospitals Penalized Under Medicare Program Rating Quality," Kaiser Health News, November 14, 2013, http://www.kaiserhealthnews.org/stories/2013/november/14/value-based-purchasing-medicare.aspx.

140. Ibid.

141. For more on patient satisfaction scores, *see* Shivan J. Mehta, MD, MBA, "Patient Satisfaction Reporting and Its Implications for Patient Care," *AMA Journal of Ethics* vol. 17, no. 7 (July 2015): 616–21, http://journalofethics.ama-assn.org/2015/07/ecas3-1507.html; see also John W. Bachman, MD, "The Problem With Patient Satisfaction Scores," *Family Practice Management* vol.1 (January/February 2016): 23-27, http://www.aafp.org/fpm/2016/0100/p23.html.

142. Jordan Rau, "When TLC Doesn't Satisfy Patients, Elite Hospitals May Pay A Price," Kaiser Health News, November 7, 2011, http://khn.org/news/patient-ratings-hospital-medicare-reimbursements/.

143. Mehta.

144. Jordan Rau, "Nearly 1,500 Hospitals Penalized Under Medicare Program Rating Quality," Kaiser Health News, November 14, 2013, http://www.kaiserhealthnews.org/stories/2013/november/14/value-based-purchasing-medicare.aspx.

145. "Early VBP Penalties Data Show Little Effect on Hospital Quality," Advisory Board, August 7, 2014, http://www.advisory.com/daily-briefing/2014/08/07/early-vbp-penalties-data-show-little-effect-on-hospital-quality.

146. HAL 9000, Robot Hall of Fame. n.d., http://www.robothalloffame.org/inductees/03inductees/hal.html.

147. Cossman.

148. Jeffrey Henry Hise, MD, "And Then Came the PACS," *JAMA (Journal of the American Medical Association)*, July 18, 2017, http://jamanetwork.com/journals/jama/fullarticle/2645110.

149. Ibid.

150. Robert O'Harrow Jr., "The Machinery Behind Health-Care Reform," *Washington Post*, May 16, 2009, http://www.washingtonpost.com/wp-dyn/content/article/2009/05/15/AR2009051503667.html.

151. Ibid.

152. Ibid.; see also Jan Walker et al., "The Value of Health Care Information Exchange and Interoperability," *Health Affairs*, January 2005, http://www.providersedge.com/ehdocs/ehr_articles/The_Value_Of_Health_Care_Information_Exchange_And_Interoperability.pdf.

153. Steve Lohr, "The Agenda Behind Electronic Health Records," *Bits* (blog), *New York Times*, May 9, 2010, http://bits.blogs.nytimes.com/2010/05/09/the-agenda-behind-electronic-health-records/?_php=true&_type=blogs&_r=0.

154. Ibid.

155. Ralph Grams, "The Obama EHR Experiment," *Journal of Medical Systems* vol. 36, no. 2 (April 2012): 951–6, http://link.springer.com/article/10.1007%2Fs10916-010-9559-z/fulltext.html.

156. Kathryn M. McDonald, MM, et al., "Chapter 4, Emerging Trends in Care Coordination Measurement," in "Care Coordination Measures Atlas Update," Agency for Healthcare Research and Quality, US Department of Health & Human Services, last updated June 2014, http://www.ahrq.gov/professionals/prevention-chronic-care/improve/coordination/atlas2014/chapter4.html.

157. HIMSS, "HIMSS18 Opening Keynote, Eric Schmidt," YouTube, March 16, 2018, from 30:30, https://www.youtube.com/watch?v=ACQes9erfsw.

158. Mansur Hasib, "EHR & Artificial Intelligence Can Reduce Medical Errors," InformationWeek, November 11, 2014, http://www.informationweek.com/healthcare/electronic-health-records/ehr-and-artificial-intelligence-can-reduce-medical-errors/a/d-id/1317389.

159. David Nather, "A Skeptical Look at a New AI Medical Initiative," Axios, August 16, 2017, https://www.axios.com/a-skeptical-look-at-a-new-ai-medical-initiative-2473347683.html.

160. Evan Sweeney, "Despite Support from AMA, Doctors Worry the Human Diagnosis Project Could Be 'Spitting Out Garbage,'" FierceHealthcare, August 18, 2017, http://www.fiercehealthcare.com/analytics/despite-support-from-ama-doctors-worry-health-diagnosis-project-could-be-spitting-out.

161. Kathryn Doyle, "Doctors Significantly Better than Google According to New Research," *HuffPost* (Reuters), last updated October 25, 2016, https://www.huffingtonpost.com/entry/doctors-significantly-better-than-google-according-to-new-research_us_57fe4d59e4b05eff55809fd9.

162. Mike Miliard, "AI is Disrupting Clinical Practice, So How Tech is Implemented Matters," *Healthcare IT News,* January 30, 2018, http://www.healthcareitnews.com/news/ai-disrupting-clinical-practice-so-how-tech-implemented-matters.

163. Mike Miliard, "Radiologists Are Paying Attention to Workflow, Career Impact of AI," *Healthcare IT News*, January 30, 2018, http://www.healthcareitnews.com/news/ai-adoption-rate-picking-and-radiologists-are-paying-attention-workflow-career-impact.

164. Sent to the author, name withheld, published with permission, 2018.

165. "Centers for Medicare & Medicaid Services Move Toward Pay-for-Performance," *Journal of Oncology Practice* vol. 1, no. 1 (May 2005): 27, https://www.ncbi.nlm.nih.gov/pmc/articles/PMC2793563/; see also "Medicare Advantage, Kaiser Family Foundation, October 10, 2017, http://www.kff.org/medicare/fact-sheet/medicare-advantage/.

166. Total Performance Score Information," Medicare, Centers for Medicare & Medicaid Services, n.d., https://www.medicare.gov/hospitalcompare/data/total-performance-scores.html.

167. "Clinical Quality Measures Basics," Centers for Medicare & Medicaid Services, last modified February 26, 2018, https://www.cms.gov/Regulations-and-Guidance/Legislation/EHRIncentivePrograms/ClinicalQualityMeasures.html.

168. Elaine Rosenblatt, MSN, "Quest for Quality: Immunizations" (PowerPoint presentation, Dane County Immunization Coalition Membership Meeting, Madison, WI, November 13, 2012), https://www.publichealthmdc.com/DCIC/documents/DCICmin20121113rosenblatt.pdf.

169. "Physician Quality Reporting System (PQRS)," Physician Compare, Medicare, Centers for Medicare & Medicaid Services, n.d., https://www.medicare.gov/physiciancompare/staticpages/data/pqrs.html.

170. Alexandra Robbins, "The Problem with Satisfied Patients," *The Atlantic*, April 17, 2015, http://www.theatlantic.com/health/archive/2015/04/the-problem-with-satisfied-patients/390684/.

171. "Measuring and Improving Quality of Care: A Report from the American Heart Association/American College of Cardiology First Scientific Forum on Assessment of Healthcare Quality in Cardiovascular Disease and Stroke," *Circulation* vol. 101, no. 12 (March 28, 2000): 1483–93, http://circ.ahajournals.org/content/101/12/1483.full.

172. "Linking Quality to Payment," Hospital Compare, Medicare, Centers for Medicare & Medicaid Services, n.d., https://www.medicare.gov/hospitalcompare/linking-quality-to-payment.html.

173. "U.S. Physicians in Four Specialties Spend $15 Billion Annually Reporting Data to Insurance Providers," Weill Cornell Medicine, March 7, 2016, https://news.weill.cornell.edu/news/2016/03/us-physicians-in-four-specialties-spend-15-billion-annually-reporting-data-to-insurance-providers.

174. Kathie McDonald-McClure, "Certified EHRs Expected to Transmit Data for Medicare's New Hospital Inpatient Value-Based Purchasing Program,"

HITECH Law (blog), Wyatt Tarrant & Combs LLP, February 8, 2011, https://wyatthitechlaw.com/2011/02/08/certified-ehrs-expected-to-transmit-data-for-medicares-new-hospital-inpatient-value-based-purchasing-program/.

175. US Department of Health & Human Services News Division, "Better, Smarter, Healthier: In Historic Announcement, HHS Sets Clear Goals and Timeline for Shifting Medicare Reimbursements from Volume to Value," The Lund Report, January 26, 2015, https://www.thelundreport.org/content/better-smarter-healthier-historic-announcement-hhs-sets-clear-goals-and-timeline-shifting.

176. Ibid.

177. Patrick Conway, MD, MSc, "CMS Updates Its Quality Strategy to Build a Better, Smarter, and Healthier Health Care Delivery System," *The CMS Blog*, Centers for Medicare & Medicaid Services, November 25, 2015, http://blog.cms.gov/2015/11/.

178. "IMPACT Act of 2014 Data Standardization & Cross Setting Measures," Centers for Medicare & Medicaid Services, last modified October 28, 2015, https://www.cms.gov/Medicare/Quality-Initiatives-Patient-Assessment-Instruments/Post-Acute-Care-Quality-Initiatives/IMPACT-Act-of-2014-and-Cross-Setting-Measures.html.

179. Bill Siwicki, "Vision for Value-Based Care Must Include Clinical Decision Support Integrated into EHR," *Healthcare IT News,* February 20, 2018, http://www.healthcareitnews.com/news/vision-value-based-care-must-include-clinical-decision-support-integrated-ehr.

180. John Commins, "Value-Based Payments Must Address Patient Mix," *HealthLeaders Media*, December 5, 2017, http://www.healthleadersmedia.com/quality/value-based-payments-must-address-patient-mix; see also Eric T. Roberts, PhD, et al., "The Value-Based Payment Modifier: Program Outcomes and Implications for Disparities," *Annals of Internal Medicine*, vol. 168, no. 4 (November 28, 2017): 255-265, http://annals.org/aim/article-abstract/2664654/value-based-payment-modifier-program-outcomes-implications-disparities.

181. "Impact of US Pay for Performance Programs 'Limited and Disappointing,' Say Experts," *The BMJ (British Medical Journal), Medical Xpress*, January 3, 2018, https://medicalxpress.com/news/2018-01-impact-limited-disappointing-experts.html.

182. Daniel Jackson et al., editors, *Software for Dependable Systems: Sufficient Evidence?* (Washington, D.C.: National Academies Press, 2007), 2, https://www.cs.drexel.edu/~spiros/teaching/CS576/papers/Software-for-dependable-systems.pdf.

183. Ben-Tzion Karsh et al., "Health Information Technology: Fallacies and Sober Realities," *Journal of the American Medical Informatics Association* vol. 17, no. 6 (Nov-Dec 2010): 617–23, https://www.ncbi.nlm.nih.gov/pmc/articles/PMC3000760/.

184. Alison Banger, MPH, and Mark L. Graber, MD, "Recent Evidence that Health IT Improves Patient Safety," RTI International, The Office of the National Coordinator for Health Information Technology, February 2015, 8, http://www.healthit.gov/sites/default/files/brief_1_final_feb11t.pdf.

185. Gerard Castro, PhD, MPH, et al., "Investigations of Health IT-Related Deaths, Serious Injuries or Unsafe Conditions," The Joint Commission, The Office of the National Coordinator for Health Information Technology, March 30, 2015, 2, https://www.healthit.gov/sites/default/files/safer/pdfs/Investigations_HealthIT_related_SE_Report_033015.pdf.

186. Ibid., 9.

187. Ibid., 27.

188. Ibid., 9.

189. Ibid., 9–10.

190. Andrew Gettinger, MD, and Kathy Kenyon, JD, "The Evidence Shows IOM Was Right on Health IT and Patient Safety," *Health IT Buzz* (blog), The Office of the National Coordinator for Health Information Technology, April 27, 2015, http://www.healthit.gov/buzz-blog/health-it-safety/evidence-shows-health-it-improves-patient-safety/.

191. Memorandum to Jeff Shuren, MD, JD, Director, CDRH, from Chuck

McCollough, Office of Surveillance and Biometrics (OSB), Center for Devices and Radiological Health (CDRH) et al., US Department of Health & Human Services, Drexel University College of Computing & Informatics, February 23, 2010, http://cci.drexel.edu/faculty/ssilverstein/Internal-FDA-Report-on-Adverse-Events-Involving-Health-Information-IT.pdf; see also "Internal FDA Memorandum of Feb. 23, 2010 to Jeffrey Shuren on HIT Risks. Smoking Gun? I Report, You Decide," *Health Care Renewal* (blog), August 5, 2010, http://hcrenewal.blogspot.com/2010/08/smoking-gun-internal-fda-memorandum-of.html.

192. "Testimony of Jeffrey Shuren, Director of FDA's Center for Devices and Radiological Health," Health Information Technology (HIT) Policy Committee Adoption/Certification Workgroup, February 25, 2010, http://www.cchfreedom.org/cchf.php/597.

193. Castro, 2.

194. Arthur Allen, "ONC Gets Ready to Shrink," Politico Morning eHealth, December 4, 2017, https://www.politico.com/newsletters/morning-ehealth/2017/12/04/onc-gets-ready-to-shrink-038972.

195. ECRI Institute PSO, "Wrong-Record, Wrong-Data Errors with Health IT Systems," *PSO Navigator* vol. 7, no. 2 (May 2015), https://www.ecri.org/Resources/In_the_News/PSONavigator_Data_Errors_in_Health_IT_Systems.pdf.

196. Allison Inserro, "EHR Usability Linked to Possible Patient Harms, Study Finds," *American Journal of Managed Care*, March 27, 2018, http://www.ajmc.com/focus-of-the-week/ehr-usability-linked-to-possible-patient-harms-study-finds.

197. Evan Sweeney, "Conservative Estimates of EHR Safety Incidents Belie Bigger Industry Concerns," FierceHealthcare, March 28, 2018, https://www.fiercehealthcare.com/tech/ehr-patient-safety-research-medstar-jama.

198. Inserro; see also Howe JL et al., "Electronic Health Record Usability Issues and Potential Contribution to Patient Harm," *JAMA (Journal of the American Medical Association)* vol. 319, no. 12 (2018): 1276-1278, https://jamanetwork.com/journals/jama/article-abstract/2676098?redirect=true.

199. Marqui's letter to Schlafly.

200. June Eichner, MS, and Maya Das, MD, JD, "Challenges and Barriers to Clinical Decision Support (CDS) Design and Implementation Experienced in the Agency for Healthcare Research and Quality CDS Demonstrations," Agency for Healthcare Research and Quality, US Department of Health & Human Services, March 2010, https://healthit.ahrq.gov/sites/default/files/docs/page/CDS_challenges_and_barriers.pdf.

201. "Clinical Decision Support (CDS)," HealthIT, last updated January 15, 2013, https://www.healthit.gov/policy-researchers-implementers/clinical-decision-support-cds.

202. Adam Wright et al., "Analysis of Clinical Decision Support System Malfunctions: A Case Series and Survey," *Journal of the American Medical Informatics Association* vol. 23, no. 6 (March 28, 2016): 1068-76, http://jamia.oxfordjournals.org/content/early/2016/03/28/jamia.ocw005.

203. Kurt Hegmann, MD, MPH, and Steven Wiesner, MD, "Integrating Evidence-Based Decision Tools Within an EHR (PowerPoint presentation), Session 197, HIMSS 2018, March 8, 2018, http://365.himss.org/sites/himss365/files/365/handouts/550237067/handout-197.pdf.

204. "Clinical Decision Support (CDS)," The Office of the National Coordinator of Health Information Technology, last updated January 15, 2013, https://www.healthit.gov/policy-researchers-implementers/clinical-decision-support-cds; *see also* Twila Brase, RN, PHN, "How Technocrats are Taking Over the Practice of Medicine: A Wake-up Call to the American People," Citizens' Council on Health Care (now Citizens' Council for Health Freedom), January 2005, http://www.cchfreedom.org/pdfreport/.

205. "Improving Physician Adherence to Clinical Practice Guidelines," New England Healthcare Institute, February 2008, 13, http://www.nehi.net/writable/publication_files/file/cpg_report_final.pdf.

206. Ibid., 12.

207. Eichner and Das, 1.

208. Ibid., 9.

209. Ibid., 15.

210. Ibid., 14.

211. Ibid., 16.

212. Ibid.

213. Ibid., 3.

214. Wright et al.

215. Ibid.

216. "Statement from FDA Commissioner Scott Gottlieb, MD, on Advancing New Digital Health Policies to Encourage Innovation, Bring Efficiency and Modernization to Regulation," US Food & Drug Administration, December 7, 2017, https://www.fda.gov/NewsEvents/Newsroom/PressAnnouncements/ucm587890.htm.

217. "Clinical and Patient Decision Support Software: Draft Guidance for Industry and Food and Drug Administration Staff," US Food & Drug Administration, December 8, 2017, 10, https://www.fda.gov/downloads/MedicalDevices/DeviceRegulationandGuidance/GuidanceDocuments/UCM587819.pdf.

218. Darius Tahir, "CR Contains Telehealth, ACO, Meaningful Use Goodies," Politico Morning eHealth, February 7, 2018, https://www.politico.com/newsletters/morning-ehealth/2018/02/07/cr-contains-telehealth-aco-meaningful-use-goodies-095946.

219. Russell Branzell and Cletis Earle, letter to Scott Gottlieb, MD, Commissioner, Food and Drug Administration, College of Healthcare Information Management Executives (CHIME), February 6, 2018, https://chimecentral.org/wp-content/uploads/2018/02/CHIME-Letter-to-FDA-on-CDS-for-board-FINAL.pdf.

220. Tahir, "CR Contains Telehealth, ACO, Meaningful Use Goodies."

221. Douglas B. Fridsma, MD, PhD, "RE: Clinical and Patient Decision Support Software Draft Guidance; Docket No. FDA-2017-D-6569-0001," letter to the US Food and Drug Administration, American Medical Informatics Association, February 6, 2018, https://www.amia.org/sites/default/files/AMIA-Response-to-FDA-Draft-Guidance-on-Clinical-and-Patient-Decision-Support-Software.pdf.

222. HIMSS, "HIMSS18 Opening Keynote, Eric Schmidt," YouTube, March 16, 2018, from 37:35, https://www.youtube.com/watch?v=ACQes9erfsw.

223. "Inquiry Launched into 450,000 Missed Breast Cancer Screenings," *New Scientist* (Associated Press), May 2, 2018, https://www.newscientist.com/article/2167926-inquiry-launched-into-450000-missed-breast-cancer-screenings/#.WunQpAeHq-M.twitter.

224. Ryan Black, "Is AI As Smart As It Thinks It Is?" *Healthcare Analytics News*, October 16, 2017, http://www.hcanews.com/news/is-ai-as-smart-as-it-thinks-it-is-1.

225. Ryan Black, "A New Ethical Wrinkle for Medical Algorithms," *Healthcare Analytics News*, March 16, 2018, http://www.hcanews.com/news/a-new-ethical-wrinkle-for-medical-algorithms; see also Danton S. Char, MD, et al., "Implementing Machine Learning in Health Care—Addressing Ethical Challenges," *New England Journal of Medicine* no. 378 (March 15, 2018): 981-983, http://www.nejm.org/doi/full/10.1056/NEJMp1714229.

226. Roger L. Sur and Philip Dahm, "History of Evidence-Based Medicine," *Indian Journal of Urology* vol. 27, no. 4 (Oct-Dec 2011): 487-489, https://www.ncbi.nlm.nih.gov/pmc/articles/PMC3263217/.

227. For more information on evidenced-base medicine, see Michel Accad, MD, "The Devolution of Evidence-Based Medicine," *Alert & Oriented* (blog), March 11, 2016, http://alertandoriented.com/the-devolution-of-evidence-based-medicine/; see also Gary Belkin, MD, MPH, PhD, "The Technocratic Wish: Making Sense and Finding Power in the 'Managed' Medical Marketplace," *Journal of Health Politics, Policy and Law* vol. 22, no. 2 (April 1997): 509-532, https://www.ncbi.nlm.nih.gov/pubmed/9159714; see also Twila Brase, RN, PHN, "How Technocrats are Taking Over the Practice of Medicine: A Wake-up Call to the American People," Citizens' Council on Health Care (now Citizens' Council for Health Freedom), January 2005, http://www.cchfreedom.org/pdfreport/.

228. Steve Hickey, PhD, and Hilary Roberts, PhD, *Tarnished Gold: The Sickness of Evidence-Based Medicine* (CreateSpace, 2011).

229. Peter Wood and David Randall, "How Bad Is the Government's Science?" *Wall Street Journal*, April 16, 2018, https://www.wsj.com/articles/how-bad-is-the-governments-science-1523915765.

230. "Computerized Provider Order Entry," Patient Safety Network, Agency for Healthcare Research and Quality, US Department of Health & Human Services last updated June 2017, https://psnet.ahrq.gov/primers/primer/6/computerized-provider-order-entry.

231. Joan S. Ash, PhD, et al., "An Unintended Consequence of CPOE Implementation: Shifts in Power, Control, and Autonomy," AMIA Annual Symposium Proceedings Archive, 2006, 11–15, https://www.ncbi.nlm.nih.gov/pmc/articles/PMC1839304/.

232. Linda T. Kohn et al., editors, *To Err is Human: Building a Safer Health System* (Washington D.C.: National Academies Press, 2000), chap. 8, http://www.ncbi.nlm.nih.gov/books/NBK225188/.

233. Mostrous.

234. Farah Magrabi, PhD, et al., "Patient Safety Problems Associated with Healthcare Information Technology: An Analysis of Adverse Events Reported to the US Food and Drug Administration," AMIA Annual Symposium Proceedings Archive, October 22, 2011, 853–7, http://www.ncbi.nlm.nih.gov/pmc/articles/PMC3243129/.

235. "Computerized Provider Order Entry," Patient Safety Network, Agency for Healthcare Research and Quality, US Department of Health & Human Services last updated June 2017, https://psnet.ahrq.gov/primers/primer/6/computerized-provider-order-entry.

236. Ross Koppel et al., "Role of Computerized Physician Order Entry Systems in Facilitating Medication Errors," *JAMA (Journal of the American Medical Association)* vol. 293, no. 10 (March 9, 2005): 1197-1203, http://jamanetwork.com/journals/jama/fullarticle/200498.

237. Erin Sparnon, MEng, and William M. Marella, MBA, "The Role of the Electronic Health Record in Patient Safety Events," Pennsylvania Patient Safety Authority, vol. 9, no. 4 (December 2012): 114, http://patientsafety.pa.gov/ADVISORIES/documents/201212_113.pdf.

238. "MAUDE Adverse Event Report: CERNER MILLENIUM CPOE, POWER CHART," US Food & Drug Administration, January 1, 2010, https://www.accessdata.fda.gov/scripts/cdrh/cfdocs/cfmaude/detail.cfm?mdrfoi__id=1584195.

239. Victoria M. Bradley et al., "Evaluation of Reported Medication Errors Before and After Implementation of Computerized Practitioner Order Entry," *Journal of Health Information Management* vol. 20, no. 4 (Fall 2006): 46–53, https://www.ncbi.nlm.nih.gov/pubmed/17091790.

240. Mostrous.

241. Stephen Soumerai and Tony Avery, "Don't Repeat the UK's Electronic Health Records Failure," *HuffPost* (blog), last updated May 25, 2011, http://www.huffingtonpost.com/stephen-soumerai/dont-repeat-the-uks-elect_b_790470.html.

242. Mike Miliard, "CPOE Cuts Medication Errors, Study Shows," *Healthcare IT News*, February 22, 2013, http://www.healthcareitnews.com/news/cpoe-cuts-medication-errors-study-shows.

243. P. Carayon et al., "EHR-related Medication Errors in Two ICUs," Patient Safety Network, Agency for Healthcare Research and Quality, US Department of Health & Human Services January 2017, https://psnet.ahrq.gov/resources/resource/30500; see also Pascale Carayon, PhD, et al., "Electronic Health Records," Patient Safety Network, Agency for Healthcare Research and Quality, US Department of Health & Human Services, updated November 2017, http://onlinelibrary.wiley.com/doi/10.1002/jhrm.21259/abstract.

244. Katie Wike, "CPOE Isn't Catching Most Medical Errors," Health IT Outcomes, February 2, 2015, https://www.healthitoutcomes.com/doc/cpoe-isn-t-catching-most-medical-errors-0001.

245. Shannon Barnet, "CPOE Systems Prevent Some Medication Errors, But Miss Nearly 40%," Beckers Clinical Leadership & Infection Control, April 7, 2016, http://www.beckershospitalreview.com/quality/

cpoe-systems-prevent-some-medication-errors-but-miss-nearly-40.html.

246. Wike.

247. Bob Wachter, "How Technology Led a Hospital to Give a Patient 38 Times His Dosage," *Wired,* March 30, 2015, https://www.wired.com/2015/03/how-technology-led-a-hospital-to-give-a-patient-38-times-his-dosage/#.kr5h1xh8q.

248. Yong Y. Han, MD, et al., "Unexpected Increased Mortality after Implementation of a Commercially Sold Computerized Physician Order Entry System," *Pediatrics* vol. 116, no. 6 (December 2005): 1506–12, http://pediatrics.aappublications.org/content/116/6/1506.

249. Ibid., 1509.

250. Ibid., 1510.

251. PRNewswire-USNewswire, "ECRI Institute PSO Uncovers Health Information Technology-Related Events in Deep Dive Analysis," ECRI Institute, February 6, 2013, http://www.prnewswire.com/news-releases/ecri-institute-pso-uncovers-health-information-technology-related-events-in-deep-dive-analysis-190064661.html.

252. "Ways EHRs Can Lead to Unintended Safety Problems," *American Medical News*, February 25, 2013, http://www.amednews.com/article/20130225/profession/130229981/4/; see also ECRI Institute PSO, "ECRI Institute PSO Deep Drive: Health Information Technology," December 2012, 4, https://www.ecri.org/components/PSOCore/Documents/Deep%20Dive/Deep%20Dive%20-%20Health%20Information%20Technology%200113.pdf.

253. Dan Childs et al., "President-Elect Urges Electronic Medical Records in 5 Years," ABC News, January 9, 2009, http://abcnews.go.com/Health/President44/story?id=6606536.

254. "Ways EHRs Can Lead to Unintended Safety Problems."

255. Cheryl Clark, "HIT Errors 'Tip of the Iceberg,' Says ECRI," *HealthLeaders Media*, April 5, 2013, http://www.healthleadersmedia.com/technology/hit-errors-tip-iceberg-says-ecri.

256. Ibid.

257. PRNewswire-USNewswire, "ECRI Institute PSO Uncovers Health Information Technology-Related Events in Deep Dive Analysis."

258. "ECRI Institute Releases Top 10 Health Technology Hazards Report for 2014," Diagnostic and Interventional Cardiology (DAIC), November 20, 2013, https://www.dicardiology.com/article/ecri-institute-releases-top-10-health-technology-hazards-report-2014.

259. Erin McCann, "HIT Systems among Top 10 Health Tech Hazards, Says ECRI," *Healthcare IT News*, November 6, 2012, http://www.healthcareitnews.com/news/top-10-health-tech-hazards-named-hit-systems-among-top.

260. ECRI Institute PSO, "Wrong-Record, Wrong-Data Errors with Health IT Systems."

261. Freudenheim.

262. "EHR and Patient Safety: A Real Danger, Even for Experienced Users," *PT in Motion News* (blog), American Physical Therapy Association, June 24, 2014, http://www.apta.org/PTinMotion/NewsNow/?blogid=10737418615&id=10737434086.

263. Ibid.

264. Susan Chapman, "Report Analyzes EHR Patient Safety Concerns," *For the Record* vol. 26, no. 11 (November 2014): 20, http://www.fortherecordmag.com/archives/1114p20.shtml.

265. Ibid.

266. Ibid.

267. S. Silverstein, "Meaningful Use Final Rule: Have the Administration and ONC Put the Cart Before the Horse on Health IT?" *Health Care Renewal* (blog), July 13, 2010, http://hcrenewal.blogspot.com/2010/07/meaningful-use-final-rule-have.html.

268. Fred Schulte and Emma Schwartz, "FDA, Obama Digital Medical Records Team at Odds Over Safety Oversight," *HuffPost* (blog), updated December 6, 2017, http://www.huffingtonpost.com/2010/08/04/fda-obama-digital-medical_n_670036.html.

269. Grams.

270. Freudenheim.

271. Marc Probst and Larry Wolf, "Comments on Patient Safety and Electronic Health Record Systems," (PowerPoint presentation, The Office of the National Coordinator for Health Information Technology, February 6, 2013), http://www.healthit.gov/FACAS/sites/faca/files/hitpc_cawg_patient_safety_hit_final.pdf.

272. Christopher Nemeth and Richard Cook, "Hiding in Plain Sight: What Koppel et al. Tell Us about Healthcare IT," *Journal of Biomedical Informatics* vol. 38 (May 5, 2005): 263, http://www.wapatientsafety.org/downloads/article-8.pdf.

273. Bernie Monegain, "3 EMRs Lead with Mid-Sized Practices," *Healthcare IT News*, January 21, 2014, http://www.healthcareitnews.com/news/3-emrs-lead-mid-sized-practices.

274. "Adam Buck," Health IT Fellows Bios, The Office of the National Coordinator of Health Information Technology, last updated November 27, 2013, https://www.healthit.gov/providers-professionals/health-it-fellows-bios.

275. Nemeth and Cook.

276. Ibid.

277. "Issue Brief: Physician Perspectives about Health Information Technology," Deloitte Center for Health Solutions, 2012, 4, http://www.scottsdaleinstitute.org/conferences/spring/2012/supp/Deloitte%20PhysicianPerspectivesAboutHIT_021612.pdf.

278. Cossman.

279. Valinoti.

280. "ECRI Institute PSO Deep Drive: Health Information Technology," December 2012, https://www.ecri.org/components/PSOCore/Documents/Deep%20Dive/Deep%20Dive%20-%20Health%20Information%20Technology%200113.pdf.

281. Mostrous.

282. Freudenheim.

283. SScot M. Silverstein, MD, "Cart before the Horse Again: AHRQ's 'Health IT Hazard Manager,'" *Contemporary Issues in Medical Informatics: Good Health IT, Bad Health IT, and Common Examples of Healthcare IT Difficulties* (blog), Drexel University, June 2012, http://www.ischool.drexel.edu/faculty/ssilverstein/cases/?loc=cases&sloc=Cart_before_horse.

284. Mostrous.

285. T. Eric Schackow, MD, PhD, et al., "EHR Meltdown: How to Protect Your Patient Data," *Family Practice Management* vol. 16, no. 6 (June 2008): A3-A8, http://www.aafp.org/fpm/2008/0600/pa3.html.

286. Schulte and Schwartz.

287. "Munson Memo Explains Systems Failure," *Traverse City Record Eagle*, June 30, 2011, http://www.record-eagle.com/archives/munson-memo-explains-systems-failure/article_5cd90906-9ae0-53ba-b2bb-ef82215a13ef.html.

288. Jonathan D. Silver, "Computer Outage at UPMC Called 'Rare,'" *Pittsburgh Post-Gazette*, December 23, 2011, http://www.post-gazette.com/local/city/2011/12/24/Computer-outage-at-UPMC-called-rare/stories/201112240115.

289. Globe Newswire, "Cerner to Present at JP Morgan Healthcare Conference," January 2, 2013, https://cernercorporation.gcs-web.com/news-releases/news-release-details/cerner-present-jp-morgan-healthcare-conference-1.

290. Ken Terry, "Cerner Hosting Outage Raises Doctor, Hospital Concerns," InformationWeek, July 26, 2012, http://www.informationweek.com/healthcare/electronic-health-records/cerner-hosting-outage-raises-doctor-hospital-concerns/d/d-id/1105525.

291. Anne Zieger, "Cerner Outage Sparks Controversy," Hospital EMR and EHR (blog), July 27, 2012, http://www.hospitalemrandehr.com/2012/07/27/cerner-outage-sparks-controversy/.

292. Erin McCann, "Setback for Sutter after $1B EHR Crashes," *Healthcare IT News*, August 28, 2013, http://www.healthcareitnews.com/news/setback-sutter-after-1b-ehr-system%20crashes.

293. Stephanie Baum, "HCA Says Hardware Storage Glitch Behind EHR Outage," MedCity News, December 7, 2015, http://medcitynews.com/2015/12/hardware-storage-glitch/?rf=1.

294. Mark Hagland, "Breaking News: Medstar Health Hacked, EHR Down, FBI Investigating," Healthcare

Informatics, March 28, 2016, https://www.healthcare-informatics.com/article/breaking-news-medstar-health-hacked-ehr-down-fbi-investigating.

295. "EHR Failures Can Be Dangerous without a Contingency Plan," *Same-Day Surgery*, March 1, 2015, https://www.ahcmedia.com/articles/134670-ehr-failures-can-be-dangerous-without-having-a-contingency-plan.

296. Joseph Conn, "Chicago-Area HIE Sues IT Vendor over Shutdown Plans," *Modern Healthcare*, April 20, 2016, http://www.modernhealthcare.com/article/20160420/NEWS/160429995/chicago-area-hie-sues-it-vendor-over-shutdown-plans.

297. Christopher Rowland, "Billing Dispute Leads to Blocked Patient Data in Maine," *Boston Globe*, September 22, 2014, http://www.bostonglobe.com/news/nation/2014/09/21/electronic-health-records-vendor-compugroup-blocks-maine-practice-from-accessing-patient-data/6ILpMv78NARDsrdU5O0T9N/story.html.

298. Ian Barker, "Ransomware Economy Grows 2500 percent since 2016," BetaNews, October 11, 2017, https://betanews.com/2017/10/11/ransomware-economy-growth/.

299. Richard Winton, "2 More Southland Hospitals Attacked by Hackers Using Ransomware," *Los Angeles Times*, March 22, 2016, http://www.latimes.com/local/lanow/la-me-ln-two-more-so-cal-hospitals-ransomware-20160322-story.html.

300. "Hospital Declares 'Internal State of Emergency' After Ransomware Infection," Krebs on Security, March 2016, https://krebsonsecurity.com/2016/03/hospital-declares-internet-state-of-emergency-after-ransomware-infection/.

301. David Bisson, "U.S. Hospitals Are at Risk of Ransomware Attacks," Tripwire, April 10, 2016, http://www.tripwire.com/state-of-security/regulatory-compliance/hipaa/how-hospitals-are-at-risk-of-ransomware-attacks/.

302. Jose Pagliery, "U.S. Hospitals are Getting Hit by Hackers," CNN Tech, March 28, 2016, http://money.cnn.com/2016/03/23/technology/hospital-ransomware/.

303. "At 2 a.m. on a Sunday, a Hospital Was Hacked. Here's How It Kept Key Departments Operating," Advisory Board, May 25, 2017, https://www.advisory.com/daily-briefing/2017/05/25/ecmc-hack.

304. Thomas Fox-Brewster, "Medical Devices Hit By Ransomware for the First Time in US Hospitals," *Forbes*, May 17, 2017, https://www.forbes.com/sites/thomasbrewster/2017/05/17/wannacry-ransomware-hit-real-medical-devices/#5b9d0899425c.

305. Rachel Clarke, MD, and Taryn Youngstein, MD, "Cyberattack on Britain's National Health Services—A Wake-up Call for Modern Medicine," *New England Journal of Medicine* vol. 377 (August 3, 2017): 409–11, http://www.nejm.org/doi/full/10.1056/NEJMp1706754.

306. Fox-Brewster.

307. Evan Sweeney, "Physician Practices Report Lost Revenue and Patient Care Disruptions Following Allscripts Ransomware Attack," FierceHealthcare, January 23, 2018, https://www.fiercehealthcare.com/privacy-security/allscripts-ransomware-ehr-scheduling-claims-billing-cybersecurity-physician.

308. Steve Ragan, "Ransomware Attack Hits MedStar Health, Network Offline," CSO, March 28, 2016, http://www.csoonline.com/article/3048825/security/ransomware-attack-hits-medstar-health-network-offline.html.

309. Chris Nerney, "Bad Choice or No Choice? Indiana Health Network Pays $47,000 to Ransomware Attackers," Connected Care Watch, January 17, 2018, http://www.connectedcarewatch.com/news/bad-choice-or-no-choice-indiana-health-network-pays-47000-ransomware-attackers.

310. Andrea Peterson, "2015 Is Already the Year of the Health-Care Hack—and It's Only Going to Get Worse," *Washington Post*, March 20, 2015, https://www.washingtonpost.com/news/the-switch/wp/2015/03/20/2015-is-already-the-year-of-the-health-care-hack-and-its-only-going-to-get-worse/?utm_term=.ff6dd6d9a5ae.

311. Susan D. Hall, "Healthcare No. 1 Target for Cyberattacks in 2015,"

FierceHealthcare, April 20, 2016, http://www.fiercehealthcare.com/it/healthcare-no-1-target-for-cyberattacks-2015.

312. Anna Wilde Mathews and Danny Yadron, "Health Insurer Anthem Hit by Hackers," *Wall Street Journal*, February 4, 2015, https://www.wsj.com/articles/health-insurer-anthem-hit-by-hackers-1423103720.

313. Fred O'Connor, "Medical Data Is Becoming the Next Revenue Stream for Hackers," *Computerworld*, March 20, 2015, http://www.computerworld.com/article/2900047/medical-data-is-becoming-the-next-revenue-stream-for-hackers.html.

314. Brendon Pierson, "Anthem to Pay Record $115 Million to Settle US Lawsuits over Data Breach," Reuters, June 23, 2017, http://www.reuters.com/article/us-anthem-cyber-settlement-idUSKBN19E2ML.

315. Beth Jones Sanborn, "Landmark $115 Million Settlement Reached in Anthem Data Breach Suit, Consumers Could Feel Sting," *Healthcare IT News*, June 27, 2017, http://www.healthcareitnews.com/news/landmark-115-million-settlement-reached-anthem-data-breach-suit-consumers-could-feel-sting.

316. O'Connor.

317. Ibid.

318. Heather Landi, "Survey: 71 Percent of Healthcare Organizations Allocate a Specific Budget to Cybersecurity," Healthcare Informatics, August 9, 2017, https://www.healthcare-informatics.com/news-item/cybersecurity/survey-71-percent-healthcare-organizations-allocate-specific-budget.

319. Heather Landi, "Survey: One Quarter of Healthcare IT Security Pros Cite Little Confidence in Ability to Manage Digital Threats," Healthcare Informatics, August 23, 2017, https://www.healthcare-informatics.com/news-item/cybersecurity/survey-one-quarter-healthcare-it-security-pros-cite-little-confidence.

320. "More Than 347,000 HITECH Breaches Reported Since 2009," EIN Newsdesk, May 1, 2018, http://www.einnews.com/pr_news/444926661/more-than-347-000-hitech-breaches-reported-since-2009; see also Julie Spitzer, "More Than 347K HITECH Breaches Since 2009—What Gives?" Beckers Health IT & CIO Report, May 2, 2018, https://www.beckershospitalreview.com/cybersecurity/more-than-347k-hitech-breaches-since-2009-what-gives.html.

321. Jessica Davis, "HHS Overhauls 'Wall of Shame' Breach Reporting Website," *Healthcare IT News*, July 26, 2017, http://www.healthcareitnews.com/news/hhs-overhauls-wall-shame-breach-reporting-website.

322. Evan Sweeney, "More than 316,000 Patient Blood Tests Exposed in Breach Linked to Home Monitoring Company," FierceHealthcare, October 11, 2017, https://www.fiercehealthcare.com/privacy-security/data-breach-medical-records-blood-tests-patient-home-monitoring-kromtech-security.

323. Linn Foster Freedman, "Second Largest Business Associate Breach in 2017," Data Privacy + Security Insider, September 28, 2017, https://www.dataprivacyandsecurityinsider.com/2017/09/second-largest-business-associate-breach-in-2017/.

324. Chris Nerney, "Clinic Discovers Network Breach That Lasted 15 Months," Connected Care Watch, July 19, 2017, http://www.hiewatch.com/news/clinic-discovers-network-breach-lasted-15-months.

325. Kira Caban, "Hacking Dominates Breaches, But One Insider Breach Took 14 Years to Discover," *Post-healthcare* (blog), Protenus, August 15, 2017, https://post-healthcare.com/hacking-dominates-breaches-but-one-insider-breach-took-14-years-to-discover-3d6a8cee34dd.

326. David Perera, "Chaffetz: OPM Data Breaches May Affect 32 Million," *Politico*, June 24, 2015, http://www.politico.com/story/2015/06/opm-data-breach-jason-chaffetz-119374.html.

327. Marina Koren, "About Those Fingerprints Stolen in the OPM Hack," *The Atlantic*, September 23, 2015, http://www.theatlantic.com/technology/archive/2015/09/opm-hack-fingerprints/406900/.

328. Ibid.

329. Aliya Sternstein, "The Puzzle of When the OPM Hack was Discovered Might Not Be Solved After All," Nextgov, May 31, 2016, http://m.nextgov.com/cybersecurity/2016/05/probe-when-opm-hack-was-discovered-might-not-be-case-closed/128698/?oref=nextgov_today_nl; see also Andy Medici, "Lawmaker: Earlier Breach Led to Massive OPM Hack," *Federal Times*, June 24, 2015, https://www.federaltimes.com/2015/06/24/lawmaker-earlier-breach-led-to-massive-opm-hack/.

330. Timothy B. Lee, "The Devastating Hack of the Federal Office of Personnel Management, Explained," Vox, September 23, 2015, https://www.vox.com/2015/6/27/8854765/opm-hack-explained; see also "Official: Hacked Federal Agency Has History of Security Failures," CBS News, June 16, 2015, http://www.cbsnews.com/news/official-hacked-federal-agency-opm-has-history-of-security-failures/.

331. Ken Dilanian, Associated Press, "Years of 'Neglected' Security Left Door Open to Hack of Millions of Fed Workers' Info," *U.S. News & World Report*, June 16, 2015, http://www.usnews.com/news/politics/articles/2015/06/16/cybertheft-of-personnel-info-rips-hole-in-espionage-defenses.

332. Akanksha Jayanthi, "It Costs $4M to Respond to a Data Breach: This and 6 More Key Findings from IBM," Becker's Health IT & CIO Report, June 15, 2016, http://www.beckershospitalreview.com/healthcare-information-technology/it-costs-4m-to-respond-to-a-data-breach-this-and-6-more-key-findings-from-ibm.html.

333. Ibid.

334. Ronald Campbell and Deborah Schoch, "Millions of Electronic Medical Records Breached," California Center for Health Reporting, University of Southern California, July 7, 2014, http://centerforhealthreporting.org/article/millions-electronic-medical-records-breached.

335. Patrick Ouellette, "Is HIPAA Fine Money Being Spent to Improve Data Security?" HealthIT Security, June 6, 2013, https://healthitsecurity.com/news/is-hipaa-fine-money-being-spent-to-improve-data-security.

336. Marianne Kolbasuk McGee, "OCR Considering HIPAA Privacy Rule, Enforcement Changes," Bank Info Security, March 28, 2018. Accessed March 29, 2018: https://www.bankinfosecurity.com/ocr-considering-hipaa-privacy-rule-enforcement-changes-a-10750.

IV. HIPAA Doesn't Protect Privacy

1. Daniel J. Solove, "HIPAA Turns 10: Analyzing the Past, Present and Future Impact," *Journal of AHIMA* vol. 84, no. 4 (April 2013): 22–8, http://library.ahima.org/doc?oid=106325#.VyOMuKteJ3Y.

2. Aja Brooks, JD, and Lucia Savage, JD, "The Real HIPAA: Permitted Uses and Disclosures," *Health IT Buzz* (blog), The Office of the National Coordinator for Health Information Technology, February 11, 2016, https://www.healthit.gov/buzz-blog/privacy-and-security-of-ehrs/the-real-hipaa-permitted-uses-and-disclosures/.

3. "HIPAA Administrative Simplification" (Unofficial Version), March 2013, 85, https://www.hhs.gov/sites/default/files/ocr/privacy/hipaa/administrative/combined/hipaa-simplification-201303.pdf.

4. "Comments," "Medicare Program; Merit-Based Incentive Payment System (MIPS) and Alternative Payment Model (APM) Incentive under the Physician Fee Schedule and Criteria for Physician-Focused Payment Models, Proposed Rule," *Federal Register*, posted May 9, 2016, https://www.regulations.gov/document?D=CMS-2016-0060-0372.

5. Sharyl J. Nass et al., editors, *Beyond the HIPAA Privacy Rule: Enhancing Privacy, Improving Health Through Research* (Washington D.C.: National Academies Press, 2009), chap. 4, https://www.ncbi.nlm.nih.gov/books/NBK9573/.

6. "Numbers at a Glance," US Department of Health & Human Services, last reviewed January 31, 2018, https://www.hhs.gov/hipaa/for-professionals/compliance-enforcement/data/numbers-glance/index.html; see also "Health Information Privacy Complaints Received by Calendar Year," US Department of Health & Human Services, last reviewed February 28, 2018, https://www.hhs.gov/hipaa/for-professionals/compliance-enforcement/

data/complaints-received-by-calendar-year/index.html?language=en.

7. Solove.

8. Bernie Monegain, "Brailer on Who Owns Medical Records," *Healthcare IT News*, May 1, 2015, http://www.healthcareitnews.com/news/brailer-who-owns-medical-records.

9. "The 18 HIPAA Identifiers," Duke University School of Medicine, n.d., https://medschool.duke.edu/research/clinical-and-translational-research/duke-office-clinical-research/irb-and-institutional-14.

10. "Guidance Regarding Methods for De-identification of Protected Health Information in Accordance with the Health Insurance Portability and Accountability Act (HIPAA) Privacy Rule," US Department of Health & Human Services, last reviewed November 6, 2015, https://www.hhs.gov/hipaa/for-professionals/privacy/special-topics/de-identification/index.html#rationale.

11. Letter to HHS Secretary Thomas E. Price, MD, National Committee on Vital and Health Statistics, February 23, 2017, https://www.ncvhs.hhs.gov/wp-content/uploads/2013/12/2017-Ltr-Privacy-DeIdentification-Feb-23-Final-w-sig.pdf.

12. Keith Loria, "Physicians Leaving Profession Over EHRs," *Medical Economics*, January 24, 2018, http://medicaleconomics.modernmedicine.com/medical-economics/news/physicians-leaving-profession-over-ehrs?page=0,0.

13. "Summary of the HIPAA Privacy Rule," US Department of Health & Human Services, last reviewed July 26, 2013, https://www.hhs.gov/hipaa/for-professionals/privacy/laws-regulations/index.html.

14. Lucia Savage, JD, "The Real HIPAA," *Health IT Buzz* (blog), The Office of the National Coordinator of Health Information Technology, n.d., https://www.healthit.gov/buzz-blog/category/privacy-and-security-of-ehrs/the-real-hipaa/.

15. "Summary of the HIPAA Privacy Rule."

16. Lucia Savage, JD, "HIPAA Supports Electronic Exchange of Health Information at the Federal, State, and Local Level," *Health IT Buzz* (blog), The Office of the National Coordinator of Health Information Technology, January 11, 2017, https://www.healthit.gov/buzz-blog/privacy-and-security-of-ehrs/the-real-hipaa/hipaa-supports-electronic-exchange-health-information-federal-state-local-level/.

17. Sue Blevins, "Proposed Changes to Privacy Rule Won't Ensure Privacy," Health Freedom Watch, September 2010, http://forhealthfreedom.org/Newsletter/September2010.html#Article3.

18. Ibid; see also "Modifications to the HIPAA Privacy, Security, and Enforcement Rules under the Health Information Technology for Economic and Clinical Health Act, Notice of Proposed Rulemaking," Office for Civil Rights, US Department of Health & Human Services, *Federal Register* vol. 75, no. 134 (July 14, 2010): 40872, 40906, 40907, and 40911, http://www.hhs.gov/sites/default/files/ocr/privacy/hipaa/understanding/coveredentities/nprmhitech.pdf.

19. "Definition of Limited Data Set," Johns Hopkins Medicine, April 2015, http://www.hopkinsmedicine.org/institutional_review_board/hipaa_research/limited_data_set.html.

20. "HITECH Act: Business Associates Subject to Certain Provisions of HIPAA Privacy and Security Rules," Carlton Fields, n.d., https://www.carltonfields.com/files/Publication/54c84388-450c-444b-9b4c-0397b07b2f14/Presentation/PublicationAttachment/d57f1d23-aa8c-4333-8774-0bd02f937805/HITECH%20ACT_Business%20Associates%20Subject%20to%20Certain%20Provisions%20of%20HIPAA.pdf.

21. "45 CFR 164.512—Uses and Disclosures for Which an Authorization or Opportunity to Agree or Object is Not Required," Legal Information Institute, Cornell University Law School, https://www.law.cornell.edu/cfr/text/45/164.512.

22. "Summary of the HIPAA Privacy Rule," OCR Privacy Brief, US Department of Health & Human Services, last revised May 2003, http://www.hhs.gov/sites/default/files/privacysummary.pdf.

23. "Definition of 'Newspeak'—English Dictionary," Cambridge Dictionary, n.d.,

https://dictionary.cambridge.org/us/dictionary/english/newspeak.

24. "Health Insurance Portability and Accountability Act (HIPAA) Privacy Rule and the National Instant Criminal Background Check System (NICS), 45 CFR Part 164, Final Rule," Office for Civil Rights, US Department of Health & Human Services, *Federal Register* vol. 81, no. 3 (January 6, 2016): 383, https://www.gpo.gov/fdsys/pkg/FR-2016-01-06/pdf/2015-33181.pdf.

25. David Humiston and Stephen M. Crane, "Will Your State's Privacy Law Be Superseded by HIPAA?" *Managed Care*, May 2002, https://www.managedcaremag.com/archives/2002/5/will-your-states-privacy-law-be-superseded-hipaa; see also Sharyl J. Nass et al., editors, *Beyond the HIPAA Privacy Rule: Enhancing Privacy, Improving Health Through Research* (Washington D.C.: National Academies Press, 2009), chap. 4, https://www.ncbi.nlm.nih.gov/books/NBK9573/.

26. Joy L. Pritts, "Altered States: State Health Privacy Laws and the Impact of the Federal Health Privacy Rule," *Yale Journal of Health Policy, Law, and Ethics* vol. 2, issue 2 (February 23, 2013): 19, http://digitalcommons.law.yale.edu/cgi/viewcontent.cgi?article=1047&context=yjhple.

27. "Notice of Privacy Practices," Mayo Clinic, 2015, http://www.mayo.edu/pmts/mc5200-mc5299/mc5256-01.pdf.

28. Representative Nick Zerwas et al., "Patient Consent to Release of Health Records Provision Modified," H.F. 3312, Minnesota State Legislature, introduced March 5, 2018, https://www.revisor.mn.gov/bills/bill.php?f=HF3312&y=2018&ssn=0&b=house; see also Senator Eric Pratt et al., "Patient consent to release of health records provisions modification," S.F. 2975, Minnesota State Legislature, introduced March 5, 2018, https://www.revisor.mn.gov/bills/bill.php?f=SF2975&y=2018&ssn=0&b=senate.

29. "How Can Covered Entities Use and Disclose Protected Health Information for Research and Comply with the Privacy Rule?" HIPAA Privacy Rule, National Institutes of Health, US Department of Health & Human Services, last updated February 2, 2007, https://privacyruleandresearch.nih.gov/pr_08.asp.

30. Ibid.

31. Aja Brooks, JD and Lucia Savage, JD, "The Real HIPAA: Permitted Uses and Disclosures," *Health IT Buzz* (blog), The Office of the National Coordinator of Health Information Technology, February 11, 2016, https://www.healthit.gov/buzz-blog/privacy-and-security-of-ehrs/the-real-hipaa-permitted-uses-and-disclosures/.

32. "Uses and Disclosures for Treatment, Payment, and Health Care Operations," OCR HIPAA Privacy, US Department of Health & Human Services, revised April 3, 2003, https://www.hhs.gov/sites/default/files/ocr/privacy/hipaa/understanding/coveredentities/sharingfortpo.pdf

33. Richard Sobel, "The HIPAA Paradox: The Privacy Rule That's Not," *Hastings Center Report* 37, no. 4 (July/August 2007): 42, http://pipatl.org/data/library/HIPAAparadox.pdf.

34. §164.501, 45 CFR Subtitle A, US Government Printing Office, October 1, 2011, https://www.gpo.gov/fdsys/pkg/CFR-2011-title45-vol1/pdf/CFR-2011-title45-vol1-sec164-501.pdf.

35. Representative Nick Zerwas et al., "Patient Consent to Release of Health Records Provision Modified."

36. "Minnesota Health Information Exchange Legislative Study Request for Public Comment," Minnesota Department of Health, October 2, 2017, 21, http://www.health.state.mn.us/e-health/hie/study/hiestudy.public-comment-2017-10-02.pdf.

37. "Connecting Health and Care for the Nation: A Shared Nationwide Interoperability Roadmap," Supplemental Materials, Version 1.0, Office of the National Coordinator for Health Information Technology, n.d., 23, https://www.healthit.gov/sites/default/files/hie-interoperability/Interoperibility-Road-Map-Supplemental.pdf.

38. "Connecting Health and Care for the Nation, A Shared Nationwide Interoperability Roadmap, Final Version 1.0," Office of the National Coordinator for Health Information Technology, n.d., 18. Accessed February 20, 2018:

https://www.yumpu.com/en/document/view/54433693/connecting-health-and-care-for-the-nation/34.

39. "NMH HIPAA Privacy Training" (PowerPoint presentation, North Memorial Health, Robbinsdale, MN, March 24, 2017), https://northmemorial.com/wp-content/uploads/2017/03/north-memorial-health-hipaa-privacy-training-032417.pdf.

40. "De-Identified Data Sets and Limited Data Sets," University of Michigan Health System, revised June 2003, http://www.ehcca.com/presentations/HIPAA7/4_04H2.pdf.

41. "Definition of Limited Data Set," Johns Hopkins Medicine, April 2015, http://www.hopkinsmedicine.org/institutional_review_board/hipaa_research/limited_data_set.html.

42. Ibid.; see also "Limited Data Sets in Research," Drexel University, n.d., https://drexel.edu/~/media/Files/research/administration/hrpp/88%20Limited%20Data%20Sets%20in%20Rearch.ashx?la=en.

43. "Definition of Limited Data Set."

44. Ibid.

45. "DUA—Limited Data Sets (LDS)," Centers for Medicare & Medicaid Services, last modified April 21, 2017, https://www.cms.gov/Research-Statistics-Data-and-Systems/Computer-Data-and-Systems/Privacy/DUA_-_LDS.html.

46. "DUA TOOLKIT: A Guide to Data Use Agreements," Health Care Systems Research Network, n.d., http://www.hcsrn.org/en/Tools%20&%20Materials/GrantsContracting/HCSRN_DUAToolkit.pdf.

47. Elizabeth A. Bankert and Robert J. Amdur, *Institutional Review Board: Management and Function*, 2nd ed. (Burlington, MA: Jones & Bartlett Publishers, 2006), 276.

48. "Definition of Limited Data Set"; see also "Must a covered entity provide an accounting for disclosures if the only information disclosed to a public health authority is in the form of a limited data set?," US Department of Health & Human Services, August 28, 2003, http://www.hhs.gov/ocr/privacy/hipaa/faq/right_to_an_accounting_of_disclosures/467.html.

49. "Connecting Health and Care for the Nation: A Shared Nationwide Interoperability Roadmap, Final Version 1.0," 18.

50. Cited with permission from "Health Data Map 1997," theDataMap, The Data Privacy Lab, Harvard University, http://thedatamap.org/map1997/index.html.

51. "Protect Your Rights," Citizens' Council for Health Freedom, http://www.cchfreedom.org/healthprivacyalert.php#.VyPHkKteJ3Y.

52. Dan Johnson, "Congress Holds the Key to Achieving Improved Healthcare through Better Use of Data," *Health Management Technology*, September 26, 2017, https://www.healthmgttech.com/congress-holds-key-achieving-improved-healthcare-better-use-data.

53. "Ensuring Patient Access to Healthcare Records Act of 2017" (H.R. 4613), 115th Congress, 1st Session, Government Publications Office, December 11, 2017, 5, https://www.congress.gov/115/bills/hr4613/BILLS-115hr4613ih.pdf.

54. "Part C—Administrative Simplification: Definitions," Social Security Adminstration, n.d., https://www.ssa.gov/OP_Home/ssact/title11/1171.htm.

55. Johnson.

56. "Our Mission," Claim Your Health Data Coalition, n.d., http://claimcoalition.org/faq/.

57. Johnson.

58. Johnson.

59. Katherine K Kim et al., "Comparison of Consumers' Views on Electronic Data Sharing for Healthcare and Research," *Journal of the American Medical Informatics Association* vol. 22, no. 4 (July 2015): 821-830, https://www.ncbi.nlm.nih.gov/pmc/articles/PMC5009901/.

60. Adrian Gropper, MD, "Open Season on Health Privacy in Washington DC," *The Health Care Blog*, May 24, 2017, http://thehealthcareblog.com/blog/2017/05/24/open-season-on-health-privacy-in-washington-dc/; see also Thomas McMullan, "What Does the Panopticon Mean in the Age of Digital Surveillance?"

The Guardian, July 23, 2015, https://www.theguardian.com/technology/2015/jul/23/panopticon-digital-surveillance-jeremy-bentham.

61. Darius Tahir, "We've Got a CMMI Head," Politico Morning eHealth, December 22, 2017, https://www.politico.com/newsletters/morning-ehealth/2017/12/22/weve-got-a-cmmi-head-061197.

62. Johnson.

63. "Notice of Privacy Practices," US Department of Health & Human Services, n.d., http://www.hhs.gov/ocr/privacy/hipaa/understanding/consumers/noticepp.html.

64. "Understanding the HIPAA Notice," Office for Civil Rights, US Department of Health & Human Services, n.d., http://www.cchfreedom.org/files/files/OCR_understanding-hipaa-notice_Highlighted.pdf.

65. Ryan P. Blaney, "HHS Empowers Consumers to Know (and Enforce) Their Rights Under under HIPAA," Proskauer Rose LLP, May 8, 2013, https://www.lexology.com/library/detail.aspx?g=a90d7264-cb4b-4997-9f5b-06f937637735.

66. "Know Your Rights—A Guide for Consumers Navigating Health Care," Office for Civil Rights, US Department of Health & Human Services, n.d., http://coveraz.org/wp-content/uploads/2013/06/HHS-Privacy-Rights-Information.docx.

67. "Get it. Check it. Use it." US Department of Health & Human Services, last reviewed September 7, 2017, https://www.hhs.gov/hipaa/for-individuals/right-to-access/index.html.

68. Email (edited for typos) sent to Citizens' Council for Health Freedom at hipaahurtme.org, February 2015.

69. Katherine G. Lusk et al., "Patient Matching in Health Information Exchanges," *Perspectives in Health Information Management*, 2014, http://perspectives.ahima.org/patient-matching-in-health-information-exchanges/#.VySy7ateJ3Y.

70. "Nationwide Health Information Network (NHIN) Exchange Architecture Overview (Draft v0.9)," US Department of Health & Human Services, April 21, 2010, 4. Accessed July 28, 2017: https://www.healthit.gov/sites/default/files/nhin-architecture-overview-draft-20100421-1.pdf.

71. "Draft Trusted Exchange Framework," Draft for Comment, Office of the National Coordinator of Health Information Technology, January 5, 2018, https://www.healthit.gov/sites/default/files/draft-trusted-exchange-framework.pdf.

72. Jessica Davis, "ONC's Draft Interoperability Framework Floats 'Network of Networks' Concept," *Healthcare IT News*, January 5, 2018, http://www.healthcareitnews.com/news/oncs-draft-interoperability-framework-floats-network-networks-concept.

73. "Draft Trusted Exchange Framework," 28.

74. "Draft Trusted Exchange Framework," 3.

75. David Blumenthal, MD, "The Future of Health Care and Electronic Records," *Health IT Buzz* (blog), The Office of the National Coordinator of Health Information Technology, July 13, 2010, https://www.healthit.gov/buzz-blog/electronic-health-and-medical-records/the-future-of-health-care-and-electronic-records/.

76. Dan Bowman, "HIE Hurdles Include Lack of Patient ID Standards and Technical Knowledge," FierceHealthcare, January 28, 2013, http://www.fiercehealthcare.com/ehr/hie-hurdles-include-lack-patient-id-standards-and-technical-knowledge.

77. "Summary of Nationwide Health Information Network (NHIN) Request for Information (RFI) Responses," Office of the National Coordinator of Health Information Technology, US Department of Health & Human Services, June 2005, 55, http://www.providersedge.com/ehdocs/ehr_articles/Summary_of_NHIN_RFI_Responses.pdf.

78. Ibid., 1.

79. Ibid.

80. Ibid., 65.

81. Ibid., 21.

82. Ibid., 63.

83. Robert E. Hoyt and Ann K. Yoshihashi, editors, *Health Informatics: Practical Guide for Healthcare and Information Technology*

Professionals, 6th ed. (Singapore: Informatics Education, 2014), 136.

84. Trimed Staff, "Brailer's Office Releases RFI on National Health Information Network," *Health Imaging*, November 18, 2004, http://www.healthimaging.com/topics/oncology-imaging/brailers-office-releases-rfi-national-health-information-network.

85. "American Health Information Community (AHIC)," Public Health Data Standards Consortium, n.d., http://www.phdsc.org/health_info/american-health-info.asp.

86. C. Stephen Redhead, "The Health Information Technology for Economic and Clinical Health (HITECH) Act," Congressional Research Service, February 23, 2009, https://digital.library.unt.edu/ark:/67531/metadc743451/m1/1/high_res_d/R40161_2009Feb23.pdf.

87. Shannon Leigh, "Healtheway's eHealth Exchange Selected as ACT-IAC Igniting Innovation 2015 Award Finalist," The Sequoia Project, January 27, 2015, http://sequoiaproject.org/sequoia-project/sequoia-project-news/healtheways-ehealth-exchange-selected-as-act-iac-igniting-innovation-2015-award-finalist/.

88. Mariann Yeager, "eHealth Exchange Transition Update" (PowerPoint presentation, Healtheway, Inc., October 2, 2012), http://docslide.net/documents/ehealth-exchange-transition-update-october-2-2012-mariann-yeager-interim-executive.html.

89. "What is eHealth Exchange?" The Sequoia Group. n.d., http://sequoiaproject.org/ehealth-exchange/.

90. "eHealth Exchange Participants," The Sequoia Project. n.d., http://sequoiaproject.org/ehealth-exchange/participants/.

91. "What's the Difference between eHealth Exchange, Carequality, and The Sequoia Project?" The Sequoia Project, n.d., http://sequoiaproject.org/about-us/whats-difference-ehealth-exchange-carequality-sequoia-project/.

92. Gary Brown et al., "Final Project—Health Information Exchange: Technology, Challenges & Opportunities," (PowerPoint presentation, MMI 402, Fall 2013, 6), http://kazirussell.weebly.com/uploads/5/2/8/9/52894915/russell_group_final.pptx.

93. Ibid.

94. "What is the eHealth Exchange?" The Office of the National Coordinator of Health Information Technology, last updated November 17, 2015, https://www.healthit.gov/providers-professionals/faqs/what-ehealth-exchange.

95. "What's the Difference between eHealth Exchange, Carequality, and The Sequoia Project?"

96. "Nationwide Health Information Network (NHIN) Exchange Architecture Overview," US Department of Health & Human Services, April 21, 2010, 6, 10, https://www.healthit.gov/sites/default/files/nhin-architecture-overview-draft-20100421-1.pdf.

97. Mariann Yeager and Jennifer Rosas, "eHealth Exchange—Healtheway Monthly Communications Call," Healtheway, November 8, 2013, https://ehealthexchange.wikispaces.com/file/view/eHealth+Exchange-Healtheway-Update-2013Nov8_FINAL+(2).pdf.

98. "Nationwide Health Information Network (NHIN) Exchange Architecture Overview."

99. Ibid.

100. Ibid.

101. "California Health Information Exchange Operational Plan" (excerpt of complete plan available at ehealth.ca.gov), March 31, 2010, http://www.sujansky.com/docs/CA_HIE_Operational_Plan-Technical_Infrastructure.pdf.

102. Ibid.

103. "Health Information Organization Connections," Minnesota Department of Health, last updated October 3, 2017, http://www.health.state.mn.us/e-health/hie/certified/hioconnections.html.

104. Yeager and Rosas.

105. Michael Matthews, "HIT Policy Committee/HIT Standards Committee Joint Meeting on January 29, 2013, Panel #3: Governance Barriers and Opportunities," January 24, 2013, https://www.healthit.gov/facas/sites/faca/files/2013-01-29_testimony_matthews_0.pdf.

106. Mariann Yeager, "eHealth Exchange Transition Update" (PowerPoint presentation, Healtheway, Inc., October 2, 2012), http://www.connectopensource.org/sites/connectopensource.org/files/ehealthexchangetransition_cat1112.pptx.

107. Matthews.

108. "eHealth Exchange Annual Participation & Testing Fees," The Sequoia Project, n.d., http://sequoiaproject.org/ehealth-exchange/onboarding/fees-2/.

109. Joseph Goedert, "Sequoia Project Starts Program to Share Patient Data During Disasters," *Health Data Management*, April 9, 2018, https://www.healthdatamanagement.com/news/sequoia-project-starts-program-to-share-patient-data-during-disasters.

110. "What is a Regional Health Information Organization (RHIO)?" Health Resources and Services Administration, US Department of Health & Human Services, n.d., https://web-beta.archive.org/web/20111015183010/http://www.hrsa.gov/healthit/toolbox/RuralHealthITtoolbox/Collaboration/whatisrhio.html.

111. "GAO Kicks Off Review of HIE Performance," *Healthcare IT News*, January 12, 2015, http://www.healthcareitnews.com/news/gao-kicks-review-hie-performance.

112. Linda Reed, RN, MBA et al., "Jersey Health Connect: A Collaborative Framework of Community Stakeholders," *Journal of Healthcare Information Management* vol. 25, no. 1 (Winter 2011): 28, https://www.longwoods.com/articles/images/JHIM-Winter.pdf.

113. Ibid.

114. Ashley Gold, "Senators Order GAO Review of ONC-Funded HIEs — Why Wearables Alone Can't Make Us Healthy — FDA Puts Out Year's List of Guidance Priorities," *Politico*, January 9, 2015, http://www.politico.com/tipsheets/morning-ehealth/2015/01/senators-order-gao-review-of-onc-funded-hies-why-wearables-alone-cant-make-us-healthy-fda-puts-out-years-list-of-guidance-priorities-212543.

115. Dr. Karen B. DeSalvo and Ahmed E. Haque, "HHS and ONC Invest $28 Million in Health Information Exchange Grants," *Health IT Buzz* (blog), The Office of the National Coordinator of Health Information Technology, February 3, 2015, http://www.healthit.gov/buzz-blog/from-the-onc-desk/health-information-exchange-grants/.

116. Prashila Dullabh et al., "Evaluation of the State Health Information Exchange Cooperative Agreement Program," NORC at the University of Chicago (presented to The Office of the National Coordinator for Health Information Technology), March 2016, 29, https://www.healthit.gov/sites/default/files/reports/finalsummativereportmarch_2016.pdf.

117. Ibid., 10.

118. Karen Boruff, "RAND: Systematic Review of Health Information Exchange," California Association of Health Information Exchanges, December 16, 2014, https://web-beta.archive.org/web/20150423194457/http://www.ca-hie.org/news/rand-systematic-review-of-health-information-exchange.

119. Ken Terry, "Public HIEs Failing, Poll Says," InformationWeek, January 30, 2014, http://www.informationweek.com/healthcare/clinical-information-systems/public-hies-failing-poll-says/d/d-id/1113645.

120. Dullabh et al., 6.

121. David Pittman, "Senators Order GAO Review of ONC-Funded Health Information Exchanges," Politico Morning eHealth, January 9, 2015. Subscriber-only email to author.

122. Doug Brown, "Payers Reject Public HIEs and Pony Up to Lead Private Enterprise Interoperability, Reveals Recent Black Book Survey," Black Book Market Research, January 28, 2014, http://www.blackbookmarketresearch.com/payers-reject-public-hies-and-pony-up-to-lead-private-enterprise-interoperability-reveals-recent-black-book-survey/.

123. Chris Nerney, "Trouble in Vermont: State's HIE Struggling, Review Shows," Connected Care Watch, January 2, 2018, http://www.connectedcarewatch.com/news/trouble-vermont-state's-hie-struggling-review-shows.

124. Mike Miliard, "SHIEC Expands 'Patient Centered Data Home' Initiative, Linking HIEs Nationwide," *Healthcare*

IT News, January 5, 2018, http://www.healthcareitnews.com/news/shiec-expands-patient-centered-data-home-initiative-linking-hies-nationwide.

125. Jennifer Bresnick, "SHIEC Expands Patient-Centered Data Home HIE Network Nationwide," *Health IT Analytics* (blog), January 4, 2018, https://healthitanalytics.com/news/shiec-expands-patient-centered-data-home-hie-network-nationwide.

126. Andrea Leeb, RN, JD, CIPP/US, "Legal Landscape for Health Information Exchange," (PowerPoint presentation, HIE in EMS Summit, Garden Grove, CA, April 19, 2016, 6), https://emsa.ca.gov/wp-content/uploads/sites/47/2017/07/Legal-Landscape-for-Health-Information-Exchange.pdf.

127. "Business Associate Contracts Required for Certain Entities," Section 13408, Health Information Technology for Economic and Clinical Health Act, The American Recovery and Reinvestment Act of 2009, (Public Law 111-5), February 17, 2009, 271, https://www.gpo.gov/fdsys/pkg/PLAW-111publ5/pdf/PLAW-111publ5.pdf.

128. "Business Associate Contracts: Sample Business Associate Agreement Provisions," US Department of Health & Human Services, January 25, 2013, https://www.hhs.gov/hipaa/for-professionals/covered-entities/sample-business-associate-agreement-provisions/index.html.

129. "Electronic Consent Management: Landscape Assessment, Challenges, and Technology," Office of the National Coordinator for Health Information Technology, October 29, 2014, https://www.healthit.gov/sites/default/files/privacy-security/ecm_finalreport_forrelease62415.pdf.

130. Leeb, 7.

131. "State HIE Consent Policies: Opt-In or Opt-Out," Clinovations, Milken Institute School of Public Health, last updated September 2016, https://www.healthit.gov/sites/default/files/State%20HIE%20Opt-In%20vs%20Opt-Out%20Policy%20Research_09-30-16_Final.pdf.

132. "CliniSync Consent FAQs," Ohio Health Information Partnership, February 11, 2016, http://www.clinisync.org/_literature_186874/Consent_FAQs.

133. "Patient Options—Opt Out/Back In," HealthShare Exchange, n.d., https://www.healthshareexchange.org/patient-options-opt-out-back.

134. Scott Mace, "How HIEs Are Becoming Essential to Clinicians," MedPage Today, September 20, 2015, https://www.medpagetoday.com/practicemanagement/practicemanagement/53644.

135. "CliniSync Consent FAQs," 7.

136. "EHR Connectivity Report," CORHIO, last updated April 5, 2017, http://www.corhio.org/services/health-information-exchange-services/ehr-connectivity-report-copy.

137. "Themes and Lessons from Capacity Building Bright Spots," State HIE Bright Spots Synthesis, State Health Information Exchange Program, The Office of the National Coordinator of Health Information Technology, December 2012, http://healthit.gov/sites/default/files/bright-spots-synthesis_capacity-builder_final_12212012.pdf.

138. "Health Information Exchange Services & Pricing Package," HealthlinkNY, Effective March 1, 2015, http://www.healthlinkny.com/editor_files/1436196088_HealthlinkNY-HIE-Services-Pricing-Package.pdf.

139. "What is the SHIN-NY?" (author unknown; locate on website of HealtheConnections, a regional health information organization), April 2015, 11, 20, http://www.healtheconnections.org/wp-content/uploads/2015/04/what-is-the-shin-ny_rob.pdf.

140. "Health Information Exchange Services & Pricing Package," HealthlinkNY, Effective March 1, 2015, http://www.healthlinkny.com/editor_files/1436196088_HealthlinkNY-HIE-Services-Pricing-Package.pdf.

141. Marla Durben Hirsch, "RAND: HIEs are still 'experiments' in need of further study," FierceHealthcare, December 1, 2014, http://www.fiercehealthcare.com/ehr/rand-hies-are-still-experiments-need-further-study.

142. Terry, "Public HIEs Failing, Poll Says."

143. Brooke Murphy, "88% of Providers Say Collaborative HIE Initiatives Improving Payer-Provider Relations: 9 Survey Findings," Becker's Health IT & CIO Report, April 8, 2016, http://www.beckershospitalreview.com/healthcare-information-technology/88-of-providers-say-collaborative-hie-initiatives-improving-payer-provider-relations-9-survey-findings.html.

144. Gold, "Senators Order GAO Review of ONC-Funded HIEs."

145. "GAO Kicks Off Review of HIE Performance."

146. Dori A. Cross et al., "Assessing Payer Perspectives on Health Information Exchange," *Journal of the American Medical Informatics Association* vol. 23, no. 2 (July 3, 2015): 290, http://jamia.oxfordjournals.org/content/jaminfo/early/2015/07/02/jamia.ocv072.full.pdf.

147. Ibid., 299.

148. Evan Sweeney, "CHIME Launches New Effort to Make DirectTrust's Data Exchange Framework Universal in Healthcare." FierceHealthcare, August 31, 2017, http://www.fiercehealthcare.com/ehr/chime-looks-to-make-directtrust-data-exchange-framework-universal-across-healthcare.

149. Evan Sweeney, "HIMSS Policy Official Praises Trusted Exchange Framework but Worries about Potential Costs," FierceHealthcare, January 31, 2018, https://www.fiercehealthcare.com/regulatory/himss-onc-jeff-coughlin-trusted-exchange-framework-costs-interoperability.

150. "CHIME and DirectTrust Announce Collaboration," DirectTrust, August 30, 2017, https://www.directtrust.org/chime-and-directtrust-announce-collaboration/.

151. "Carequality and CommonWell Health Alliance Agree on Connectivity and Collaboration to Advance Interoperability," CommonWell Health Alliance, December 13, 2016, http://www.commonwellalliance.org/news/carequality-commonwell-health-alliance-collaboration/.

152. Ibid.

153. Ibid.

154. Matthew J. Belvedere, "No Security Ever Built into Obamacare Site: Hacker," CNBC, November 25, 2013, https://www.cnbc.com/2013/11/25/no-security-ever-built-into-obamacare-site-hacker.html.

155. Jim Finkle and Alina Selyukh, "Some Cyber Security Experts Recommend Shutting Obamacare Site," Reuters, November 20, 2013, http://www.reuters.com/article/2013/11/20/us-usa-healthcare-security-idUSBRE9AI0NR20131120.

156. Ibid.

157. Dr. Nabajyoti Barkakati and Gregory C. Wilshusen, "Healthcare.gov: Actions Needed to Enhance Information Security and Privacy Controls," US Government Accountability Office, March 2016, http://www.gao.gov/assets/680/676003.pdf.

158. Erin Mershon and Natalie Villacorta, "Republicans May Wait on Using Reconciliation to Repeal ACA—Medicare Wants to Pay Docs for End-of-Life Talks—White House Wants to Improve Cures," Politico Pulse, July 9, 2015, http://www.politico.com/tipsheets/politico-pulse/2015/07/republicans-may-wait-on-using-reconciliation-to-repeal-aca-medicare-wants-to-pay-docs-for-end-of-life-talks-white-house-wants-to-improve-cures-212543.

159. Marianne Kolbasuk McGee, "Shoring Up HealthCare.gov Security," Healthcare Info Security, June 26, 2015, http://www.healthcareinfosecurity.com/shoring-up-healthcaregov-security-a-8357/op-1.

160. "H.R. 3600, Health Security Act," US Representative Richard Gephardt, 103d Congress, 1st session, November 20, 1993, 869-871, https://www.gpo.gov/fdsys/pkg/BILLS-103hr3600ih/pdf/BILLS-103hr3600ih.pdf.

161. Sheryl Gay Stolberg, "Health Identifier for All Americans Runs Into Hurdles," *New York Times*, July 20, 1998, http://www.nytimes.com/1998/07/20/us/health-identifier-for-all-americans-runs-into-hurdles.html.

162. "HHS has stated that it is prohibited from implementing a national patient identifier and has referred to the Omnibus Consolidated and Emergency Supplemental Appropriations Act of 1999. The act prohibits HHS from using any funds to promulgate or

adopt any final standard providing for, or providing for the assignment of, a unique health identifier for an individual until legislation is enacted specifically approving the standard. See Public Law No. 105-277, § 516, 112 Stat. 2681, 2681-386 (1998)." "Electronic Health Records: Nonfederal Efforts to Help Achieve Health Information Interoperability," US Government Accountability Office, September 16, 2015: http://www.gao.gov/assets/680/672585.pdf.

163. Carl Bergman, "Congress Getting Real About Interoperability—Kills Paul's Unique Patient ID Gag Rule," *EMR and EHR* (blog), December 22, 2014, http://www.emrandehr.com/2014/12/22/congress-getting-real-about-interoperability-kills-pauls-patient-id-gag-rule/.

164. David Wagner, "CHIME, HeroX Patient ID Challenge Gains Momentum," InformationWeek, March 14, 2016, http://www.informationweek.com/healthcare/chime-herox-patient-id-challenge-gains-momentum/d/d-id/1323935.

165. Twila Brase, "National Patient ID," Policy Insights, Citizens' Council for Health Freedom, July 2012, http://www.cchfreedom.org/files/files/Final_UPI_Report-Use(1).pdf.

166. Carl Bergman, "The New Congressional Rider: Unique Patient ID Lemonade?" *EMR and EHR* (blog), January 8, 2015, http://www.emrandehr.com/tag/unique-patient-identifier/.

167. Ibid.

168. Ibid.

169. "Electronic Health Records: Nonfederal Efforts to Help Achieve Health Information Interoperability," US Government Accountability Office, September 16, 2015, http://www.gao.gov/assets/680/672585.pdf.

170. Darius Tahir, "Unique Patient Identifier Again on the Top of the Wish List," Politico Pro eHealth Whiteboard (subscription required), July 7, 2015.

171. Wagner.

172. Jennifer Bresnick, "CHIME Offers $1M for 100% Accurate Patient Matching Solution," *HealthITAnalytics* (blog), March 18, 2015, http://healthitanalytics.com/news/chime-offers-1m-for-100-accurate-patient-matching-solution/.

173. "CHIME National Patient ID Challenge," HeroX, n.d., https://herox.com/PatientIDChallenge/timeline.

174. Shaun Sutner, "Delays for $1 million CHIME National Patient ID Challenge," SearchHealthIT, August 9, 2017, http://searchhealthit.techtarget.com/news/450424138/Delays-for-1-million-CHIME-national-patient-ID-challenge.

175. College of Healthcare Information Management Executives, "CHIME Sharpens Focus on Patient Identification Mission, Encourages Stakeholders to Join in Solution," press release, November 15, 2017, https://herox.com/PatientIDChallenge/update/1678.

176. "S.2511 - Improving Health Information Technology Act," 114th Congress, February 8, 2016, https://www.congress.gov/bill/114th-congress/senate-bill/2511/text.

177. Consolidated Appropriations Act, 2017, Public Law No. 115-31, 131 Stat. 135 (May 5, 2017), https://www.congress.gov/115/plaws/publ31/PLAW-115publ31.pdf.

178. "Dear Chairman Frelinghuysen, Chairman Cochran, Ranking Member Lowey, Ranking Member Leahy, Chairman Cole, Ranking Member DeLauro, and Committee Members," (Letter found on HIMSS website, signed by 25 groups), April 5, 2017, http://www.himss.org/sites/himssorg/files/newsletters/HITPU/FY1718%20Labor-H%20Patient%20Matching%20Report%20Langauge%20Support%20Letter%20v%20FINAL%281%29.pdf.

179. Ibid.

180. Consolidated Appropriations Act, 2017, Title V, Section 510, 563.

181. "Report together with Minority Views and Additional Views," Departments of Labor, Health & Human Services, and Education, and Related Agencies Appropriations Bill, 2017, House of Representatives, 114th Congress, 2nd Session, Report 114-699, July 22, 2016, 110, https://www.gpo.gov/fdsys/pkg/CRPT-114hrpt699/pdf/CRPT-114hrpt699.pdf.

182. Carla Smith, MA, FHIMSS, CNM, "After Nearly Two Decades, a Win in Congress for Patient Data Matching," Healthcare Information and Management Systems Society (HIMSS), May 9, 2017, http://www.himss.org/news/after-nearly-two-decades-win-congress-patient-data-matching.

183. Kate Monica, "National Patient Identifier Gains Congressional Support," EHR Intelligence, May 11, 2017, https://ehrintelligence.com/news/national-patient-identifier-gains-congressional-support.

184. "Patient Matching Algorithm Challenge," Patient Matching Algorithm Challenge, June 12, 2017, https://www.patientmatchingchallenge.com.

185. "Regenstrief Developing and Testing Novel, Real-World Automated Patient Identification," IUSM Newsroom, Indiana University, August 8, 2017, http://news.medicine.iu.edu/releases/2017/08/regenstrief-developing-testing-real-world-automated-patient-identification.shtml.

186. "New Jersey Innovation Institute Awarded $2.9M Federal Grant to Advance Health Information Technology Services," *New Jersey Business*, July 30, 2015, https://njbmagazine.com/njb-news-now/new-jersey-innovation-institute-awarded-2-9m-federal-grant-to-advance-health-information-technology-services/.

187. Michael C. Ksiazek, "NJ Is Creating A 'Master Person Index' to Counter Medical Errors," *Personal Injury Law Journal* (blog), Lexology, August 24, 2017, https://www.lexology.com/library/detail.aspx?g=d1361672-57fe-456c-942a-992b6546dbc8.

188. "Health Information Exchange Grants Criteria," State of New Jersey Recovery and Reinvestment Plan, n.d., http://www.nj.gov/recovery/grant/docs/hieg_narrative.pdf.

189. "Equifax Data Breach Affected Millions More than First Thought," CBS News, October 2, 2017, https://www.cbsnews.com/news/equifax-data-breach-millions-more-affected/.

190. John McCrank and Jim Finkle, "Equifax Breach Could Be Most Costly in Corporate History," Reuters, March 2, 2018, https://www.reuters.com/article/us-equifax-cyber/equifax-breach-could-be-most-costly-in-corporate-history-idUSKCN1GE257.

191. Rachel Z. Arndt, "Experian Takes on Patient ID," *Modern Healthcare*, September 8, 2017, http://www.modernhealthcare.com/article/20170908/TRANSFORMATION02/170909929#.

192. Jeff Smith, "Taking Stock: Interoperability and National Health IT Week," Medium, October 6, 2017, https://medium.com/@jefferyrlsmith/taking-stock-interoperability-and-national-health-it-week-6354e00f38d6; see also "List of Different Types of Health Data," Health Data Knowledge, August 13, 2014, http://www.healthdataknowledge.com/list-of-different-types-of-health-data/.

193. Jeff Byers, "Jonathan Bush on athenahealth's Next Steps—and Why Doctors Should Get on Board," Healthcare Dive, March 8, 2017, https://www.healthcaredive.com/news/jonathan-bush-new-crazy-ones-networked-health/437390/.

194. Dan Johnson.

195. Dan Cidon, "HIT Think: Why a National Patient Identifier Won't Solve Matching Concerns," *Health Data Management*, November 29, 2017, https://www.healthdatamanagement.com/opinion/why-a-national-patient-identifier-wont-solve-matching-concerns.

196. Mohana Ravindranath, "Survey: Baby Boomers Worry About Cybersecurity but Most Shrug Off Their Role in It." Nextgov, October 31, 2017, http://www.nextgov.com/cybersecurity/2017/10/survey-baby-boomers-worry-about-cybersecurity-most-shrug-their-role-it/142181/.

197. "State-of-the-Art New Born Safety System," McLaren Northern Michigan, October 17, 2017, http://www.mclaren.org/northernmichigan/redesignnews/stateoftheart_new_born_safety_system__2037.aspx.

198. Rick Shrum, "Washington First Hospital in State to Use Newborn Safety System," *Observer-Reporter*, December 27, 2017, https://observer-reporter.com/news/localnews/washington-first-hospital-in-state-to-use-newborn-safety-system/article_b7acd8ec-eb15-11e7-9ce3-ef3066fe25d1.html.

199. "OT–Morpho Becomes IDEMIA, the Global Leader in Trusted Identities," IDEMIA, September 28, 2017, https://www.morpho.com/en/media/ot-morpho-becomes-idemia-global-leader-trusted-identities-20170928; see also http://www.morphotrust.com/News.aspx.

200. Eduard Goodman, "Biometrics Won't Solve Our Data-Security Crisis," *Harvard Business Review,* December 6, 2017, https://hbr.org/2017/12/biometrics-wont-solve-our-data-security-crisis.

201. "OT and Morpho Finalise Deal," Security Document World, May 6, 2017, http://www.securitydocumentworld.com/article-details/i/13207/.

202. "OT–Morpho Becomes IDEMIA, the Global Leader in Trusted Identities."

203. Business Wire, "OT-Morpho Signs Up 5 Million US Travelers for TSA PreCheck®," July 6, 2017, http://www.businesswire.com/news/home/20170706005763/en; see also Josh Noel, "Applying for PreCheck? Here's Where Your Fingerprints Go," *Seattle Times*, March 1, 2014, https://www.seattletimes.com/life/travel/applying-for-precheck-herersquos-where-your-fingerprints-go/.

204. "AADHAAR Program Achieves A Milestone: 1 Billion Digital Identities Created," IDEMIA, n.d., https://www.morpho.com/aadhaar.

205. "MorphoTrust Solutions Produce North American Driver Licenses," IDEMIA, n.d., https://www.morpho.com/en/media/morphotrust-solutions-produce-north-american-driver-licenses-20140424.

206. Twila Brase and Matt Flanders, "Exposing Idemia: The Push for National Biometric IDs in America," Policy Insights, Citizens' Council for Health Freedom, February 2018, http://www.cchfreedom.org/files/files/Policy%20Insights%20-%20Idemia.pdf.

207. "Emergency Supplemental Appropriations Act, 2005," *Congressional Record—Senate* (109th Congress, 1st Session), vol. 151, no. 43, April 13, 2015, S3529, https://www.congress.gov/crec/2005/04/13/CREC-2005-04-13.pdf.

208. "ACLU Scorecard on Final Real ID Regulations," American Civil Liberties Union, January 17, 2008, https://www.aclu.org/files/images/general/asset_upload_file162_33700.pdf.

209. Senator Will Kraus et al., letter to President Donald Trump, Missouri General Assembly, March 8, 2017, http://www.cchfreedom.org/files/files/2017%20REAL%20ID%20Pres_%20Trump%20Letter%20(signed).pdf; see also Representative Daryl D. Metcalfe et al., letter to President Donald Trump, House of Representatives, Commonwealth of Pennsylvania, January 24, 2017, http://www.cchfreedom.org/files/files/PA%20Letter%20to%20Trump%20-%20REAL%20ID%20-%20Condensed.pdf.

210. Molly Ramsdell, "REAL ID is For Real," *State Legislatures* vol. 40, no. 3 (March 1, 2014), http://www.ncsl.org/research/transportation/real-id-is-for-real.aspx.

211. "Privacy Impact Assessment for the REAL ID Final Rule, US Department of Homeland Security, January 11, 2008, 8. https://www.dhs.gov/xlibrary/assets/privacy/privacy_pia_realidfr.pdf.

212. "How the REAL–ID Act is Creating a National ID Database," The Identity Project, February 11, 2016, https://papersplease.org/wp/2016/02/11/how-the-real-id-act-is-creating-a-national-id-database/.

213. Debbie Schaeffer, "Letter: Real ID Law an Abuse of Senior Citizens," *Carroll County Times*, January 18, 2018, http://www.carrollcountytimes.com/cc-op-letters-schaeffer-20180118-story.html.

214. "Section 201. Definitions," Real ID Act—Title II, H.R. 1268 (2005), US Department of Homeland Security, https://www.dhs.gov/xlibrary/assets/real-id-act-text.pdf.

215. "Total Number of Medicare Beneficiaries" Kaiser Family Foundation, n.d., http://www.kff.org/medicare/state-indicator/total-medicare-beneficiaries/?currentTimeframe=0&sortModel=%7B%22colId%22:%22Location%22,%22sort%22:%22asc%22%7D.

216. "December 2017 Medicaid and CHIP Enrollment Data Highlight," Medicaid, n.d., https://www.medicaid.gov/medicaid/program-information/medicaid-and-chip-enrollment-data/report-highlights/index.html.

217. "Identity Solutions for Motor Vehicle Agencies," IDEMIA, n.d., http://www.

morphotrust.com/IdentitySolutions/ForMotorVehicleAgencies/Issuance360/SecureCredentials.aspx.

218. "Real ID - Federal Control over Identification and Movement," Citizens' Council for Health Freedom, n.d., http://www.cchfreedom.org/issue.php/39?lim=20.

219. Notes taken by the author at "A HIPAA Compliance, Enforcement, and Policy Update from the HHS Office for Civil Rights," HIMSS 18 Conference, March 6, 2018.

220. Adam Tanner, "How Data Brokers Make Money off Your Medical Records," *Scientific American*, February 1, 2016, http://www.scientificamerican.com/article/how-data-brokers-make-money-off-your-medical-records/.

221. Ibid.

222. Ibid.

223. Rachel Z. Arndt, "How Third Parties Harvest Health Data From Providers, Payers and Pharmacies," *Modern Healthcare*, April 7, 2018, http://www.modernhealthcare.com/article/20180407/NEWS/180409938.

224. Ibid.

225. Mark Reilly, "Epic Systems Pays $46M to Buy Mayo Clinic Data Center," *Milwaukee Business Journal*, January 5, 2016, http://www.bizjournals.com/milwaukee/news/2016/01/05/epic-systems-pays-46m-to-buy-mayo-clinic-data.html.

226. Skip Snow, "Q&A: Epic President Carl Dvorak," *Healthcare IT News*, November 11, 2015, http://www.healthcareitnews.com/news/qa-epic-president-carl-dvorak.

227. Rich Kirchen, "Epic Systems Collaborates with IBM Watson Health, Mayo Clinic," *Milwaukee Business Journal*, May 6, 2015, http://www.bizjournals.com/milwaukee/news/2015/05/06/epic-systems-collaborates-with-ibm-watson-health.html.

228. Lt. Dan, "Epic Teams Up with IBM Watson and Mayo Clinic to Improve Clinical Decision Support," HIStalk, May 7, 2015, http://histalkmobile.com/epic-teams-up-with-ibm-watson-and-mayo-clinic-to-improve-clinical-decision-support/.

229. Kirchen.

230. Wendy K. Mariner, "Reconsidering Constitutional Protection for Health Information Privacy," *Journal of Constitutional Law* vol. 18, no. 3 (November 17, 2015): 988, http://scholarship.law.upenn.edu/cgi/viewcontent.cgi?article=1597&context=jcl.

231. Aditi Pai, "Rock Health: Venture Funding in 2015 Surpassed $4.3 Billion," MobiHealthNews, December 14, 2015, http://mobihealthnews.com/content/rock-health-venture-funding-2015-surpassed-43-billion.

232. "Diagnostic Wearable Medical Devices Market Overview, Growth Opportunities, Emerging Market Demands, Market Analysis & Forecast," Arun Patil, Market Reports Press Releases, *WIREPRNEWS*, November 6, 2017, http://wireprnews.com/index.php/2017/11/06/diagnostic-wearable-medical-devices-market-overview-growth-opportunities-emerging-market-demands-market-analysis-forecast/.

233. Sara Heath, "ECRI: Healthcare Internet of Things to Boost Population Health," *HealthITAnalytics* (blog), January 20, 2016, http://healthitanalytics.com/news/ecri-healthcare-internet-of-things-to-boost-population-health.

234. James Stables, "22 Essential Fitness Apps that Work with Apple Health," Wareable, July 13, 2015, https://web.archive.org/web/20150820095359/http://www.wareable.com/sport/apps-that-work-with-apple-health-kit-compatible.

235. David Pittman, "Appropriations Battle Marches On," Politico Morning eHealth, December 14, 2015, http://www.politico.com/tipsheets/morning-ehealth/2015/12/politicos-morning-ehealth-appropriations-battle-marches-on-stage-3-comments-due-this-week-finance-committee-makes-progress-on-chronic-care-work-211744.

236. Stephanie M. Lee, "Who Owns Your Steps?" BuzzFeed News, July 6, 2015, http://www.buzzfeed.com/stephaniemlee/who-owns-your-steps#.rce9ZGAGN9.

237. Jessica Kim Cohen, "AAP to Collect Data from EHRs, Payers to Develop Clinical Registry of US Children," Becker's Health IT & CIO Report, November 30, 2017,

https://www.beckershospitalreview.com/data-analytics-precision-medicine/aap-to-collect-data-from-ehrs-payers-to-develop-clinical-registry-of-us-children.html.

238. Council on Child and Adolescent Health, "The Role of Home-Visitation Programs in Improving Health Outcomes for Children and Families," *Pediatrics* vol. 101, no. 3 (March 1998), http://pediatrics.aappublications.org/content/101/3/486.

239. James Bell Asssociates, Inc., "The Maternal, Infant, and Early Childhood Home Visiting Program: Form 2 Performance Indicators and Systems Outcomes Data Collection & Reporting Manual and Grantee Plan," Health Resources & Services Administration, Office of Planning, Research and Evaluation, Administration for Children and Families, US Department of Health & Human Services, updated October 2016, https://mchb.hrsa.gov/sites/default/files/mchb/MaternalChildHealthInitiatives/HomeVisiting/performanceresources/performancemeasurementtoolkit.pdf.

240. Karen R. Effrem, MD, "Federal Education and Labor in School Based Health Clinics," Written Testimony to the Subcommittee on Oversight and Investigations, Committee of Education and the Workforce, US House of Representatives, June 6, 2000, http://archives-republicans-edlabor.house.gov/archive/hearings/106th/oi/schoice6600/effrem.pdf.

241. Anna Gorman, "Home Visits Help Parents Overcome Tough Histories, Raise Healthy Children, National Public Radio, August 21, 2017, https://www.npr.org/sections/health-shots/2017/08/21/544214492/home-visits-help-parents-overcome-tough-histories-raise-healthy-children.

242. Mohamed Abdelhamid, PhD, et al., "Putting the Focus Back on the Patient: How Privacy Concerns Affect Personal Health Information Sharing Intentions," *Journal of Medical Internet Research* vol. 19, no. 9 (September 13, 2017), https://www.jmir.org/2017/9/e169/.

243. Katherine K Kim et al., "Comparison of Views on Electronic Data Sharing for Healthcare and Research," Journal of the American Medical Informatics Association vol. 22, no. 4 (July 2015): 821-830, https://www.ncbi.nlm.nih.gov/pmc/articles/PMC5009901/.

244. "Gallup Survey Finds Americans' Concern About Medical Privacy Runs Deep," Institute for Health Freedom, September 26, 2000, http://www.forhealthfreedom.org/Publications/Privacy/NR20000926.html.

245. Ibid.

246. Heather Landi, "Survey: Patients Skeptical of Health IT Due to Privacy, Security Concerns," Healthcare Informatics, January 3, 2017, https://www.healthcare-informatics.com/news-item/cybersecurity/survey-patients-distrusthealth-it-due-privacy-security-concerns.

247. Kim, et al.

248. Katrina J. Serrano, PhD, et al., "Willingness to Exchange Health Information Via Mobile Devices: Findings from a Population-Based Survey," *Annals of Family Medicine* vol. 14, no. 1 (January/February 2016): 34-40, http://www.annfammed.org/content/14/1/34.full#T2.

249. Vaishali Patel, PhD, MPH, et al., "Individuals' Perceptions of the Privacy and Security of Medical Records," ONC Data Brief No. 27, Office of the National Coordinator for Health Information Technology, June 2015, https://www.healthit.gov/sites/default/files/briefs/oncdatabrief27june2015privacyandsecurity.pdf.

250. "Medical Privacy and Confidentiality Survey: Summary and Overview," California Health Care Foundation, January 28, 1999, https://www.chcf.org/wp-content/uploads/2017/12/PDF-survey.pdf.

251. Mariner, 1050-1,

252. Joy L. Pritts, JD, "The Importance and Value of Protecting the Privacy of Health Information: The Roles of the HIPAA Privacy Rule and the Common Rule in Health Research," National Academy of Sciences, 2008, http://www.nationalacademies.org/hmd/~/media/Files/Activity%20Files/Research/HIPAAandResearch/PrittsPrivacyFinalDraftweb.ashx.

253. Mariner, 982-3.

254. "Understanding Health Disparities: Data Collection and Analysis," Section 4302, Patient Protection and Affordable Care Act, Public Law No. 111-148, 124 Stat. 119 (March 23, 2010), https://www.gpo.gov/fdsys/pkg/PLAW-111publ148/pdf/PLAW-111publ148.pdf.

255. Gregory Rodriguez, "President Obama: At Odds with Clear Demographic Trends toward Multiracial Pride," *Los Angeles Times*, April 4, 2011, http://www.latimes.com/opinion/opinion-la/la-oe-rodriguez-column-obama-race-20110404-column.html.

256. US Commission on Civil Rights, "Dissenting Statement by Commissioner Carl A. Anderson and Commissioner Russell G. Redenbaugh" in *The Health Care Challenge: Acknowledging Disparity, Confronting Discrimination, and Ensuring Equality: Volume I The Role of Governmental and Private Health Care Programs and Initiatives,* September 1999, 228, https://archive.org/stream/healthcarechalle00unse#page/n0/mode/2up.

257. Fourth Amendment, US Constitution, FindLaw, n.d., http://constitution.findlaw.com/amendment4.html.

258. Mariner, 998.

259. Ibid., 990.

260. Ibid., 977.

261. "Olmstead v. United States 277 U.S. 438," Supreme Court of the United States, June 4, 1928, https://supreme.justia.com/cases/federal/us/277/438/case.html.

262. Information acquired during the author's conversation with an electronic signature pad vendor at the HIMSS 2018 conference.

263. Christopher A. Harle et al., "Patient Preferences Toward an Interactive E-Consent Application for Research Using Electronic Health Records," *Journal of the American Medical Informatics Association* vol. 25, issue 3 (March 1, 2018): 360-368, https://academic.oup.com/jamia/advance-article/doi/10.1093/jamia/ocx145/4762499.

264. Anonymous, comment on "Patients Doing Digital Document Signing," Practice Fusion, July 28, 2015, https://knowledgebase.practicefusion.com/forums/276361-product-ideas/suggestions/7159902-patients-doing-digital-document-signing.

265. "What Is the Difference between 'Consent' and 'Authorization' Under the HIPAA Privacy Rule?" Office of Civil Rights, US Department of Health & Human Services, last reviewed July 26, 2013, https://www.hhs.gov/hipaa/for-professionals/faq/264/what-is-the-difference-between-consent-and-authorization/index.html.

266. Sharyl J. Nass et al., editors, *Beyond the HIPAA Privacy Rule: Enhancing Privacy, Improving Health Through Research*, 1st ed. (Washington D.C.: National Academies Press, (March 24, 2009), chap. 4, https://www.ncbi.nlm.nih.gov/books/NBK9573/; see also "HIPAA Procedure 5031: Authorization Requirements for Use and Disclosure of Protected Health Information, Including Verification of Identification," 14, Yale, revised December 6, 2017, https://hipaa.yale.edu/sites/default/files/files/5031-PR.pdf.

267. "Consent for Services," North Memorial Clinic, January 2014, http://www.cchfreedom.org/files/files/North%20Memorial%20Consent%20Form.pdf.

V. Government Intrusion

1. "Moving Forward with Comparative Effectiveness Research," Health, Biomedical Science & Society Initiative, May 2012, https://assets.aspeninstitute.org/content/uploads/files/content/docs/pubs/Moving_Forward_with_CER.pdf.

2. "PCORnet Committees and Members," PCORnet, last updated January 9, 2018, http://pcornet.org/about-pcornet/pcornet-committees-members/.

3. Dave Ranney, "The Controversy Behind Comparative Effectiveness Research," April 20, 2009, http://www.khi.org/news/article/controversy-behind-comparative-effectiveness-resea.

4. Senator Pat Roberts, "Senator Roberts Introduces Bill to Stop Health Care Rationing in Obamacare," YouTube, February 27, 2014, from 3:40–4:03, and 5:52 onward, https://www.youtube.com/watch?v=83rohum_VxY&feature=youtu.be.

5. Peter R. Orszag, "Research on the Comparative Effectiveness of Medical Treatments: Options for an Expanded Federal Role," Testimony before Subcommittee on Health Committee on Ways and Means U.S. House of Representatives, June 12, 2007, https://www.cbo.gov/sites/default/files/110th-congress-2007-2008/reports/comparative_testimony.pdf.

6. Peter R. Orszag, "Increasing the Value of Federal Spending on Health Care," testimony before the Committee on the Budget US House of Representatives, Congressional Budget Office, July 16, 2008, https://www.cbo.gov/sites/default/files/cbofiles/ftpdocs/95xx/doc9563/07-16-healthreform.pdf.

7. Darius Tahir, "The GOP's Misguided War on Comparative Effectiveness Research," *New Republic*, October 5, 2011, https://newrepublic.com/article/95890/the-gops-misguided-war-comparative-effectiveness-research.

8. Ronald Bailey, "Tom Daschle's Plan for Health Care Rationing," Reason, December 23, 2008, http://reason.com/archives/2008/12/23/tom-daschles-plan-for-health-c.

9. Ben Smith, "Budget to Kick Off Health Care Rewrite," *Politico*, February 19, 2009, http://www.politico.com/story/2009/02/budget-to-kick-off-health-care-rewrite-019017.

10. Ariana Eunjung Cha, "Scientists Embark on Unprecedented Effort to Connect Millions of Patient Medical Records," *Washington Post*, April 15, 2014, http://www.washingtonpost.com/national/health-science/scientists-embark-on-unprecedented-effort-to-connect-millions-of-patient-medical-records/2014/04/15/ea7c966a-b12e-11e3-9627-c65021d6d572_story.html.

11. "About PCORnet," PCORnet, last updated Februrary 13, 2018, http://www.pcornet.org/about-pcornet/; see also "PCORI Board Approves $142.5 Million to Fund Expansion Phase of PCORnet, the National Patient-Centered Clinical Research Network," Patient-Centered Outcomes Research Institute, July 21, 2015, https://www.pcori.org/news-release/pcori-board-approves-142-5-million-fund-expansion-phase-pcornet-national-patient.

12. "PCORnet Releases Refreshed Data and Expanded Conditions of Interest," PCORnet, May 4, 2017, http://www.pcornet.org/2017/05/pcornet-releases-refreshed-data-expanded-conditions-interest/.

13. "Partner Networks," PCORnet, last updated February 27, 2018, http://pcornet.org/participating-networks/.

14. Elizabeth Zimmerman, "Mayo Clinic-Led Networks Approved for More than $10 million to Participate in PCORnet, the National Patient-Centered Clinical Research Network," Mayo Clinic, August 13, 2015, http://newsnetwork.mayoclinic.org/discussion/mayo-clinic-led-networks-approved-for-more-than-10-million-to-participate-in-pcornet-the-national-patient-centered-clinical-research-network/.

15. "Welcome to the Greater Plains Collaborative!" Greater Plains Collaborative, n.d., http://www.gpcnetwork.org.

16. Rainu Kaushal et al., "Changing the Research Landscape: the New York City Clinical Data Research Network," *Journal of the American Medical Informatics Association* vol. 21 (2014): 589, http://jamia.oxfordjournals.org/content/jaminfo/21/4/587.full.pdf.

17. Cha.

18. Kaushal et al., 590.

19. Cha.

20. "PCORnet Releases Refreshed Data and Expanded Conditions of Interest."

21. Patient Protection and Affordable Care Act, Public Law, No. 111-148, 124 Stat. 119 (March 23, 2010), https://www.gpo.gov/fdsys/pkg/PLAW-111publ148/pdf/PLAW-111publ148.pdf.

22. We found the search feature of some browsers fails to accurately find or identify each mention of these phrases. Try another browser if you come up with a different number.

23. "PCORI Announces Funding for First Comparative Effectiveness Research Projects," Patient-Centered Outcomes Research Institute, December 18, 2012,

https://www.pcori.org/news-release/pcori-announces-funding-first-comparative-effectiveness-research-projects.

24. "PCORI Awards $88.6 Million in Funding for Comparative Effectiveness Research Projects," Patient-Centered Outcomes Research Institute, May 7, 2013, http://www.pcori.org/news-release/pcori-awards-886-million-funding-comparative-effectiveness-research-projects.

25. "PCORI Board Approves $153 Million to Support Patient-Centered Comparative Clinical Effectiveness Research," Patient-Centered Outcomes Research Institute, July 19, 2016, http://www.pcori.org/news-release/pcori-board-approves-153-million-support-patient-centered-comparative-clinical.

26. "PCORI Board Approves $115 Million to Support 20 New Patient-Centered Comparative Clinical Effectiveness Research Studies," Patient-Centered Outcomes Research Institute, August 15, 2017, https://www.pcori.org/news-release/pcori-board-approves-115-million-support-20-new-patient-centered-comparative-clinical.

27. Patient Protection and Affordable Care Act, 740.

28. Patient Protection and Affordable Care Act, 738.

29. Patient Protection and Affordable Care Act, 740.

30. Ranney.

31. Brian Rye, "The Controversy Surrounding Comparative Effectiveness Research," Bloomberg Government, February 21, 2014, https://web-beta.archive.org/web/20150320172050/http://about.bgov.com:80/2014-02-21/the-controversy-surrounding-comparative-effectiveness-research/.

32. Cha.

33. Section 6301 of the Patient Protection and Affordable Care Act, 2010 established the PCOR Trust Fund under Sec. 9511 of the Internal Revenue Code of 1986, http://www.cchfreedom.org/pdf/ppaca-consolidated.pdf.

34. "Trust Fund Transfers to Patient-Centered Outcomes Research Trust Fund," Social Security Act §1183, http://www.ssa.gov/OP_Home/ssact/title11/1183.htm.

35. "Connecting Health and Care for the Nation: A 10-Year Vision to Achieve an Interoperable Health IT Infrastructure," The Office of the National Coordinator for Health Information Technology, n.d., 2, http://www.healthit.gov/sites/default/files/ONC10yearInteroperabilityConceptPaper.pdf.

36. Ibid., 3.

37. "HHS Proposes Path to Improve Health Technology and Transform Care" US Department of Health & Human Services, January 30, 2015, http://wayback.archive-it.org/3926/20170127185444/https://www.hhs.gov/about/news/2015/01/30/hhs-proposes-path-to-improve-health-technology-and-transform-care.html.

38. Andrew Robertson, "Interoperability Begins at Home: Three Lessons from Community Hospitals," *Healthcare IT News*, March 23, 2015, http://www.healthcareitnews.com/blog/interoperability-begins-home-three-lessons-community-hospitals.

39. Andrew Robertson, "Interoperability Begins at Home: Three Lessons from Community Hospitals," *Healthcare IT News*, March 23, 2015, http://www.healthcareitnews.com/blog/interoperability-begins-home-three-lessons-community-hospitals.

40. "Draft Interoperability Roadmap (web page), The Office of the National Coordinator for Health Information Technology, last updated November 10, 2015. https://www.healthit.gov/policy-researchers-implementers/draft-interoperability-roadmap.

41. "Interoperability Roadmap Public Comments," The Office of the National Coordinator for Health Information Technology, last updated April 4, 2015, http://www.healthit.gov/policy-researchers-implementers/interoperability-roadmap-public-comments.

42. "Statements of Support," Interoperability, The Office of the National Coordinator for Health Information Technology, last updated November 16, 2015, https://

www.healthit.gov/policy-researchers-implementers/interoperability/support-statements.

43. "Connecting Health and Care for the Nation: A Shared Nationwide Interoperability Roadmap, Final Version 1.0," The Office of the National Coordinator for Health Information Technology, n.d., https://www.healthit.gov/sites/default/files/nationwide-interoperability-roadmap-version-1.0.pdf.

44. "Shared Nationwide Interoperability Roadmap: The Journey to Better Health" (Infographic), The Office of the National Coordinator for Health Information Technology, n.d., https://www.healthit.gov/newsroom/shared-nationwide-interoperability-roadmap-journey-better-health-and-care.

45. "A Shared Nationwide Interoperability Roadmap Version 1.0," The Office of the National Coordinator of Health Information Technology, last updated December 22, 2015, https://www.healthit.gov/policy-researchers-implementers/interoperability; see also "Interoperability Roadmap Public Comments," The Office of the National Coordinator for Health Information Technology, updated April 4, 2015, http://www.healthit.gov/policy-researchers-implementers/interoperability-roadmap-public-comments.

46. "HHS Publishes a Roadmap to Advance Health Information Sharing and Transform Care," The Office of the National Coordinator for Health Information Technology, October 6, 2015, https://archive-it.org/collections/3926?fc=meta_Date:2015&page=2&totalResultCount=225.

47. "Connecting Health and Care for the Nation: A Shared Nationwide Interoperability Roadmap," Supplemental Materials, Version 1.0, The Office of the National Coordinator for Health Information Technology, n.d., 23, https://www.healthit.gov/sites/default/files/hie-interoperability/Interoperibility-Road-Map-Supplemental.pdf.

48. "Connecting Health and Care for the Nation: A Shared Nationwide Interoperability Roadmap," Final Version 1.0, The Office of the National Coordinator for Health Information Technology, n.d., 127, https://www.healthit.gov/sites/default/files/nationwide-interoperability-roadmap-version-1.0.pdf.

49. "Connecting Health and Care for the Nation: A Shared Nationwide Interoperability Roadmap, Final Version 1.0," The Office of the National Coordinator for Health Information Technology, n.d., 127, https://www.healthit.gov/sites/default/files/nationwide-interoperability-roadmap-version-1.0.pdf.

50. "Connecting Health and Care for the Nation: A Shared Nationwide Interoperability Roadmap," Final Version 1.0, 127.

51. "Connecting Health and Care for the Nation: A Shared Nationwide Interoperability Roadmap, Final Version 1.0," 127.

52. Kate Monica, "AHRQ, PCORI to Fund Learning HealthSystem Research, Training," EHR Intelligence, September 14, 2017, https://ehrintelligence.com/news/ahrq-pcori-to-fund-learning-health-system-research-training.

53. Meg Bryant, "AMA Launches Shared Framework for Health Data," Healthcare Dive, October 17, 2017, https://www.healthcaredive.com/news/ama-launches-shared-framework-for-health-data/507415/; see also "Be Part of Our Health Care Solution," Integrated Health Model Initiative, American Medical Association, n.d., https://ama-ihmi.org.

54. "Be Part of Our Health Care Solution."

55. Jennifer Bresnick, "AMA Launches Integrated Healthcare Big Data Analytics Platform," *HealthITAnalytics* (blog), October 16, 2017, https://healthitanalytics.com/news/ama-launches-integrated-healthcare-big-data-analytics-platform.

56. "Federal Policy for the Protection of Human Subjects," Notice of Proposed Rulemaking, US Department of Health & Human Services, *Federal Register* vol. 80, no. 173 (September 8, 2015), https://www.regulations.gov/#!documentDetail;D=HHS-OPHS-2015-0008-0001.

57. "Federal Policy for the Protection of Human Subjects, Notice of Proposed

Rulemaking," US Office for Human Research Protections, Department of Health & Human Services, *Federal Register* vol. 80, no. 173 (September 8, 2015), https://www.regulations.gov/#!documentDetail;D=HHS-OPHS-2015-0008-0001.

58. Letter to Jerry Menikoff, MD, JD, Office for Human Research Protections, from Twila Brase, RN, PHN, Citizens' Council for Health Freedom, January 4, 2016, http://www.cchfreedom.org/files/files/CCHF%20NIH%20COMMON%20RULE%20COMMENTS%20JAN%20 4,%202016.pdf.

59. "Federal Policy for the Protection of Human Subjects," 53947.

60. "Federal Policy for the Protection of Human Subjects," *Federal Register* vol. 82, no. 12 (January 19, 2017): 7261-7262, https://www.regulations.gov/document?D=VA-2015-OTHER-0027-0006.

61. "Federal Policy for the Protection of Human Subjects, Final Rule," *Federal Register* vol. 82, no. 12 (January 19, 2017): 7261-7262, https://www.regulations.gov/document?D=VA-2015-OTHER-0027-0006.

62. Associated Press, "Lawsuit Alleges Michigan Illegally Obtains Newborns' Blood," Associated Press, April 12, 2018, https://www.usnews.com/news/best-states/michigan/articles/2018-04-12/lawsuit-alleges-michigan-stole-newborns-blood.

63. Associated Press, "Lawsuit Alleges Michigan Illegally Obtains Newborns' Blood," April 12, 2018, https://www.usnews.com/news/best-states/michigan/articles/2018-04-12/lawsuit-alleges-michigan-stole-newborns-blood.

64. "Sycamore Examines Newborn Screening Practices, Issue of Genetic Ownership," Indiana State University Newsroom, November 21, 2016, http://www2.indstate.edu/news/news.php?newsid=4800.

65. "Legal & Legislative Issues in Newborn Screening," Association of Public Health Laboratories, n.d. Accessed April 11, 2018: https://www.aphl.org/programs/newborn_screening/Pages/legal.aspx.

66. "Legal & Legislative Issues in Newborn Screening," Association of Public Health Laboratories, n.d, https://www.aphl.org/programs/newborn_screening/Pages/legal.aspx

67. "Federal Policy for the Protection of Human Subjects, Final Rule," 2017, 7152.

68. "Federal Policy for the Protection of Human Subjects, Final Rule," 2017, 7170.

69. Ibid., 7170.

70. "NIH Program Explores the Use of Genomic Sequencing in Newborn Healthcare," National Institutes of Health, September 4, 2013, https://www.nih.gov/news-events/news-releases/nih-program-explores-use-genomic-sequencing-newborn-healthcare.

71. Monica Heger, "Newborn Sequencing Projects Demonstrate Successes, Challenges of Widespread Implementation," GenomeWeb, March 16, 2017, https://www.genomeweb.com/sequencing/newborn-sequencing-projects-demonstrate-successes-challenges-widespread-implementation.

72. Jocelyn Kaiser, "Surprisingly Few New Parents Enlist in Study to Have Baby's Genome Sequenced," *Science*, October 19, 2016, http://www.sciencemag.org/news/2016/10/surprisingly-few-new-parents-enlist-study-have-baby-s-genome-sequenced.

73. "Genetic Testing for Newborns Raising Concerns About Privacy & Discrimination," CBS New York, October 24, 2017, http://newyork.cbslocal.com/2017/10/24/genetic-testing-for-newborns-raising-concerns-about-privacy-discrimination/.

74. Heger.

75. "Newborn Screening Specimens Use and Storage," California Department of Public Health, Last updated January 2, 2018, https://www.cdph.ca.gov/Programs/CFH/DGDS/Pages/nbs/NBSDBS-Storage.aspx.

76. "Newborn Screening Specimens Use and Storage," California Department of Public Health, Last updated January 2, 2018, https://www.cdph.ca.gov/Programs/CFH/DGDS/Pages/nbs/NBSDBS-Storage.aspx; see also, "California Biobank Stores Every Baby's DNA. Who Else Has Access?" Julie Watts, CBS SF Bay Area, May 8, 2018, http://sanfrancisco.cbslocal.

com/2018/05/08/california-biobank-stores-baby-dna-access/.

77. Kaiser.

78. "Genetic Testing For Newborns Raising Concerns About Privacy & Discrimination."

79. Michael Cook, "Nuffield Council Issues Brief Note on Whole Genome Sequencing of Babies," BioEdge, April 7, 2018, https://www.bioedge.org/bioethics/nuffield-council-issues-brief-note-on-whole-genome-sequencing-of-babies/12638.

80. David Pittman, "Precision Medicine Initiative Hits a Snag," Politico Morning eHealth, October 10, 2017, http://www.politico.com/tipsheets/morning-ehealth/2017/10/10/precision-medicine-initiative-hits-a-snag-222722; see also Arthur Allen, "Giant NIH Research Project Finds Some Reluctance to Share EHRs," *Politico*, October 25, 2017, https://www.politico.com/story/2017/10/25/giant-nih-research-project-finds-some-reluctance-to-share-ehrs-244160.

81. "Beta Testing Begins for NIH's All of Us Research Program," All of Us Research Program, National Institutes of Health, June 5, 2017, https://allofus.nih.gov/news-events-and-media/announcements/beta-testing-begins-nihs-all-us-research-program.

82. Pittman.

83. "The Precision Medicine Initiative," CRS Insight, October 25, 2016, https://fas.org/sgp/crs/misc/IN10227.pdf.

84. "Program FAQ" All of Us Research Program, National Institutes of Health, n.d., https://allofus.nih.gov/about/program-faq.

85. "Program FAQ" All of Us Research Program, National Institutes of Health, n.d., https://allofus.nih.gov/about/program-faq; see also "The Future of Health Has Begun," All of Us Research Program, n.d., https://launch.joinallofus.org.

86. Marla Durben Hirsch, "EMR Users Given Preference in CMS Payment Bundling Program," FierceHealthcare, August 31, 2011, http://www.fiercehealthcare.com/ehr/emr-users-given-preference-cms-payment-bundling-program.

87. Patient Protection and Affordable Care Act, 390.

88. "Accreditation of Advanced Diagnostic Imaging Suppliers," Centers for Medicare & Medicaid Services, last modified January 16, 2018, https://www.cms.gov/Medicare/Provider-Enrollment-and-Certification/SurveyCertificationGenInfo/Accreditation-of-Advanced-Diagnostic-Imaging-Suppliers.html.

89. "Oncology Care Model," Centers for Medicare & Medicaid Services, last updated March 16, 2018, https://innovation.cms.gov/initiatives/Oncology-Care/.

90. "Medicare Program: Revisions to Payment Policies under the Physician Fee Schedule, Clinical Laboratory Fee Schedule, Access to Identifiable Data for the Center for Medicare & Medicaid Innovation Models & Other Revisions to Part B for CY 2015; Proposed Rule," US Department of Health & Human Services, *Federal Register* vol. 79, no. 133 (July 11, 2014): 40376, http://www.gpo.gov/fdsys/pkg/FR-2014-07-11/pdf/2014-15948.pdf.

91. "Medicare Program: Revisions to Payment Policies under the Physician Fee Schedule, Clinical Laboratory Fee Schedule, Access to Identifiable Data for the Center for Medicare & Medicaid Innovation Models & Other Revisions to Part B for CY 2015, Proposed Rule," US Department of Health & Human Services, *Federal Register* vol. 79, no. 133 (July 11, 2014): 40376, http://www.gpo.gov/fdsys/pkg/FR-2014-07-11/pdf/2014-15948.pdf.

92. Ibid., 40377.

93. Ibid., 40377.

94. Ibid., 40376–7.

95. Ibid., 40378.

96. Ibid., 40377.

97. "Medicaid MCO Enrollment," Kaiser Family Foundation, September 2017, http://www.kff.org/other/state-indicator/medicaid-enrollment-by-mco/?currentTimeframe=0&sortModel=%7B%22colId%22:%22State%22,%22sort%22:%22asc%22%7D.

98. Gretchen Jacobson et al., "Medicare Advantage 2016 Spotlight: Enrollment Market Update," Kaiser Family

Foundation, May 11, 2016, https://www.kff.org/medicare/issue-brief/medicare-advantage-2016-spotlight-enrollment-market-update/.

99. Gretchen Jacobson et al., "Medicare Advantage Plans in 2017: Short-Term Outlook Is Stable," Kaiser Family Foundation, December 21, 2016, http://www.kff.org/report-section/medicare-advantage-plans-in-2017-issue-brief/.

100. "Medicare Program: Revisions to Payment Policies under the Physician Fee Schedule," 40378.

101. "Medicare Program; Revisions to Payment Policies Under the Physician Fee Schedule, Clinical Laboratory Fee Schedule, Access to Identifiable Data for the Center for Medicare and Medicaid Innovation Models & Other Revisions to Part B for CY 2015, Final Rule with Comment Period," Centers for Medicare & Medicaid Services, *Federal Register* vol. 79, No. 219 (November 13, 2014): 67755, https://www.regulations.gov/#!documentDetail;D=CMS-2014-0094-2364.

102. "Innovation Models," Centers for Medicare & Medicaid Services, n.d., https://innovation.cms.gov/initiatives/index.html#views=models; see also "CMS Innovation Center: Model Implementation and Center Performance," Report to Congressional Requesters, US Government Accountability Office, March 2018, https://www.gao.gov/assets/700/690875.pdf.

103. "Medicare Program: Comprehensive Care for Joint Replacement Payment Model for Acute Care Hospitals Furnishing Lower Extremity Joint Replacement Services, Final Rule," Centers for Medicare & Medicaid Services, *Federal Register* vol. 80, No. 226 (November 24, 2015), https://www.regulations.gov/#!documentDetail;D=CMS-2015-0082-0395.

104. "Medicare Program; Cancellation of Advancing Care Coordination through Episode Payment and Cardiac Rehabilitation Incentive Payment Models; Changes to Comprehensive Care for Joint Replacement Payment Model: Extreme and Uncontrollable Circumstances Policy for the Comprehensive Care for Joint Replacement Payment Model, Final Rule, Interim Final Rule with Comment Period," Centers for Medicare & Medicaid Services, US Department of Health & Human Services, *Federal Register* vol. 82, No. 230 (December 1, 2017): 57097, https://www.gpo.gov/fdsys/pkg/FR-2017-12-01/pdf/2017-25979.pdf.

105. Todd Neff, "Joint-Replacement Program Seems to Work, But Hangs in the Balance," UCHealth, January 23, 2017, https://www.uchealth.org/today/2017/01/23/joint-replacement-program-seems-to-work-but-hangs-in-the-balance/.

106. "Medicare Program: Comprehensive Care for Joint Replacement Payment Model for Acute Care Hospitals Furnishing Lower Extremity Joint Replacement Services, Final Rule," 73294.

107. "Medicare Program: Comprehensive Care for Joint Replacement Payment Model for Acute Care Hospitals Furnishing Lower Extremity Joint Replacement Services, Final Rule," 73277-8.

108. Ibid., 73310.

109. Ibid., 73281.

110. Ibid., 73519.

111. Ibid., 73463.

112. Ibid., 73463.

113. Reince Priebus, "Memorandum for the Heads of Executive Departments and Agencies," The White House, January 20, 2017, https://www.whitehouse.gov/the-press-office/2017/01/20/memorandum-heads-executive-departments-and-agencies.

114. "Startup of Cardiac Bundling Program, CJR Expansion, Delayed Until at Least October 1," *PT in Motion News* (blog), March 21, 2017, http://www.apta.org/PTinMotion/News/2017/3/21/BundleDelayOct/; see also "Medicare Program; Advancing Care Coordination through Episode Payment Models (EPMs); Cardiac Rehabilitation Incentive Payment Model; and Changes to the Comprehensive Care for Joint Replacement Model (CJR); Delay of Effective Date, Interim Final Rule with Comment Period" Centers for Medicare & Medicaid Services, *Federal Register* vol. 82, no. 53 (March 21, 2017), https://www.gpo.gov/fdsys/pkg/FR-2017-03-21/pdf/2017-05692.pdf; see also "Medicare Program;

Advancing Care Coordination Through Episode Payment Models (EPMs); Cardiac Rehabilitation Incentive Payment Model; and Changes to the Comprehensive Care for Joint Replacement Model (CJR); Delay of Effective Date, Final Rule," Centers for Medicare & Medicaid Services, *Federal Register* vol. 82, no. 96 (May 19, 2017), https://www.gpo.gov/fdsys/pkg/FR-2017-05-19/pdf/2017-10340.pdf.

115. "Medicare Program; Cancellation of Advancing Care Coordination Through Episode Payment and Cardiac Rehabilitation Incentive Payment Models; Changes to Comprehensive Care for Joint Replacement Payment Model (CMS-5524-P), Proposed Rule," Centers for Medicare & Medicaid Services, *Federal Register* vol. 82, No. 158 (August 17, 2017), https://www.gpo.gov/fdsys/pkg/FR-2017-08-17/pdf/2017-17446.pdf.

116. "Medicare Program; Cancellation of Advancing Care Coordination Through Episode Payment and Cardiac Rehabilitation Incentive Payment Models; Changes to Comprehensive Care for Joint Replacement Payment Model (CMS-5524-P), Proposed Rule," Centers for Medicare & Medicaid Services, *Federal Register* vol. 82, No. 158 (August 17, 2017): 39310, https://www.gpo.gov/fdsys/pkg/FR-2017-08-17/pdf/2017-17446.pdf.

117. "Medicare Program; Cancellation of Advancing Care Coordination through Episode Payment and Cardiac Rehabilitation Incentive Payment Models; Changes to Comprehensive Care for Joint Replacement Payment Model: Extreme and Uncontrollable Circumstances Policy for the Comprehensive Care for Joint Replacement Payment Model, Final Rule, Interim Final Rule with Comment Period," Centers for Medicare & Medicaid Services, *Federal Register* vol. 82, No. 230 (December 1, 2017): 57066, 57072–4, 57097–8, and 57103, https://www.gpo.gov/fdsys/pkg/FR-2017-12-01/pdf/2017-25979.pdf.

118. "About the Program" (Shared Savings Program), Centers for Medicare and Medicaid Services, last modified March 27, 2018, https://www.cms.gov/Medicare/Medicare-Fee-for-Service-Payment/sharedsavingsprogram/about.html.

119. Joanne Finnegan, "Medicare ACOs Don't Disclose How They Pay Their Doctors," FierceHealthcare, July 13, 2017, http://www.fiercehealthcare.com/practices/medicare-acos-don-t-disclose-how-they-pay-their-doctors.

120. John Goodman, "The HMO in Your Future," Independent Institute, June 23, 2012, http://www.independent.org/newsroom/article.asp?id=3372.

121. Ibid.

122. Finnegan.

123. Aaron Carroll, "One-Sided Versus Two-Sided ACOs," *The Incidental Economist* (blog), April 1, 2011, http://theincidentaleconomist.com/wordpress/one-sided-versus-two-sided-acos/.

124. "Accountable Care Organization (ACO) Participation Agreement," Ochsner Health System, 2015, 8, https://www.ochsner.org/img/uploads/opp/Advancing_the_Network_ACO_Participant_Agreement_2015_EXECUTION_COPY_6_8_15.pdf.

125. "Accountable Care Organizations & You: Frequently Asked Questions (FAQs) for People with Medicare," Centers for Medicare & Medicaid Services, August 2015, 2, https://www.medicare.gov/Pubs/pdf/11588.pdf.

126. Philip Moeller, "The Hidden Risks of Those Popular Medicare Advantage Plans," *Money*, May 26, 2016, http://time.com/money/4347183/medicare-advantage-risks/.

127. "Medicare Shared Savings Program: Shared Savings and Losses and Assignment Methodology (Specifications)," Version 5, Centers for Medicare & Medicaid Services, April 2017, 4, https://www.cms.gov/Medicare/Medicare-Fee-for-Service-Payment/sharedsavingsprogram/Downloads/Shared-Savings-Losses-Assignment-Spec-V5.pdf.

128. Jenny Gold, "Accountable Care Organizations, Explained," Kaiser Health News, September 14, 2015, http://kaiserhealthnews.org/news/aco-accountable-care-organization-faq/.

129. "Fast Facts: All Medicare Shared Savings Program (Shared Savings Program) Accountable Care Organizations (ACOs)," Centers for Medicare & Medicaid Services, January 2017, https://www.

cms.gov/Medicare/Medicare-Fee-for-Service-Payment/sharedsavingsprogram/Downloads/All-Starts-MSSP-ACO.pdf.

130. CMS writes, "A plurality refers to a greater proportion of primary care services as measured in allowed charges within the ACO than from services outside the ACO (such as from other ACOS, individual providers, or provider organizations). The plurality can be less than a majority of total services." "Medicare Shared Savings Program: Shared Savings and Losses and Assignment Methodology (Specifications)," Version 5, 5.

131. "Medicare Shared Savings Program: Shared Savings and Losses and Assignment Methodology (Specifications)," Version 5, 88.

132. Finnegan.

133. "Medicare Shared Savings Program: Shared Savings and Loses and Assignment Methodology (Specifications)," Version 3, Centers for Medicare & Medicaid Services, December 2014, 2, https://www.cms.gov/Medicare/Medicare-Fee-for-Service-Payment/sharedsavingsprogram/Downloads/Shared-Savings-Losses-Assignment-Spec-v2.pdf.

134. Carroll.

135. "Medicare Shared Savings Program: Shared Savings and Losses and Assignment Methodology (Specifications)," Version 5, 7-9.

136. Dylan Matthews, "The Sequester: Absolutely Everything You Could Possibly Need to Know, in One FAQ," *Wonkblog, Washington Post*, February 20, 2013, https://www.washingtonpost.com/news/wonk/wp/2013/02/20/the-sequester-absolutely-everything-you-could-possibly-need-to-know-in-one-faq/?utm_term=.7fa3158cbcd9.

137. "Medicare Shared Savings Program: Shared Savings and Losses and Assignment Methodology (Specifications)," Version 5, 8.

138. Josh Seidman, John Feore, Neil Rosacker, "Medicare Accountable Care Organizations Have Increased Federal Spending Contrary to Projections That They Would Produce Net Savings," Avalere, March 29, 2018, http://avalere.com/expertise/managed-care/insights/medicare-accountable-care-organizations-have-increased-federal-spending-con.

139. Ibid., 9.

140. J. D. Whitlock, MPH, MBA, CPHIMS, "Accountable Care Obstacles: The Holy Grail of Value Based Analytics and Why We Aren't Close Yet," (PowerPoint presentation, HIMSS Clinical & Business Intelligence Community of Practice, June 26, 2014), Healthcare Information and Management Systems Society, http://www.himss.org/file/1241741/download?token=a5_HITFZ.

141. Eugene A. Kroch, PhD, "ACO Readiness: 6 Chief Determinants," *Becker's Hospital Review*, January 29, 2013, http://www.beckershospitalreview.com/hospital-physician-relationships/aco-readiness-6-chief-determinants.html.

142. Gold.

143. Farhad Manjoo, "A Start-Up Suggests a Fix to the Health Care Morass," August 16, 2017, https://www.nytimes.com/2017/08/16/technology/a-start-up-suggests-a-fix-to-the-health-care-morass.html.

144. Brianna Ehley, "Trump's Budget Targets Health Programs," Politico Pulse, February 13, 2018, https://www.politico.com/newsletters/politico-pulse/2018/02/13/trumps-budget-targets-health-programs-103470; see also "Eliminating Barriers to Care Coordination Under Accountable Care Organizations," Section 50341, Bipartisan Budget Act of 2018, Public Law No. 115-123 (February 9, 2018), https://www.congress.gov/115/bills/hr1892/BILLS-115hr1892enr.pdf.

145. Brianna Ehley, "Trump's Budget Targets Health Programs," Politico Pulse, February 13, 2018, https://www.politico.com/newsletters/politico-pulse/2018/02/13/trumps-budget-targets-health-programs-103470; see also "Eliminating Barriers to Care Coordination Under Accountable Care Organizations," Section 50341, Bipartisan Budget Act of 2018, Public Law No. 115-123, 132 Stat. 64 (February 9, 2018), https://budgetcounsel.com/§030-laws-public-statutes/x§068-pub-l-115-123-bipartisan-budget-act-of-2018/.

146. Ibid., 3.

147. "Accountable Care Organizations: What Providers Need to Know," Centers for Medicare & Medicaid Services, US Department of Health & Human Services, March 2016, 7, https://www.cms.gov/Medicare/Medicare-Fee-for-Service-Payment/sharedsavingsprogram/Downloads/ACO_Providers_Factsheet_ICN907406.pdf.

148. Gold.

149. John Goodman, PhD, "ACOs and the Nationalization of Healthcare," *Psychology Today*, January 21, 2018, https://www.psychologytoday.com/blog/curing-the-healthcare-crisis/201301/acos-and-the-nationalization-healthcare.

150. Cynthia Cox et al., "Explaining Health Care Reform: Risk Adjustment, Reinsurance, and Risk Corridors, Kaiser Family Foundation, August 17, 2016, http://www.kff.org/health-reform/issue-brief/explaining-health-care-reform-risk-adjustment-reinsurance-and-risk-corridors/.

151. "A 10-Year Vision to Achieve an Interoperable Health IT Infrastructure," 1.

152. Stephen L. Isaacs and David C. Colby, "To Improve Health and Health Care—Editors' Introduction," *Robert Wood Johnson Foundation Anthology*, vol. XII, February 26, 2009. Accessed July 18, 2017: http://www.rwjf.org/en/library/research/2009/01/to-improve-health-and-health-care-volume-xii-editors-introduction.html.

153. "Care Beyond the Clinic: Public Health Lessons from Electronic Health Record Data," *New Public Health*, Robert Wood Johnson Foundation, July 23, 2013. Accessed July 3, 2017: https://web-beta.archive.org/web/20130802072353/http://www.rwjf.org/en/blogs/new-public-health/2013/07/care_beyond_the_clin.html.

154. Mike Miliard, "Former ONC Chief Karen DeSalvo to Join Dell Medical School," *Healthcare IT News*, December 19, 2017. Accessed January 2, 2018: http://www.healthcareitnews.com/news/former-onc-chief-karen-desalvo-join-dell-medical-school.

155. Karen B. DeSalvo, MD, MPH, MSc, "Connect for Care," HealthIT.gov, December 11, 2015. Accessed December 15, 2015: http://www.healthit.gov/buzz-blog/uncategorized/connect-care/.

156. Karen B. DeSalvo, MD, MPH, MSc, "Connect for Care," *Health IT Buzz* (blog) The Office of the National Coordinator for Health Information Technology, December 11, 2015. Accessed December 15, 2015: http://www.healthit.gov/buzz-blog/uncategorized/connect-care/.

157. "Roundtable on Population Health Improvement, Workshop 2: Speaker Biographies," Institute of Medicine. n.d. Accessed October 3, 2017: http://www.nationalacademies.org/hmd/~/media/6E92C4AC2C5C42649D8B07D8E11B0AF2.ashx.

158. "Interview: David S. Oderberg," *Bioedge*, December 15, 2015. Accessed December 16, 2015: http://www.bioedge.org/bioethics/interview-david-s.-oderberg/11695.

159. "Interview: David S. Oderberg," Bioedge, December 15, 2015. Accessed December 16, 2015: http://www.bioedge.org/bioethics/interview-david-s.-oderberg/11695.

160. "Population Health Implications of the Affordable Care Act: Workshop Summary."

161. "Politico Panel Discussion—Partial Transcript by CCHF: Outside, In: Will Population Health Solve What's Ailing the Health Care System," November 23, 2015, 4. Accessed August 1, 2017: http://www.cchfreedom.org/files/files/transcript%20population%20health%20politico-1.pdf.

162. "Population Health Implications of the Affordable Care Act: Workshop Summary."

163. Dave Muoio, "Healthcare is Moving from Episodic to 'Life-Based Care,'" *Healthcare IT News*, March 5, 2018. Accessed March 24, 2018: http://www.healthcareitnews.com/news/healthcare-moving-episodic-life-based-care.

164. "Population Health Implications of the Affordable Care Act: Workshop Summary."

165. "Pathologist Finds Natural Niche in Population Health," *Hospitals & Health Networks*, August 1, 2017: http://www.hhnmag.com/articles/8488-pathologist-finds-natural-niche-in-population-health.

166. Chris Nerney, "How Including 'Social Determinants' in EHRs Can Improve Patient Care," Connected Care Watch, August 8, 2017. Accessed September 24, 2017: http://www.hiewatch.com/news/how-including-social-determinants-ehrs-can-improve-patient-care.

167. Chris Nerney, "How Including 'Social Determinants' in EHRs Can Improve Patient Care," Connected Care Watch, August 8, 2017, http://www.hiewatch.com/news/how-including-social-determinants-ehrs-can-improve-patient-care.

168. "Politico Panel Discussion—Partial Transcript by CCHF," 3.

169. Gary Baldwin, "Tracking Population Health," *Health Data Management*, August 1, 2013, http://www.healthdatamanagement.com/issues/21_8/ehr-analytics-health-information-exchange-population-health-46443-1.html; also found at http://www.reliancecg.com/uploads/2_2013_Tracking_Population_Health.pdf

170. "Politico Panel Discussion—Partial Transcript by CCHF," 3-4.

171. "Population Health Management IT North America Market Report 2017 Edition," Signify Research, April 2017, http://signifyresearch.net/wp-content/uploads/2017/04/PHM-North-America-Q1-2017-Brochure.pdf.

172. Heather Landi, "Population Health Management Market Will Double in Size to $31.9B by 2020," Healthcare Informatics, December 10, 2015, http://www.healthcare-informatics.com/news-item/population-health-management-market-will-double-size-319b-2020.

173. Christina Farr and Jordan Novet, "Amazon's Cloud Is about to Announce a Huge Health-Care Deal with Cerner, Sources Say," CNBC, November 22, 2017, https://www.cnbc.com/2017/11/22/aws-is-partnering-with-cerner-on-cloud-deal-for-healtheintent.html.

174. Mike Miliard, "Amazon Web Services Exec: We're Interested in Longitudinal Health Records for Analytics and Pop Health," *Healthcare IT News*, January 30, 2018, http://www.healthcareitnews.com/news/amazon-web-services-exec-were-interested-longitudinal-health-records-analytics-and-pop-health.

175. HIMSS, "HIMSS18 Opening Keynote, Eric Schmidt," YouTube, March 16, 2018, quote at 2:15, https://www.youtube.com/watch?v=ACQes9erfsw; see also Dan Bowman, "HIMSS 2018: 'Run to the Cloud,' Says Former Google CEO Eric Schmidt," Health Tech, March 6, 2018, https://healthtechmagazine.net/article/2018/03/himss-2018-run-cloud-says-former-google-ceo-eric-schmidt.

176. HIMSS, "HIMSS18 Opening Keynote, Eric Schmidt," YouTube, March 5 speech posted on March 16, 2018, quote at 2:15, https://www.youtube.com/watch?v=ACQes9erfsw; see also Dan Bowman, "HIMSS 2018: 'Run to the Cloud,' Says Former Google CEO Eric Schmidt," Health Tech, March 6, 2018, https://healthtechmagazine.net/article/2018/03/himss-2018-run-cloud-says-former-google-ceo-eric-schmidt.

177. HIMSS, "HIMSS18 Opening Keynote, Eric Schmidt," quote at 22:25.

178. HIMSS, "HIMSS18 Opening Keynote, Eric Schmidt," quote at 10:19.

179. Bowman.

180. Skip Snow, "Q&A: Epic President Carl Dvorak," *Healthcare IT News*, November 11, 2015, http://www.healthcareitnews.com/news/qa-epic-president-carl-dvorak.

181. Kenneth L. Davis, "Hospital Mergers Can Lower Costs and Improve Medical Care," *Wall Street Journal*, September 16, 2014, http://www.wsj.com/articles/kenneth-l-davis-hospital-mergers-can-lower-costs-and-improve-medical-care-1410823048.

182. Ibid.

183. Grant McArthur, "Newborn Test to Head Off Obesity," *The Daily Telegraph* (Sydney), December 8, 2017, https://www.pressreader.com/australia/the-daily-telegraph-sydney/20171208/281522226423297.

184. Doug Thompson, "Genetic Counselor Joins Staff of Arkansas Hospital; Goal is to Find, Explain Risk of Cancer," *Arkansas*

Democrat-Gazette (ArkansasOnline), December 31, 2017, http://www.arkansasonline.com/news/2017/dec/31/counselor-offers-genetic-expertise-2017/.

185. Samantha Olson, "When Genome Sequencing Tells Too Much, Doctors May Have to Keep Secrets," Medical Daily, September 28, 2015, http://www.medicaldaily.com/when-genome-sequencing-tells-too-much-doctors-may-have-keep-secrets-354296.

186. Cara Livernois, "Intermountain Healthcare Asks for Consumers' Genetic Data to Build Global DNA Database," Clinical Innovation + Technology, March 22, 2018, http://www.clinical-innovation.com/topics/clinical-practice/intermountain-healthcare-asks-consumer-genetic-data-23andme-ancestrydna.

187. Matt Kuhrt, "NorthShore University HealthSystem Now Gives Patients Option for Genetic Testing During Annual Checkups," FierceHealthcare, August 31, 2017., http://www.fiercehealthcare.com/healthcare/hospital-gives-patients-option-for-genetic-testing-during-annual-checkups.

188. Matt Kuhrt, "NorthShore University HealthSystem Now Gives Patients Option for Genetic Testing During Annual Checkups," FierceHealthcare, August 31, 2017. http://www.fiercehealthcare.com/healthcare/hospital-gives-patients-option-for-genetic-testing-during-annual-checkups.

189. Kuhrt.

190. Bree Allen, MPH, Karen Soderberg, MS, Marty Laventure, PhD (Director, Office of Health IT, Minnesota Department of Health), "Connecting Community Data for Population Health: Supporting Use of EHR Data for Community Health Assessments, *NACCHO Voice* (blog), June 22, 2017, https://nacchovoice.naccho.org/2017/06/22/connecting-community-data-for-population-health-supporting-use-of-ehr-data-for-community-health-assessments/.

191. "Committee Update," *Senate Briefly*, January 19, 2007, 10–11, http://www.senate.mn/briefly/2007/brief0119.pdf.

192. Kari Bomash, "Privacy and Public Health in the Information Age: Minnesota Electronic Health Records and the Minnesota Health Records Act," *Minnesota Journal of Law, Science & Technology* vol. 10, Issue 1 (2009): 117, https://pdfs.semanticscholar.org/ae09/c73d5746ffbdb5c5aee2c3063989201823fc.pdf; see also "Summary of 2007 HHS Omnibus Bill," Minnesota Department of Health, June 1, 2017, http://www.health.state.mn.us/divs/opa/07legsumm.pdf.

193. Chapter 147–H.F. 1078, 2007, Minnesota Session Laws, May 25, 2007, https://www.revisor.mn.gov/laws/?id=147&year=2007&type=0.

194. "Jennifer Bresnick, "MA Gives Details on EHR Proficiency Requirement for Licensure," EHR Intelligence, December 23, 2014, https://ehrintelligence.com/news/ma-gives-details-on-ehr-proficiency-requirement-for-licensure.

195. Chapter 358–S.F. 3780, 2008 Minnesota Session Laws, May 29, 2008, https://www.revisor.mn.gov/laws/?id=358&year=2008&type=0.

196. "Protecting Medical Privacy in Minnesota," Informational Hearing Civil Law and Data Practices Committee, Minnesota House of Representatives, February 17, 2015, http://www.house.leg.state.mn.us/cmte/minutes/minutes.aspx?comm=89005&id=5885&ls_year=89; see also "Transcript of Manny Munson-Regala's (MN Dept of Health) Response to Chairwoman Rep. Peggy Scott," Citizens' Council for Health Freedom, February 17, 2015, http://www.cchfreedom.org/cchf.php/1333.

197. "Minutes," Civil Law and Data Practices Committee, Minnesota House of Representatives, March 26, 2017, http://www.house.leg.state.mn.us/cmte/minutes/minutes.aspx?comm=89005&id=26201&ls_year=89; see also Chapter 78–H.F. 1535, 2015 Minnesota Session Laws, May 22, 2015, https://www.revisor.mn.gov/laws/?id=78&year=2015&type=0.

198. "Minutes," Civil Law and Data Practices Committee, Minnesota House of Representatives, March 26, 2015, http://www.house.leg.state.mn.us/cmte/minutes/minutes.aspx?comm=89005&id=26201&ls_year=89; see also Chapter 78–H.F. 1535,

2015 Minnesota Session Laws, May 22, 2015, https://www.revisor.mn.gov/laws/?id=78&year=2015&type=0.

199. Evan Sweeney, "CDC Plans to Improve Public Health Data Collection by Moving to the Cloud and Accessing EHRs," FierceHealthcare, June 14, 2017, http://www.fiercehealthcare.com/analytics/cdc-plans-to-improve-surveillance-data-by-moving-to-cloud-and-accessing-ehrs.

200. Chesley L. Richards, MD, MPH et al., "Advances in Public Health Surveillance and Information Dissemination at the Centers for Disease Control and Prevention," *Public Health Reports* vol. 132, no. 4 (June 13, 2017): 403-410, http://journals.sagepub.com/eprint/RRk96GrgDJhWcwJjYjh4/full.

201. "Public Health Surveillance," World Health Organization, n.d., http://www.who.int/topics/public_health_surveillance/en/.

202. Richards.

203. Ibid.

204. "About," Digital Bridge, n.d., http://www.digitalbridge.us/about/.

205. Bernie Monegain, "Digital Bridge Initiative Aims to Connect EHRs to Public Health," *Healthcare IT News,* February 20, 2018, http://www.healthcareitnews.com/news/digital-bridge-collaboration-cerner-epic-cdc-and-others-hope-connect-ehrs-public-health.

206. "About," Digital Bridge.

207. Stephen F. Hayes, "Code Chaos," *Weekly Standard*, March 10, 2014, http://www.weeklystandard.com/code-chaos/article/783576.

208. Carl Natale, "Should Hospitals Use ICD-10-PCS Codes for Outpatient Procedures?" ICD10 Watch, November 13, 2013, http://www.icd10watch.com/blog/should-hospitals-use-icd-10-pcs-codes-outpatient-procedures.

209. Pat Brooks, "ICD-10 Overview" (PowerPoint presentation), Centers for Medicare & Medicaid Services, n.d., https://www.cms.gov/Medicare/Medicare-Contracting/ContractorLearningResources/downloads/ICD-10_Overview_Presentation.pdf.

210. "ICD-10," Centers for Medicare & Medicaid Services, last modified August 31, 2017, https://www.cms.gov/Medicare/Coding/ICD10/index.html.

211. Anna Wilde Mathews, "Walked Into a Lamppost? Hurt While Crocheting? Help Is on the Way," *Wall Street Journal*, September 13, 2011, http://online.wsj.com/articles/SB10001424053111904103404576560742746021106.

212. Bill Frist, "What My Doctor Thinks of ObamaCare," *The Week*, August 29, 2012, http://theweek.com/article/index/232510/what-my-doctor-thinks-of-obamacare.

213. Mathews.

214. "ICD-10."

215. "ICD-10 Coding," HealthFusion, n.d., http://www.icd10codesearch.com/coding.php; see also "Are You Ready for the October 1, Deadline?" *PESlinc* (blog), August 28, 2015, https://www.pesi.com/blog/details/852/are-you-ready-for-the-october-1-deadline.

216. Chad Terhune, "Our Costly Addiction to Health Care Jobs," *New York Times*, April 22, 2017, https://www.nytimes.com/2017/04/22/opinion/sunday/our-costly-addiction-to-health-care-jobs.html?_r=0.

217. Personal conversation with author, June 2016.

218. "ICD-10 Code Set to Replace ICD-9," possibly from the American Medical Association, n.d., http://adam.curry.com/art/1428501947_6SZe7VFd.html.

219. Mike Miliard, "ICD-10 Cost a 'Crushing Burden' for Docs," *Healthcare IT News*, February 12, 2014, http://www.healthcareitnews.com/news/icd-10-cost-markedly-higher-docs.

220. Mary Butler, "Not So Fast! Congress Delays ICD-10-CM/PCS: Examining How the Delay Happened, Its Industry Impact, and How Best to Proceed," *Journal of AHIMA* vol. 85, no. 6 (June 2014): 24–8, http://library.ahima.org/xpedio/groups/public/documents/ahima/bok1_050674.hcsp?dDocName=bok1_050674.

221. Ibid.

222. D'Arcy Guerin Gue, "ICD-10: Not One But Two Deadlines Coming in 2015," ICD10Monitor, October 27, 2014, http://

icd10monitor.com/enews/item/1298-icd-10-not-one-but-two-deadlines-coming-in-2015.

223. "International Classification of Diseases (ICD) Information Sheet," World Health Organization, n.d., http://www.who.int/classifications/icd/factsheet/en/.

224. "About," Coalition for ICD-10, n.d., http://coalitionforicd10.org/about/.

225. "About Us," Health IT Now, https://www.healthitnow.org/thecoalition/.

226. "About," Coalition for ICD-10, n.d., http://coalitionforicd10.org/about/.

227. Butler.

228. Kelly Gooch, "The 800+ ICD-10 Code Changes 2017 Brings," Becker's Hospital Review CFO Report, August 15, 2017, http://www.beckershospitalreview.com/finance/the-800-icd-10-code-changes-2017-brings.html.

229. "Patient Protection and Affordable Care Act; HHS Notice of Benefit and Payment Parameters for 2015; Final Rule," US Department of Health & Human Services, *Federal Register* vol. 79, no. 47 (March 11, 2014): 13753, https://www.gpo.gov/fdsys/pkg/FR-2014-03-11/pdf/2014-05052.pdfhttps:/www.gpo.gov/fdsys/pkg/FR-2014-03-11/pdf/2014-05052.pdf#page=10.

230. "Patient Protection and Affordable Care Act; HHS Notice of Benefit and Payment Parameters for 2015; Final Rule," US Department of Health & Human Services, *Federal Register* vol. 79, no. 47 (March 11, 2014): 13753, https://www.gpo.gov/fdsys/pkg/FR-2014-03-11/pdf/2014-05052.pdfhttps:/www.gpo.gov/fdsys/pkg/FR-2014-03-11/pdf/2014-05052.pdf#page=10. Cox et al.

231. "Patient Protection and Affordable Care Act; HHS Notice of Benefit and Payment Parameters for 2015; Final Rule," 13752.

232. Cox et al.

233. "What Is An Edge Server/Router/Device?" Server Fault, n.d., https://serverfault.com/questions/67484/what-is-an-edge-server-router-device.

234. Cox et al.

235. "EDGE Server Data Bulletin—INFORMATION," Centers for Medicare & Medicaid Services's Center for Consumer Information & Insurance Oversight, March 18, 2016, 4, https://www.cms.gov/CCIIO/Resources/Regulations-and-Guidance/Downloads/Part-2-EDGE-Q_Q-Guidance_03182016.pdf.

236. "Patient Protection and Affordable Care Act; HHS Notice of Benefit and Payment Parameters for 2015; Final Rule," 13759.

237. Ibid., 13756.

238. "Guidance Regarding Methods for De-identification of Protected Health Information in Accordance with the Health Insurance Portability and Accountability Act (HIPAA) Privacy Rule," US Department of Health & Human Services, last reviewed November 6, 2015, https://www.hhs.gov/hipaa/for-professionals/privacy/special-topics/de-identification/index.html.

239. "Patient Protection and Affordable Care Act; HHS Notice of Benefit and Payment Parameters for 2015; Final Rule," 13761.

240. "Privacy Act of 1974; Report of New System of Records: Notice of New System of Records," US Department of Health & Human Services, Centers for Medicare & Medicaid Services, *Federal Register* vol. 81, no. 85 (May 3, 2016): 26567, https://www.gpo.gov/fdsys/pkg/FR-2016-05-03/pdf/2016-10253.pdf.

241. "Patient Protection and Affordable Care Act; HHS Notice of Benefit and Payment Parameters for 2015; Final Rule," 13770, 13759.

242. "Privacy Act of 1974; Report of New System of Records: Notice of New System of Records," 26566–7.

243. Ibid., 26567.

244. Ibid., 26568.

245. "Overview of the Privacy Act of 1974, 2015 Edition," US Department of Justice, updated June 14, 2016, https://www.justice.gov/opcl/overview-privacy-act-1974-2015-edition.

246. "Conditions of Disclosure to Third Parties: A. The 'No Disclosure Without Consent' Rule," in Overview of the Privacy Act of 1974, US Department of Justice, updated July 16, 2015, https://www.justice.gov/opcl/conditions-disclosure-third-parties#consent.

247. "Medicare Coverage of Annual Wellness Visit Providing a Personalized Prevention Plan," Section 4103, Patient Protection and Affordable Care Act, Public Law No. 111-148, 124 Stat. 119 (March 23, 2010), https://www.gpo.gov/fdsys/pkg/PLAW-111publ148/pdf/PLAW-111publ148.pdf.

248. Email with attachment sent to CCHF from Medicare patient on October 11, 2017. Permission received to share the communication without name and corporate identifiers.

249. Ibid.

250. "42 CFR Parts 405, 409, 410, et al.: Medicare Program; Payment Policies Under the Physician Fee Schedule and Other Revisions to Part B for CY 2011; Final Rule," *Federal Register* vol. 75, no. 228 (November 29, 2010): 73411, https://www.gpo.gov/fdsys/pkg/FR-2010-11-29/pdf/2010-27969.pdf.

251. "42 CFR Parts 405, 409, 410, et al.: Medicare Program; Payment Policies Under the Physician Fee Schedule and Other Revisions to Part B for CY 2011, Final Rule," *Federal Register* vol. 75, no. 228 (November 29, 2010): 73411, https://www.gpo.gov/fdsys/pkg/FR-2010-11-29/pdf/2010-27969.pdf.

252. "§410.16 Initial Preventive Physical Examination: Conditions for and Limitations on Coverage," Title 42, Chapter IV, Subchapter B, Part 410, Subpart B, Electronic Code of Federal Regulations, March 29, 2018, https://www.ecfr.gov/cgi-bin/text-idx?c=ecfr&sid=04c3b2a97efe713fc6bdcd6935ece2ed&rgn=div8&view=text&node=42:2.0.1.2.10.2.35.5&idno=42.

253. Sam Baker, "Medicare Advantage Star Ratings Are Nigh," Axios, October 10, 2017, https://www.axios.com/vitals-2494956808.html.

254. "2017 Star Ratings," Center for Medicare & Medicaid Services. October 12, 2016, https://www.cms.gov/Newsroom/MediaReleaseDatabase/Fact-sheets/2016-Fact-sheets-items/2016-10-12.html.

255. Baker.

256. Phil Galewitz, "Medicare Plans Score Higher Ratings and Millions in Bonuses," Kaiser Health News, March 7, 2016, https://khn.org/news/medicare-plans-score-higher-ratings-and-millions-in-bonuses/.

257. Shannon Muchmore, "CMS Updates Hospital Star Ratings Formula," Healthcare Dive, December 22, 2017, https://www.healthcaredive.com/news/cms-updates-hospital-star-ratings-formula/513724/.

258. Dave Philipps, "At Veterans Hospital in Oregon, a Push for Better Ratings Puts Patients at Risk, Doctors Say," *New York Times*, January 1, 2018, https://www.nytimes.com/2018/01/01/us/at-veterans-hospital-in-oregon-a-push-for-better-ratings-puts-patients-at-risk-doctors-say.html?smid=tw-share.

259. Gregory Curfman, "All-Payer Claims Databases after Gobeille," *Health Affairs Blog*, March 3, 2017, http://healthaffairs.org/blog/2017/03/03/all-payer-claims-databases-after-gobeille/.

260. Ibid.

261. "Collecting Health Data: All-Payer Claims Databases," National Conference of State Legislatures, updated December 1, 2017, http://www.ncsl.org/research/health/collecting-health-data-all-payer-claims-database.aspx.

262. "All-Payer Claims Databases (APCDS)," National Conference of State Legislators, January 1, 2018, http://www.ncsl.org/research/health/apcd-postcard.aspx; see also "Interactive State Report Map," APCD Council, n.d., http://www.apcdcouncil.org/state/map.

263. Mike Doyle, "The Value of Claims Versus EHR Data in Care Management and Population Health Analytics Strategies," Health Catalyst, n.d., https://www.healthcatalyst.com/population-health-analytics-needs-claims-and-EHR-data.

264. "Collecting Health Data: All-Payer Claims Databases."

265. Craig Konnoth, "Governing Health Information," University of Pennsylvania Law Review, vol. 65, no. 6 (2017): 1331, https://scholarship.law.upenn.edu/penn_law_review/vol165/iss6/; see also "Frequently Asked Questions," APCD Council, n.d. https://www.apcdcouncil.org/frequently-asked-questions.

266. Marla Durben Hirsch, "All-Payer Database Lawsuit before Supreme Court

Could Hurt HIEs," FierceHealthcare, December 2, 2015, http://www.fiercehealthcare.com/ehr/all-payer-database-lawsuit-before-supreme-court-could-hurt-hies.

267. "Gobeille, Chair of the Vermont Green Mountain Care Board v. Liberty Mutual Insurance Co.," Supreme Court of the United States, March 1, 2016, https://www.supremecourt.gov/opinions/15pdf/14-181_5426.pdf.

268. Ibid.

269. Durben Hirsch.

270. "Annual Reporting and Disclosure: Proposed Rule," *Federal Register* vol. 81, no. 140 (July 21, 2016), https://www.gpo.gov/fdsys/pkg/FR-2016-07-21/html/2016-14892.htm; see also Curfman.

271. "Annual Reporting and Disclosure; Proposed Rule," Employee Benefits Security Administration, US Department of Labor, *Federal Register* vol. 81, no. 140 (July 21, 2016), https://www.gpo.gov/fdsys/pkg/FR-2016-07-21/html/2016-14892.htm; see also Curfman.

272. Curfman.

273. "Physician Compare Data FAQ," Centers for Medicare & Medicaid Services, last modified June 15, 2016, https://www.cms.gov/Medicare/Quality-Initiatives-Patient-Assessment-Instruments/physician-compare-initiative/Physician-Compare-Data-FAQ-.html#What%20is%20Physician%20Compare's%20primary%20data%20source?.

274. "Medicare Program; Revisions to Payment Policies Under the Physician Fee Schedule, Clinical Laboratory Fee Schedule, Access to Identifiable Data for the Center for Medicare and Medicaid Innovation Models & Other Revisions to Part B for CY 2015," US Department of Health & Human Services, *Federal Register* vol. 79, no. 219 (November 13, 2014): 67761, https://www.gpo.gov/fdsys/pkg/FR-2014-11-13/pdf/2014-26183.pdf.

275. "Medicare Program; Revisions to Payment Policies Under the Physician Fee Schedule, Clinical Laboratory Fee Schedule, Access to Identifiable Data for the Center for Medicare and Medicaid Innovation Models & Other Revisions to Part B for CY 2015, Final Rule with Comment Period," Centers for Medicare & Medicaid Services, *Federal Register* vol. 79, no. 219 (November 13, 2014): 67761, https://www.gpo.gov/fdsys/pkg/FR-2014-11-13/pdf/2014-26183.pdf.

276. "Medicare Program; Revisions to Payment Policies Under the Physician Fee Schedule, Clinical Laboratory Fee Schedule, Access to Identifiable Data for the Center for Medicare and Medicaid Innovation Models & Other Revisions to Part B for CY 2015," US Department of Health & Human Services, *Federal Register* vol. 79, no. 133 (July 11, 2014): 40385, http://www.gpo.gov/fdsys/pkg/FR-2014-07-11/pdf/2014-15948.pdf.

277. "Medicare Program; Revisions to Payment Policies Under the Physician Fee Schedule, Clinical Laboratory Fee Schedule, Access to Identifiable Data for the Center for Medicare and Medicaid Innovation Models & Other Revisions to Part B for CY 2015, Proposed Rule," Centers for Medicare & Medicaid Services, *Federal Register* vol. 79, no. 133 (July 11, 2014): 40385, http://www.gpo.gov/fdsys/pkg/FR-2014-07-11/pdf/2014-15948.pdf.

278. "Physician's Guide to Enrollment in Medicare PECOS: Provider Enrollment, Chain and Ownership System," LHC Group, 2012, http://lhcgroup.com/wp-content/uploads/2012/11/PECOS_P1.pdf.

279. "Medicare Program; Revisions to Payment Policies, Proposed Rule," 40386.

280. "How Original Medicare Works," Medicare, n.d., https://www.medicare.gov/sign-up-change-plans/decide-how-to-get-medicare/original-medicare/how-original-medicare-works.html.

281. "Medicare Program; Revisions to Payment Policies, Proposed Rule," 40386.

282. Ibid., 40389.

283. "Medicare Program; Merit-Based Incentive Payment System (MIPS) and Alternative Payment Model (APM) Incentive under the Physician Fee Schedule and Criteria for Physician-Focused Payment Models," *Federal Register* vol. 81, No. 214 (November 4, 2016), comment posted May 9, 2016, https://www.regulations.gov/docket?D=CMS-2016-0060.

284. John Commins, "Value-based Payments Must Address Patient Mix," *HealthLeaders Media*, December 5, 2017, http://www.healthleadersmedia.com/quality/value-based-payments-must-address-patient-mix.

285. Deborah J. Cohen et al., "Primary Care Practices' Abilities and Challenges in Using Electronic Health Record Data for Quality Improvement," *Health Affairs* vol. 37 no. 4 (April 2018): https://www.healthaffairs.org/doi/abs/10.1377/hlthaff.2017.1254.

286. Robert Lowes, "Referrals and Word of Mouth Trump Online Doctor Ratings," Medscape, February 18, 2014, http://www.medscape.com/viewarticle/820787; see also H. T. Tu and J. R. Lauer, "Word of Mouth and Physician Referral Still Drive Health Care Provider Choice," *Research Brief* vol. 9 (December 2008): 1–8, https://www.ncbi.nlm.nih.gov/pubmed/19054900.

287. Steven Findlay, "Health Policy Brief: Physician Compare," *Health Affairs*, updated October 29, 2015, https://www.healthaffairs.org/do/10.1377/hpb20151029.358498/full/.

288. "Step 5: Achieve Meaningful Use," Office of the National Coordinator of Health Information Technology, last updated April 21, 2014, https://www.healthit.gov/providers-professionals/step-5-achieve-meaningful-use-stage-2.

289. Twila Brase, RN, PHN, "Profiled from Birth, Vol. 1: Not Just a Birth Certificate," Policy Insights, Citizens' Council for Health Freedom, February 2015, http://www.cchfreedom.org/files/files/Birth%20Certificate%20Report.pdf.

290. Twila Brase, RN, PHN, "Patient Privacy and Public Trust: How Health Surveillance Systems Are Undermining Both," Citizens' Council for Health Freedom, August 2013, 2, http://www.cchfreedom.org/cchf.php/720.

291. Ibid.

292. Kristin Finklea et al., "Prescription Drug Monitoring Programs," Congressional Research Service, March 24, 2014, Summary, https://fas.org/sgp/crs/misc/R42593.pdf.

293. Theo Douglas, "Missouri Governor Signs Executive Order to Create Statewide Prescription Drug Monitoring Program," *Government Technology*, July 17, 2017, http://www.govtech.com/policy/Missouri-Governor-Signs-Execurive-Orderto-Create-Statewide-Prescription-Drug-Monitoring-Program.html.

294. "Prescription Drug Monitoring Frequently Asked Questions (FAQ)," Prescription Drug Monitoring Program, Training and Technical Assistance Center, n.d., http://www.pdmpassist.org/pdf/PDMP_FAQs.pdf.

295. Bernie Monegain, "Nebraska Becomes First State to Require All Drugs Be Reported to Prescription Monitoring Program," *Healthcare IT News*, January 31, 2018, http://www.healthcareitnews.com/news/nebraska-becomes-first-state-require-all-drugs-be-reported-prescription-monitoring-program.

296. Finklea et al., 4.

297. Ibid., 11.

298. Rebecca L. Haffajee, JD, MPH, et al., "Mandatory Use of Prescription Drug Monitoring Programs," *JAMA (Journal of the American Medical Association)* vol. 313, no. 9 (March 3, 2015): 891-892, https://www.ncbi.nlm.nih.gov/pmc/articles/PMC4465450/

299. Finklea et al., 11.

300. Jim Slater, Associated Press, "Meth Flourishes Despite Tracking Laws," MPR News, January 10, 2011, https://www.mprnews.org/story/2011/01/10/meth-flourishes-despite-tracking-laws.

301. Abby Goodnough, "States Battling Meth Makers Look to Limit Ingredients," *New York Times*, March 28, 2011, http://www.nytimes.com/2011/03/29/us/29meth.html.

302. Slater.

303. Chapter 147—H.F. No. 1078, 2007 Minnesota Session Laws, The Office of the Revisor of Statutes, May 25, 2007, https://www.revisor.mn.gov/laws/?id=147&year=2007&type=0.

304. Heather J. Carlson, "Drug Database Generates Data-Privacy Concerns for Some Lawmakers," *Post-Bulletin*, April 25, 2014, http://www.postbulletin.com/news/politics/drug-database-generates-data-privacy-concerns-for-some-lawmakers/article_a993bbea-7815-52a4-843e-99b5173e0811.html.

305. "Prescription Monitoring Program," Minnesota Statutes 152.126, The Office of the Revisor of Statutes, n.d., https://www.revisor.mn.gov/statutes/?id=152.126.

306. "Prescription Monitoring Program."

307. HF 1137, Section 1, Subd. 6a, "Use of Prescription Monitoring Program," Rep. Dave Baker et al., February 13, 2017, https://www.revisor.mn.gov/bills/text.php?number=HF1137&session=ls90&version=list&session_number=0&session_year=2017.

308. Haffajee; see also "Mandating PDMP Participation by Medical Providers: Current Status and Experience in Selected States," CEO Briefing, Prescription Drug Monitoring Program Center of Excellence at Brandeis University, Revision 1, February 2014, https://www.ncjrs.gov/pdffiles1/bja/247134.pdf.

309. Associated Press, "New Law Requires Michigan Doctors to Use Prescription Drug Database," *Detroit Free Press,* December 27, 2017, https://www.freep.com/story/news/local/michigan/2017/12/27/michigan-doctor-prescription-drug-database/985144001/.

310. Carlson.

311. Nick Budnick, "Hundreds of High-Prescribers Don't Check Pharmacy-Monitoring Program," *The Oregonian,* December 18, 2012, http://www.oregonlive.com/health/index.ssf/2012/12/hundreds_of_high-prescribers_d.html.

312. Haffajee.

313. Evan Sweeney, "Indiana Announces Plans to Integrate PDMP Data into EHRs Across the State," FierceHealthcare, August 25, 2017, http://www.fiercehealthcare.com/ehr/indiana-announces-plans-to-integrate-pdmp-data-into-ehrs-across-state.

314. "Governors' Recommendations for Federal Action to End the Nation's Opioid Crisis," National Governors Association, January 18, 2018, https://www.nga.org/cms/governors-recommendations-opioid-crisis.

315. Bernie Monegain, "Ochsner Integrates Opioid Monitoring Tool Into its Epic Electronic Health Record," *Healthcare IT News,* January 10 2018, http://www.healthcareitnews.com/news/ochsner-integrates-opioid-monitoring-tool-its-epic-ehr.

316. Mohana Ravindranath, "House E&C to Consider PDMP Bill Next Week," Politico eHealth Whiteboard, April 4, 2018, https://www.politicopro.com/ehealth/whiteboard/2018/04/house-e-c-to-consider-pdmp-bill-next-week-954756.

317. Finklea et al., 23.

318. Evan Sweeney, "White House Opioid Commission Calls for Data Sharing between State and Federal PDMPs by Next Year," FierceHealthcare, August 1, 2017, http://www.fiercehealthcare.com/regulatory/white-house-opioid-commission-calls-for-data-sharing-between-state-and-federal-pdmps-by.

319. Members of the Commission on Combating Drug Addiction and the Opioid Crisis, "Dear Mr. President" letter to President Trump, n.d., https://www.whitehouse.gov/sites/whitehouse.gov/files/ondcp/commission-interim-report.pdf.

320. Senator Joe Manchin et al., "Protecting Jessica Grubb's Legacy Act," S. 1850, 115th Congress, September 25, 2017, https://www.congress.gov/115/bills/s1850/BILLS-115s1850is.pdf; see also Rep. Tim Murphy et al., "Overdose Prevention and Patient Safety Act," H.R. 3545, 115th Congress, July 28, 2017, https://www.congress.gov/115/bills/hr3545/BILLS-115hr3545ih.pdf.

321. Rajiv Leventhal, "New Legislation Intends to Align Substance Abuse Treatment Records with HIPAA," Healthcare Informatics, September 27, 2017, https://www.healthcare-informatics.com/news-item/privacy/new-legislation-intends-align-substance-abuse-treatment-records-hipaa.

322. Members of the Commission on Combating Drug Addiction and the Opioid Crisis, "Dear Mr. President" Letter to President Trump, n.d., https://www.whitehouse.gov/sites/whitehouse.gov/files/ondcp/commission-interim-report.pdf.

VI. The Cost of Coercion

1. "Electronic Health Records: The Time Is Now," Healthcare Information

and Management Systems Society (HIMSS), January 28, 2009, http://www.himss.org/News/NewsDetail.aspx?ItemNumber=5357.

2. Jan Walker et al., "The Value of Health Care Information Exchange and Interoperability," National Center for Biotechnology Information, January 2005, http://www.providersedge.com/ehdocs/ehr_articles/The_Value_Of_Health_Care_Information_Exchange_And_Interoperability.pdf; see also Blackford Middleton, MD, MPH "Assessing Value/Calculating ROI," 17, 33 (PowerPoint presentation, Health Information Technology Summit, Washington D.C., October 20, 2004), http://www.ehcca.com/presentations/hitsummit1/middleton.pdf.

3. Walker et al.

4. Bernie Monegain, "Foundation for eHealth Initiative Called to Task on Federal Grants," *Healthcare IT News*, September 1, 2005, http://www.healthcareitnews.com/news/foundation-ehealth-initiative-called-task-federal-grants.

5. "Analysis of Health IT," RAND Corporation, n.d., http://www.rand.org/pubs/technical_reports/TR562z5/analysis-of-health-it.html.

6. Federico Girosi et al., *Extrapolating Evidence of Health Information Technology Savings and Costs* (Santa Monica: RAND Corporation, 2005), http://www.rand.org/pubs/monographs/MG410.html.

7. "Health Information Technology," Congressional Budget Office, May 20, 2008, https://www.cbo.gov/publication/24787.

8. Stuart Hagen and Peter Richmond, "Evidence on the Costs and Benefits of Health Information Technology," Congressional Budget Office, May 2008, 3–4, https://www.cbo.gov/sites/default/files/110th-congress-2007-2008/reports/05-20-healthit.pdf.

9. "Budget Options Volume 1: Health Care," Congressional Budget Office, December 2008, 5, https://www.cbo.gov/sites/default/files/110th-congress-2007-2008/reports/12-18-healthoptions.pdf.

10. Jan Walker et al.

11. "Evidence on the Costs and Benefits of Health Information Technology," 3.

12. "QuickStats: Percentage of Physicians with Electronic Health Record (EHR) Systems that Meet Federal Standards," by Physician Specialty—Physician Workflow Survey, United States, 2011," *Morbidity and Mortality Weekly Report* vol. 61 no, 35 (September 7, 2012), US Centers for Disease Control and Prevention, http://www.cdc.gov/mmwr/preview/mmwrhtml/mm6135a4.htm.

13. Ken Terry, "EHR Adoption Passes the Tipping Point," InformationWeek, October 2, 2012, http://www.informationweek.com/healthcare/electronic-health-records/ehr-adoption-passes-the-tipping-point/d/d-id/1106616?.

14. "Doctors and Hospitals' Use of Health IT More Than Doubles Since 2012," Centers for Medicare & Medicaid Services, May 22, 2013, https://www.cms.gov/Newsroom/MediaReleaseDatabase/Press-releases/2013-Press-releases-items/2013-05-22.html.

15. Aaron Young, PhD, et al., "A Census of Actively Licensed Physicians in the United States, 2014," *Journal of Medical Regulation* vol. 101, no. 2 (2015): 8, http://citeseerx.ist.psu.edu/viewdoc/download;jsessionid=6A0C57E9CC9CE90B9BB8AA68B4A5D5CA?doi=10.1.1.730.735&rep=rep1&type=pdf; see also Health Forum, *AHA Hospital Statistics™ 2018 Edition* (Chicago: American Hospital Association, January 31, 2018), "Fast Facts on US Hospitals," updated February 2018, http://www.aha.org/research/rc/stat-studies/fast-facts.shtml.

16. Anthony Brino, "EHR Incentive Payments Blast Toward $18 Billion," *Healthcare IT News*, January 14, 2014, http://www.healthcareitnews.com/news/incentive-payments-approach-20-billion.

17. Dustin Charles, MPH, et al., "Adoption of Electronic Health Record Systems among U.S. Non-Federal Acute Care Hospitals: 2008–2014," The Office of the National Coordinator of Health Information Technology, ONC Data Brief, no. 23, April 2015, 1, https://www.healthit.gov/sites/default/files/data-brief/2014HospitalAdoptionDataBrief.pdf.

18. David Cossman, MD, "HAL," *General Surgery News*, May 8, 2012, http://www.

generalsurgerynews.com/Opinions-Letters/Article/05-12/HAL/20816/ses=ogst.

19. "Budget Options Volume I: Health Care," 89.
20. "How Much Is This Going to Cost Me?" The Office of the National Coordinator of Health Information Technology, last updated November 12, 2014, http://www.healthit.gov/providers-professionals/faqs/how-much-going-cost-me.
21. Olga Khazan, "For Some Doctors, Electronic Records Aren't a Miracle Cure," *Washington Post*, November 5, 2012, https://www.washingtonpost.com/national/health-science/for-some-doctors-electronic-records-arent-a-miracle-cure/2012/11/05/f12c3400-f1fb-11e1-a612-3cfc842a6d89_story.html.
22. Mark W. Friedberg et al., *Factors Affecting Physician Professional Satisfaction and Their Implications for Patient Care, Health Systems, and Health Policy* (Santa Monica: RAND Corporation, October 9, 2013), 41, http://www.rand.org/content/dam/rand/pubs/research_reports/RR400/RR439/RAND_RR439.pdf.
23. Khazan.
24. Patricia Kirk, "Experts Say Vendors Charge Excessive Fees to Interface EHRs with Clinical Pathology Laboratories, Other Providers, and Networks," Dark Daily, October 4, 2013, https://www.darkdaily.com/experts-say-vendors-charge-excessive-fees-to-interface-ehrs-with-clinical-pathology-laboratories-other-providers-and-networks-1004.
25. Ibid.
26. Walker et al.
27. Drew Nietert, "The 6 Hidden Costs of EHRs," *Healthcare IT News*, October 27, 2011, http://www.healthcareitnews.com/news/6-hidden-costs-ehrs.
28. Marla Durben Hirsch, "EHR Transition May Be Financially Risky for Hospitals," FierceHealthcare, April 30, 2013, http://www.fiercehealthcare.com/ehr/ehr-transition-may-be-financially-risky-for-hospitals.
29. Glenn Steele Jr., MD, PhD, "The Geisinger Model: Innovations in Healthcare Delivery," (PowerPoint presentation, The Future of Health Care Innovation Conference, University of Colorado Law School, October 16, 2013), http://www.silicon-flatirons.org/documents/conferences/2013.10.16%20Health%20Care/Steele_Glenn_Presentation.pdf.
30. Michael Lotti, "On the (Electronic Medical) Records," *Twin Cities Business*, October 1, 2009, http://tcbmag.com/Industries/Health-Care/On-the-(Electronic-Medical)-Records?page=1.
31. "8 Epic EHR Implementations with the Biggest Price Tags in 2015," Becker's Health IT & CIO Report, July 1, 2015, http://www.beckershospitalreview.com/healthcare-information-technology/8-epic-ehr-implementations-with-the-biggest-price-tags-in-2015.html.
32. Jennifer Dennard, "Will Rip and Replace EHR Software Ever Be a Thing of the Past?" *EMR and EHR* (blog), April 25, 2012, http://www.emrandehr.com/2012/04/25/will-rip-and-replace-ehr-software-ever-be-a-thing-of-the-past/.
33. John A. Gale, MS, et al., "Adoption and Use of Electronic Health Records by Rural Health Clinics: Results of a National Survey," Maine Rural Health Research Center, Working Paper no. 58, September 2015, 10, https://muskie.usm.maine.edu/Publications/rural/EHR-use-RHCs.pdf.
34. Aine Cryts, "3 Reasons to Stay With Your Current EHR Vendor," Physicians Practice, Septemer 16, 2017, http://www.physicianspractice.com/ehr/3-reasons-stay-your-current-ehr-vendor.
35. Stephanie Innes, "Banner Scrapping $115M UA Health Records System," *Arizona Daily Star*, September 5, 2015, http://tucson.com/business/local/banner-scrapping-m-ua-health-records-system/article_f2673df0-4f67-5c92-b30a-9b17f30b63e6.html.
36. Akanksha Jayanthi, Kelly Gooch, Max Green, Carrie Pallardy, "50 Things to Know about Epic and Judy Faulkner," Becker's Health IT & CIO Report, June 22, 2015, https://www.beckershospitalreview.com/healthcare-information-technology/50-things-to-know-about-epic-and-judy-faulknerjan-27.html.
37. "8 Epic EHR Implementations."

38. Marla Durben Hirsch, "Massachusetts Health System Lays Off 95 Due to Unanticipated Costs of Epic Roll Out," FierceHealthcare, March 16, 2016, http://www.fiercehealthcare.com/ehr/massachusetts-health-system-lays-off-95-due-to-unanticipated-costs-epic-roll-out.

39. Michael Gartland, "Hospital Exec Quits, Compares $764M Upgrade to Challenger Disaster," *New York Post*, March 16, 2016, http://nypost.com/2016/03/16/hospital-exec-quits-compares-764m-upgrade-to-challenger-disaster/.

40. Dan Bowman, "Hospital IT Official Resigns, Compares Organization's EHR Launch to Challenger Disaster," FierceHealthcare, March 17, 2016, http://www.fiercehealthcare.com/ehr/hospital-it-official-resigns-compares-organization-s-ehr-launch-to-challenger-disaster.

41. Jennifer Bresnick, "Small, Rural Hospitals Continue EHR Adoption, HIE Struggles," *HealthITAnalytics* (blog), November 16, 2015, https://healthitanalytics.com/news/small-rural-hospitals-continue-ehr-adoption-hie-struggles.

42. "Getting Meaningful Use Right," American Hospital Association, September 2016, http://www.aha.org/advocacy-issues/factsheets/fs-meaningfuluse.pdf.

43. Meg Bryant, "In Rural America, Some Hospitals Find a Way to Prosper and Grow," Healthcare Dive, October 31, 2017, https://www.healthcaredive.com/news/in-rural-america-some-hospitals-find-a-way-to-prosper-and-grow/507840/.

44. Heather Landi, "AHA Calls on CMS to Cancel Stage 3 of Meaningful Use," Healthcare Informatics, June 15, 2017, https://www.healthcare-informatics.com/news-item/payment/aha-calls-cms-cancel-stage-3-meaningful-use.

45. "Regulatory Overload," American Hospital Association, October 2017, https://www.aha.org/system/files/2018-02/regulatory-overload-report.pdf.

46. "EHR Incentive Payment Timeline," Office of the National Coordinator of Health Information Technology, updated March 4, 2014, https://www.healthit.gov/providers-professionals/ehr-incentive-payment-timeline.

47. "Getting Meaningful Use Right."

48. "Medicare & Medicaid EHR Incentive Program: Meaningful Use Stage 1 Requirements Overview" (PowerPoint presentation, Centers for Medicare & Medicaid Services, 2010), https://www.cms.gov/Regulations-and-Guidance/Legislation/EHRIncentivePrograms/downloads/MU_Stage1_ReqOverview.pdf.

49. "Medicare and Medicaid EHR Incentive Program Basics," Centers for Medicare & Medicaid Services, last modified February 6, 2018, https://www.cms.gov/regulations-and-guidance/legislation/ehrincentiveprograms/basics.html.

50. Daniel R. Verdon, "Physician Outcry on EHR Functionality, Cost Will Shake the Health Information Technology Sector," *Medical Economics*, February 10, 2014, http://medicaleconomics.modernmedicine.com/medical-economics/content/tags/ehr/physician-outcry-ehr-functionality-cost-will-shake-health-informa?page=full.

51. Jessica Kim Cohen, "61% of Healthcare Officials Indicate Terrible, Poor ROI on EHRs, Survey Finds," Becker's Health IT & CIO Report, September 18, 2017, http://www.beckershospitalreview.com/ehrs/61-of-healthcare-officials-indicate-terrible-poor-roi-on-ehrs-survey-finds.html.

52. "EHR Incentive Program for Medicare Hospitals: Calculating Payments," Centers for Medicare & Medicaid Services, last updated May 2013, http://www.cms.gov/Regulations-and-Guidance/Legislation/EHRIncentivePrograms/Downloads/MLN_TipSheet_MedicareHospitals.pdf.

53. Mary Mosquera, "EHR Incentive Payments Top $8B in October," *Healthcare IT News*, November 9, 2012, http://www.healthcareitnews.com/news/ehr-incentive-payments-top-8b-october.

54. David Muntz et al., "No Easy Wins with an EHR," *Trustee*, September 8, 2014, http://www.trusteemag.com/display/TRU-news-article.dhtml?dcrPath=/templatedata/HF_Common/NewsArticle/data/TRU/Magazine/2014/Sep/Fea-EHR-benefits-value-innovation.

55. Henry Powderly, "Healthcare Providers Earn Billions in EHR Incentives, See Which State Has the Most," *Healthcare Finance*, April 9, 2015, http://www.healthcarefinancenews.com/news/

healthcare-providers-earn-billions-ehr-incentives-see-which-state-has-most.

56. "State Breakdown of Payments to Medicare and Medicaid Providers through January 31, 2018," Data and Program Reports, EHR Incentive Program, Centers for Medicare & Medicaid Services, last modified March 19, 2018, http://www.cms.gov/Regulations-and-Guidance/Legislation/EHRIncentivePrograms/DataAndReports.html.

57. "CMS Medicare & Medicaid EHR Incentive Programs: Milestone Timeline," Centers for Medicare & Medicaid Services, n.d., http://www.cms.gov/Regulations-and-Guidance/Legislation/EHRIncentivePrograms/Downloads/EHRIncentProgtimeline508V1.pdf.

58. Innes.

59. Neil S. Fleming et al., "The Financial and Nonfinancial Costs of Implementing Electronic Health Records in Primary Care Practices," *Health Affairs* vol. 30, no. 3 (March 2011): 481, https://www.healthaffairs.org/doi/full/10.1377/hlthaff.2010.0768

60. Drew Nietert, CPHIMS, "The Hidden Costs of EHRs," Healthcare Information and Management Systems Society (HIMSS), October 25, 2011, http://www.himss.org/news/hidden-costs-ehrs.

61. Anne Zieger, "EMR Uptake by Doctors Slowed by Lack of Time and Knowledge, Not Just Cash," *Hospital EMR and EHR* (blog), October 15, 2012, http://www.hospitalemrandehr.com/2012/10/15/emr-uptake-by-doctors-slowed-by-lack-of-time-and-knowledge-not-just-cash/.

62. Fleming et al.

63. Christopher Snowbeck, "Mayo Rolls Out Big Health Record Project," *Star Tribune*, September 15, 2017, http://m.startribune.com/mayo-rolls-out-big-health-record-project/444757193/.

64. Bernie Monegain, "Mayo Clinic's Epic EHR Go-Live: A Look at Major Milestones Leading Up to Big Switch," *Healthcare IT News*, April 25, 2018, http://www.healthcareitnews.com/news/mayo-clinics-epic-ehr-go-live-look-major-milestones-leading-big-switch.

65. Bernie Monegain, "Mayo Clinic CIO Christopher Ross on Breaking the $1 Billion HER and IT Modernization Rollout Barrier," *Healthcare IT News,* May 1, 2018, http://www.healthcareitnews.com/news/mayo-clinic-cio-christopher-ross-breaking-1-billion-ehr-and-it-modernization-rollout-barrier.

66. John Lynn, "Will Cerner Let Mayo Clinic Move to Epic Easily?" *Hospital EMR and EHR* (blog), February 9, 2015, http://www.hospitalemrandehr.com/2015/02/09/will-cerner-let-mayo-clinic-move-to-epic-easily/.

67. Patricia Kime, "DoD, VA Showcase Software for Viewing Medical Records," Military Times, November 20, 2015, http://www.militarytimes.com/story/military/benefits/health-care/2015/11/20/dod-va-showcase-software-viewing-medical-records/76070650/.

68. Fred Pennic, "Investigation Finds VA/DoD Wasted $1.3 Billion on Cancelled EHR System," HIT Consultant, August 30, 2013, http://hitconsultant.net/2013/08/30/investigation-finds-vadod-wasted-1-3-billion-on-cancelled-ehr-system/; see also Frank Konkel, "Veterans Affairs Wasted Closer to $2 Billion on Failed IT Projects," Nextgov, January 31 2018, http://www.nextgov.com/it-modernization/2018/01/veterans-affairs-wasted-almost-2-billion-failed-it-projects/145626/.

69. Kime.

70. Pennic.

71. Dan Verton, "Pentagon Awards Massive Electronic Health Record Contract," FedScoop, July 29, 2015, http://fedscoop.com/pentagon-awards-10-billion-electronic-health-record-contract.

72. Kime.

73. "MHS Genesis Rolls Out as Name for New Electronic Health Record," Military Health System Communications Office, Health, April 5, 2016, http://www.health.mil/News/Articles/2016/04/05/MHS-GENESIS-rolls-out-as-name-for-new-electronic-health-record; see also Heather Landi, "DoD Plans to Roll out New EHR System, MHS Genesis, By End of 2016," Healthcare Informatics, April 11, 2016, http://www.healthcare-informatics.com/news-item/dod-plans-roll-out-new-ehr-system-mhr-genesis-end-2016.

74. Billy Mitchell, "Audit: DOD e-Health Timeline 'Not Realistic,'" FedScoop, June 1, 2016, http://fedscoop.com/dod-ig-e-health-system-timeline-not-realistic.

75. Jessica Davis, "VA Picks Cerner to Replace VistA; Trump Says EHR Will Fix Agency's Data Sharing 'Once and for All,'" *Healthcare IT News*, June 5, 2017, http://www.healthcareitnews.com/news/va-picks-cerner-replace-vista-trump-says-ehr-will-fix-agencys-data-sharing-once-and-all.

76. Meg Bryant, "VA Says Transition to Cerner EHR Could Take 8 Years," Healthcare Dive, October 26, 2017, https://www.healthcaredive.com/news/vas-shulkin-says-7-to-8-years-for-transition-to-cerner-ehr/508170/.

77. "VA Signs $10 Billion Health Records Contract With Cerner," Frank Konkel and Heather Kuldell, Nextgov, May 17, 2018, https://www.nextgov.com/it-modernization/2018/05/va-signs-10-billion-health-records-contract-cerner/148300/.

78. Konkel.

79. Arthur Allen, "Coast Guard Docs Return to the Age of Paper," Politico Morning eHealth, April 22, 2016, http://www.politico.com/tipsheets/morning-ehealth/2016/04/coast-guard-docs-return-to-the-age-of-paper-hhs-cyber-task-force-underway-213914.

80. "Electronic Health Record Project Management Support Services (PMSS)," Solicitation Number: SAQMMA1610047, US Department of State, FedBizOpps, June 3, 2016, https://www.fbo.gov/index?s=opportunity&mode=form&id=22fc638658d9eeff9deca4eede4be8d0&tab=core&_cview=0; see also David Pittman, "State Seeks a Cloud-Based EHR," Politico Morning eHealth, June 13, 2016, http://www.politico.com/tipsheets/morning-ehealth/2016/06/politicos-morning-ehealth-ama-meeting-under-way-in-chicago-hipaa-confusion-in-orlando-shooting-state-seeks-cloud-based-ehr-214786.

81. Tom Sullivan, "How the Coast Guard's Ugly, Epic EHR Break-up Played Out," *Healthcare IT News*, April 26, 2017, http://www.healthcareitnews.com/news/how-coast-guards-ugly-epic-ehr-break-played-out.

82. David A. Powner, "Coast Guard Health Records: Timely Acquisition of New System is Critical to Overcoming Challenges with Paper Process," Testimony Before the Subcommittee on Coast Guard and Maritime Transportation, Committee on Transportation and Infrastructure, House of Representatives, January 30, 2018, https://transportation.house.gov/uploadedfiles/2018-01-30_-_powner_testimony.pdf.

83. "Examination of Reports on the EL FARO Marine Casualty and Coast Guard's Electronic Health Records," hearing, US House Transportation and Infrastructure Committee, Transcription by the author, January 30, 2018, https://transportation.house.gov/calendar/eventsingle.aspx?EventID=402127.

84. Jessica Davis, "Coast Guard Reveals How It Will Adopt DoD's $4.3 Billion Cerner EHR," *Healthcare IT News,* April 10, 2018, http://www.healthcareitnews.com/news/coast-guard-reveals-how-it-will-adopt-dods-43-billion-cerner-ehr.

85. Meg Bryant, "Lawsuit Accuses Cerner of Installing Faulty Software," Healthcare Dive, September 26, 2017, http://www.healthcaredive.com/news/lawsuit-accuses-cerner-of-installing-faulty-software/505819/.

86. "HHS Awards $94 Million to Health Centers to Help Treat the Prescription Opioid Abuse and Heroin Epidemic in America," US Department of Health & Human Services, March 11, 2016, https://wayback.archive-it.org/3926/20170127185615/https://www.hhs.gov/about/news/2016/03/11/hhs-awards-94-million-to-health-centers.html.

87. Daniel Levinson, "Progress in Electronic Health Record Implementation through HRSA Grants to Health Center Controlled Networks," Office of Inspector General, US Department of Health & Human Services, January 2014, 2, 13, http://oig.hhs.gov/oei/reports/oei-09-11-00380.pdf.

88. Ibid., 14.

89. Gale et al., 12; see also Lee A. Green MD, MPH, et al., "Sustaining 'Meaningful Use' of Health Information Technology in Low-Resource Practices," *Annals of Family*

Medicine vol. 13, no.1 (January/February 2015): 17-22, http://www.annfammed.org/content/13/1/17.full.

90. "Amendment to S. 1347," US Senate, http://docs.house.gov/billsthisweek/20151214/s1347amd_01_xml.pdf.

91. Sheri Porter, "EHR Meaningful Use Dropout Rate Soars in 2012," AAFP News Now, July 3, 2013, http://www.aafp.org/news-now/practice-professional-issues/20130703mudropoutrate.html.

92. Joseph Conn, "Final Stage 3 EHR Rule is Out, But HHS Signals More Changes Ahead," *Modern Healthcare*, October 6, 2015, http://www.modernhealthcare.com/article/20151006/NEWS/151009952.

93. Marla Durben Hirsch, "EHR Adoption Up, But Doc Satisfaction Lags," FierceHealthcare, May 31, 2013, http://www.fierceemr.com/story/ehr-adoption-doc-satisfaction-lags/2013-05-31.

94. Tom Sullivan, "Inching Upward: Meaningful Use Stage 2 Attestations," Medical Practice Insider, August 6, 2014, http://www.medicalpracticeinsider.com/news/inching-upward-meaningful-use-stage-2-attestations.

95. David Pittman, "States Fail to Track Medicaid EHR Payments," Politico Pro, December 22, 2014, https://www.politicopro.com/story/ehealth/?id=42076.

96. Nina Youngstrom, "CMS Recoups All Meaningful Use Money from Providers if Audits Turn Up Errors," *Health Business Daily*, Atlantic Information Services, Inc., September 9, 2013, https://web-beta.archive.org/web/20150719081123/http://aishealth.com:80/archive/rmc090913-01.

97. Jim Tate, "Hospital System Returns $31 Million in EHR Incentives," HITECH Answers, November 13, 2013, https://www.hitechanswers.net/meaningful-use-incentives-big-giveback/.

98. "RAND Study Says Computerizing Medical Records Could Save $81 Billion Annually and Improve the Quality of Medical Care," RAND Corporation, September 14, 2005, http://www.rand.org/news/press/2005/09/14.html.

99. Arthur L. Kellermann and Spencer S. Jones, "What It Will Take to Achieve the As-Yet-Unfulfilled Promises of Health Information Technology," *Health Affairs* vol. 32 no. 1 (2013): 63, https://www.healthaffairs.org/doi/full/10.1377/hlthaff.2012.0693.

100. "RAND Study Says Computerizing Medical Records Could Save $81 Billion Annually and Improve the Quality of Medical Care."

101. Greg Scandlen, "HIT Apologia," *Health Policy Blog*, National Center for Policy Analysis, February 10, 2014, http://healthblog.ncpa.org/hit-apologia/.

102. Kellermann and Jones, 63.

103. Scandlen.

104. Daria O'Reilly et al., "The Economics of Health Information Technology in Medication Management: A Systematic Review of Economic Evaluations," *Journal of the American Medical Informatics Association* vol. 19, no. 3 (May–June 2012): 423–38, http://www.ncbi.nlm.nih.gov/pmc/articles/PMC3341783/.

105. Kelly Gooch, "17 Things to Know about Medical Scribes," *Becker's Hospital Review*, January 26, 2016, https://www.beckershospitalreview.com/hospital-physician-relationships/17-things-to-know-about-medical-scribes.html.

106. Reed Abelson et al., "Medicare Bills Rise as Records Turn Electronic," *New York Times*, September 21, 2012, http://www.nytimes.com/2012/09/22/business/medicare-billing-rises-at-hospitals-with-electronic-records.html?pagewanted=all.

107. Rachel Z. Arndt, "EHRs Do Not Lower Administrative Billing Costs, Study Finds," *Modern Healthcare*, February 20, 2018, http://www.modernhealthcare.com/article/20180220/NEWS/180229998/ehrs-do-not-lower-administrative-billing-costs-study-finds.

108. "The Road to Meaningful Use: What it Takes to Implement Electronic Health Record Systems in Hospitals" (PowerPoint presentation, Avalere Health, American Hospital Association, April 2010), https://www.aha.org/guidesreports/2010-04-22-chartpack-road-meaningful-use-what-it-takes-implement-ehr-systems.

109. Zieger.

110. Tom aka Rusty Rustbelt, "Health Care Thoughts: Business Model Angst," *Angry Bear Blog*, Business Insider, November 4,

2012, http://www.businessinsider.com/health-care-thoughts-business-model-angst-2012-11.

111. Dan Schuyler, "Get in Line, No Technology Vendor Available," *Leavitt Partners Blog*, January 13, 2012, http://leavittpartners.com/2012/01/get-in-line-no-technology-vendor-available/.

112. Debra Beaulieu-Volk, "Behind the EHR Headache is Patient Care," FierceHealthcare, October 19, 2011, http://www.fiercehealthcare.com/practices/behind-ehr-headache-patient-care.

113. Lindsey Nolen, "HIM Faculty Shortages," *Advance Healthcare Network*, March 16, 2016, https://web-beta.archive.org/web/20160511030243/http://health-information.advanceweb.com/Features/Articles/HIM-Faculty-Shortages.aspx.

114. Heather Landi, "Healthcare Industry Faces Shortage in Experienced Cybersecurity Experts," Healthcare Informatics, October 28, 2015, http://www.healthcare-informatics.com/news-item/healthcare-industry-faces-shortage-experienced-cybersecurity-experts; see also "Job Market Intelligence: Cybersecurity Jobs, 2015," Burning Glass Technologies, 2015, http://burning-glass.com/wp-content/uploads/Cybersecurity_Jobs_Report_2015.pdf.

115. Jon Oltsik, "Cybersecurity Job Fatigue Affects Many Security Professionals," CSO, February 6, 2018, https://www.csoonline.com/article/3253627/leadership-management/cybersecurity-job-fatigue-affects-many-security-professionals.html.

116. Evan Sweeney, "Cybersecurity Tops ECRI's List of Technology Hazards in 2018," FierceHealthcare, November 6, 2017, https://www.fiercehealthcare.com/privacy-security/cybersecurity-ransomware-ecri-healthcare-technology-hazards-patient-safety.

117. Bob Violino, "Data Breaches Rising Because of Lack of Cybersecurity Acumen," *Health Data Management*, December 27, 2017, https://www.healthdatamanagement.com/news/data-breaches-rising-because-of-lack-of-cybersecurity-acumen.

118. Meg Bryant, "Cerner Bookings Hit Record High in 2nd Quarter," Healthcare Dive, August 1, 2017, http://www.healthcaredive.com/news/cerner-bookings-hit-record-high-in-2nd-quarter/448321/.

119. "Corporate Member Directory," Healthcare Information and Management Systems Society (HIMSS), n.d., http://marketplace.himss.org/CompanyDirectory/Corporate.

120. Rachel Z. Arndt, "Internet-Based EHRs Gaining Some Customers But Still a Small Segment," *Modern Healthcare*, August 7, 2017, http://www.modernhealthcare.com/article/20170807/TRANSFORMATION02/170809936.

121. Ibid.

VII. Future Considerations

1. "Project Seeks to Help People Interact With Medical Records," *VUMC Reporter*, Vanderbilt University Medical Center, January 4 ,2018, https://news.vanderbilt.edu/2018/01/04/project-seeks-to-help-patients-interact-with-medical-records/.

2. Bill Siwicki, "Vanderbilt Creates AI and Natural Language Processing Voice Assistant for its Epic EHR," *Healthcare IT News*, April 5, 2018, http://www.healthcareitnews.com/news/vanderbilt-creates-ai-and-natural-language-processing-voice-assistant-its-epic-ehr.

3. Ibid.

4. Robert Wachter and Jeff Goldsmith, "To Combat Physician Burnout and Imrove Care, Fix the Electronic Health Record," *Harvard Business Review*, March 30, 2018, https://hbr.org/2018/03/to-combat-physician-burnout-and-improve-care-fix-the-electronic-health-record?utm_medium=email&utm_source=newsletter_daily&utm_campaign=dailyalert&referral=00563&deliveryName=DM3643.

5. "Speech: Remarks by CMS Administrator Seema Verma at the HIMSS18 Conference," Centers for Medicare & Medicaid Services, March 6, 2018, https://www.cms.gov/Newsroom/MediaReleaseDatabase/Press-releases/2018-Press-releases-items/2018-03-06-2.html.

6. "Trump Administration Announces MyHealthEData Initiative at HIMSS18,"

Centers for Medicare & Medicaid Services, March 6, 2018, https://www.cms.gov/Newsroom/MediaReleaseDatabase/Fact-sheets/2018-Fact-sheets-items/2018-03-06.html.

7. Casey Ross, "The Government Wants to Free Your Health Data. Will That Unleash Innovation?" *STAT*, March 29, 2018, https://www.statnews.com/2018/03/29/government-health-data-innovation/.

8. "Speech: Remarks by CMS Administrator Seema Verma at the HIMSS18 Conference."

9. "2019 Medicare Advantage and Part D Rate Announcement and Call Letter," Centers for Medicare & Medicaid Services, April 2, 2018, https://www.cms.gov/Newsroom/MediaReleaseDatabase/Fact-sheets/2018-Fact-sheets-items/2018-04-02-2.html.

10. Drew Schiller, "EHRs and Healthcare Interoperability: The Challenges, Complexities, Opportunities and Reality," *Healthcare IT News*, November 30, 2015, http://www.healthcareitnews.com/blog/ehrs-healthcare-interoperability-challenges-complexities-opportunities-reality.

11. Patient Protection and Affordable Care Act, Public Law No. 111-148, 124 Stat. 119 (March 23, 2010), https://www.congress.gov/111/plaws/publ148/PLAW-111publ148.pdf.

12. "Health Information Technology for Economic and Clinical Health Act."

13. "Alexander: Committee Working to Identify Immediate Solutions to Electronic Health Records Program that Has Physicians 'Terrified,'" US Senate Committee on Health, Education, Labor & Pensions, June 10, 2015, http://www.help.senate.gov/chair/newsroom/press/alexander-committee-working-to-identify-immediate-solutions-to-electronic-health-records-program-that-has-physicians-terrified.

14. John Graham, "Health Data 'Interoperability': A $30 Billion Unicorn Hunt," *Forbes*, September 3, 2014, http://www.forbes.com/sites/theapothecary/2014/09/03/health-data-interoperability-a-30-billion-unicorn-hunt/#32b113ff515e.

15. Neil Versel, "AMIA: Why Interoperability is 'Taking So Darn Long,'" *Healthcare IT News*, November 8, 2012, http://www.healthcareitnews.com/news/amia-why-interoperability-taking-so-darn-long.

16. Bernie Monegain, "GAO: 5 Barriers to Interoperability," *Healthcare IT News*, October 5, 2015, http://www.healthcareitnews.com/news/gao-5-barriers-interoperability.

17. "Connecting Health and Care for the Nation: A Shared Nationwide Interoperability Roadmap: Final Version 1.0," Office of the National Coordinator for Health Information Technology, n.d., 63, https://www.healthit.gov/sites/default/files/nationwide-interoperability-roadmap-version-1.0.pdf.

18. "Report to Congress: Update on the Adoption of Health Information Technology and Related Efforts to Facilitate the Electronic Use and Exchange of Health Information," US Department of Health & Human Services, February 2016, https://www.healthit.gov/sites/default/files/Attachment_1_-_2-26-16_RTC_Health_IT_Progress.pdf.

19. "Electronic Health Records: Nonfederal Efforts to Help Achieve Health Information Interoperability," US Government Accountability Office, September 16, 2015, http://www.gao.gov/assets/680/672585.pdf.

20. Jennifer Bresnick, "Top 10 Challenges of Population Health Management," *HealthITAnalytics* (blog), July 14, 2017, https://healthitanalytics.com/news/top-10-challenges-of-population-health-management.

21. Daniel Essin, MA, MD, "Interoperability in Healthcare—Easy to Say, Hard to Do," Physicians Practice, July 30, 2012, http://www.physicianspractice.com/blog/interoperability-healthcare—easy-say-hard-do.

22. H.R. 6—21st Century Cures Act (Title II, Subtitle A, Sec. 3001(e)(B)(ii)), Congress.gov, p. 266. Introduced May 19, 2015, https://www.congress.gov/bill/114th-congress/house-bill/6.

23. "Comparison of Health IT Provisions in H.R. 6 (21st Century Cures Act) and S. 2511 (Improving Health Information

Technology Act)," CHIME Public Policy, n.d., https://chimecentral.org/wp-content/uploads/2014/10/Comparison-of-Health-IT-Provisions-in-HR6-and-S2511.pdf; see also "Information Blocking in Health IT: Myth or Reality?" HIT Consultant, June 15, 2015, http://hitconsultant.net/2015/06/15/information-blocking-in-health-it-myth-or-reality/.

24. "Senate Committee Reviews Biomedical Innovations Bills," American College of Radiology, Februrary 12, 2016, https://www.acr.org/Advocacy-and-Economics/Advocacy-News/Advocacy-News-Issues/In-the-February-12-2016-Issue/Senate-Committee-Reviews-Biomedical-Innovations-Bills; see also Senator Lamar Alexander et al., "S.2511—Improving Health Information Technology Act," Introduced February 8, 2016, https://www.congress.gov/114/bills/s2511/BILLS-114s2511rs.pdf.

25. Gregory Korte, "Obama Signs $6.3 Billion Law for Cancer Research, Drug Treatment," *USA TODAY*, December 13, 2016, https://www.usatoday.com/story/news/politics/2016/12/13/obama-signs-63-billion-law-cancer-research-drug-treadment/95382708/.

26. "Information blocking," Section 4004, 21st Century Cures Act, Public Law No. 114-255, 130 Stat. 1033 (December 13, 2016), 1176, https://www.gpo.gov/fdsys/pkg/PLAW-114publ255/pdf/PLAW-114publ255.pdf.

27. Jeff Green, "What the 21st Century Cures Act Means for the EHR Market," EHR in Practice, December 15, 2016, http://www.ehrinpractice.com/what-the-21st-century-cures-act-means-for-the-ehr-market.html.

28. Dan Golder, "Specific HIT Provisions of the 21st Century Cures Act," Impact Advisors, n.d., http://www.impact-advisors.com/regulatory/specific-hit-provisions-of-the-21st-century-cures-act/.

29. "Health Information Technology Leadership Panel: Final Report," The Lewin Group, Inc., March 2005, http://www.providersedge.com/ehdocs/ehr_articles/HIT_Leadership_Panel-Final_Report.pdf.

30. "Comparison of Health IT Provisions in H.R. 6 (21st Century Cures Act) and S. 2511 (Improving Health Information Technology Act)."

31. 21st Century Cures Act, 1177.

32. Ibid., 1178

33. "Information Blocking in Health IT: Myth or Reality?"

34. "Report to Congress: Report on Health Information Blocking," Office of the National Coordinator of Health Information Technology, April 2015, 15, https://www.healthit.gov/sites/default/files/reports/info_blocking_040915.pdf.

35. Lichtenwald.

36. Mohana Ravindranath, "Information Blocking Rule Likely Delayed," Politico Morning eHealth, April 6, 2018, https://www.politico.com/newsletters/morning-ehealth/2018/04/06/information-blocking-rule-likely-delayed-160750.

37. Rachel Z. Arndt, "Epic's 'Wizards' Announce New Cognitive Computing, Patient-Engagement Tools," *Modern Healthcare*, September 27, 2017, http://www.modernhealthcare.com/article/20170927/NEWS/170929906.

38. Rachel Z. Arndt, "Epic Allows Patients to Share Medical Records With New Tool," *Modern Healthcare*, September 13, 2017, http://www.modernhealthcare.com/article/20170913/NEWS/170919961.

39. "About Us," Epic Systems, Inc., n.d., http://www.epic.com/About.

40. Arndt, "Epic Allows Patients to Share Medical Records With New Tool."

41. Jennifer Bresnick, "Epic Systems: Machine Learning Is the EHR Usability Solution," *HealthITAnalytics* (blog), n.d., https://healthitanalytics.com/features/epic-systems-machine-learning-is-the-ehr-usability-solution; see also Erin Dietsche, "Key Takeaways from Judy Faulkner at Epic UGM," MedCity News, September 26, 2017, https://medcitynews.com/2017/09/epic-ugm/.

42. Bernie Monegain, "Epic CEO Judy Faulkner is Standing Behind Switch from EHRs to 'CHRs,'" *Healthcare IT News*, October 6, 2017, http://www.healthcareitnews.com/news/epic-ceo-judy-faulkner-standing-behind-switch-ehrs-chrs.

43. Bresnick, "Epic Systems: Machine Learning Is the EHR Usability Solution."

44. Monegain.

45. Ibid.

46. "Pine Rest Makes Multi-Million Dollar Investment In New Electronic Health Record," *Pine Rest Blog*, Pine Rest Christian Mental Health Services, October 3, 2017, https://www.pinerest.org/pine-rest-makes-multi-million-dollar-investment-new-electronic-health-record/.

47. Bresnick, "Epic Systems: Machine Learning Is the EHR Usability Solution."

48. "Judy Faulkner," *Forbes*, April 1, 2018, https://www.forbes.com/profile/judy-faulkner/.

49. Monegain.

50. Jaime Grimes, "What is Epic Healthy Planet?" Healthcare IT Leaders, February 10, 2016, https://www.healthcareitleaders.com/blog/what-is-epic-healthy-planet/.

51. Justin Campbell, "Using Epic Cogito Data Warehouse For Population Health Management," *HealthIT and mHealth* (blog), September 20, 2017, http://healthitmhealth.com/tag/epic-population-health-management/.

52. David Pittman, "Cancer Moonshot Head Recounts Exchange with Epic's Faulkner," Politico Morning eHealth, August 2, 2017, http://www.politico.com/tipsheets/morning-ehealth/2017/08/02/cancer-moonshot-head-recounts-exchange-with-epics-faulkner-221658.

53. Ibid.

54. Monegain.

55. Christina Farr, "Facebook Sent a Doctor on a Secret Mission to Ask Hospitals to Share Patient Data," CNBC, April 5, 2018, https://www.cnbc.com/2018/04/05/facebook-building-8-explored-data-sharing-agreement-with-hospitals.html

56. Ibid.

57. "Registries," National Cardiovascular Data Registry, American College of Cardiology, n.d. Accessed April 6, 2018: https://cvquality.acc.org/NCDR-Home/Registries.

58. "How to Collect Data," National Cardiovascular Data Registry, American College of Cardiology, n.d., https://cvquality.acc.org/NCDR-Home/Data-Collection/How-to-Collect-Data.

59. "What Each Registry Collects," National Cardiovascular Data Registry, American College of Cardiology, n.d., https://cvquality.acc.org/NCDR-Home/Data-Collection/What-Each-Registry-Collects.

60. "MACRA," National Cardiovascular Data Registry, American College of Cardiology, n.d., https://cvquality.acc.org/NCDR-Home/macra.

61. Farr.

62. Arjun Kharpal, "Google DeepMind Patient Data Deal with UK Health Service Illegal, Watchdog Says," CNBC, July 3, 2017, https://www.cnbc.com/2017/07/03/google-deepmind-nhs-deal-health-data-illegal-ico-says.html.

63. Kalev Leetaru, "Facebook's Medical Research Project Shows It Just Doesn't Understand Consent," *Forbes*, April 5, 2018, https://www.forbes.com/sites/kalevleetaru/2018/04/05/facebooks-medical-research-project-shows-it-just-doesnt-understand-consent/#367c60ec453a.

64. Farr.

65. Ibid.

66. Emily Stewart, "Mark Zuckerberg's Testimonies Before Congress: How and Where to Watch," Vox, April 4, 2018, https://www.vox.com/policy-and-politics/2018/4/4/17197540/facebook-mark-zuckerberg-congress-testimony-watch.

67. Joseph Conn, "EHR Vendors, Tech-Savvy Providers Unite around Internet-Like Interoperability," *Modern Healthcare*, December 4, 2014, http://www.modernhealthcare.com/article/20141204/NEWS/312049998.

68. Ibid.; see also "API," Tech Terms, June 20, 2016, https://techterms.com/definition/api.

69. Donna Marbury, "Are EHRs Delivering on Expectations," *Managed Healthcare Executive*, March 30, 2016, http://managedhealthcareexecutive.modernmedicine.com/managed-healthcare-executive/news/are-ehrs-delivering-expectations?cfcache=true.

70. Conn, "EHR Vendors, Tech-Savvy Providers Unite around Internet-Like Interoperability."

71. Steven Posnack, MS, MHS, "Get Ready for a Showdown! – The Secure API Server Showdown Challenge," *Health IT Buzz* (blog), The Office of the National Coordinator of Health Information Technology, October 10, 2017, https://www.healthit.gov/buzz-blog/interoperability/get-ready-for-a-showdown/.

72. Chris Nerney, "Despite Its Great Promise, FHIR Won't Replace Older Standards Just Yet, Expert Says," Connected Care Watch, November 21, 2017, http://www.connectedcarewatch.com/news/despite-its-great-promise-fhir-wont-replace-older-standards-just-yet-expert-says.

73. Ken Mandl, MD, "Apple Will Finally Replace the Fax Machine in Health Care," CNBC, January 30, 2018, https://www.cnbc.com/2018/01/30/apple-will-finally-replace-the-fax-machine-in-health-care-commentary.html.

74. Carolyn Bernucca, "The iPhone Health App Can Get Your Medical Records, So That's Interesting," n.d., Elite Daily, https://www.elitedaily.com/p/the-iphone-health-app-can-get-your-medical-records-so-thats-interesting-8015662.

75. Evan Sweeney, "27 More Health Systems Join Apple Health Records Platform," FierceHealthcare, March 30, 2018, https://www.fiercehealthcare.com/tech/apple-health-records-dignity-health-patient-access.

76. "Former Epic Employees Raise $3.5 Million for EHR Integration API," HIT Consultant, October 20, 2015, http://hitconsultant.net/2015/10/20/former-epic-employees-raises-3-5m-for-ehr-integration-api/.

77. "Human API," Silicon Badia, https://www.siliconbadia.com/portfolio/human-api/.

78. "Our Data Network," Human API, n.d., https://www.humanapi.co/data-network/

79. "Fact Sheet: Electronic Health Record Incentive Program and Health IT Certification Program Final Rule," Centers for Medicare & Medicaid Services, October 6, 2015, https://www.cms.gov/Newsroom/MediaReleaseDatabase/Fact-sheets/2015-Fact-sheets-items/2015-10-06.html.

80. "Secure API Server Showdown Challenge," CCC Innovation Center, n.d., https://www.cccinnovationcenter.com/challenges/secure-api-server-showdown-challenge/.

81. Thomas Stringham, "Healthcare's Game Changer: The IoT (Internet of Things)," *American EHR* (blog), November 18, 2014, http://www.americanehr.com/blog/2014/11/healthcares-game-changer-the-iot-internet-of-things/.

82. Jonah Comstock, "Digital Health Trends and Predictions for 2018, Part 2," MobiHealthNews, January 26, 2018, http://www.mobihealthnews.com/content/digital-health-trends-and-predictions-2018-part-2.

83. Tom Sullivan, "Digital Transformation Recipe for Hospitals: Consumerism, IoT and Personalized Medicine," *Healthcare IT News,* February 8, 2018, http://www.healthcareitnews.com/news/digital-transformation-recipe-hospitals-consumerism-iot-and-personalized-medicine.

84. Mandl, MD, "Apple Will Finally Replace the Fax Machine in Health Care."

85. "Telehealth," Medicare, n.d., https://www.medicare.gov/coverage/telehealth.html.

86. Jennifer Bresnick, "MA Docs Stand to Lose Licenses Without Proof of EHR Ability," EHR Intelligence, February 21, 2014, https://ehrintelligence.com/news/ma-docs-stand-to-lose-licenses-without-proof-of-ehr-ability.

87. Jennifer Bresnick, "MA Gives Details on EHR Proficiency Requirement for Licensure," EHR Intelligence, December 23, 2014, https://ehrintelligence.com/news/ma-gives-details-on-ehr-proficiency-requirement-for-licensure.

88. Bresnick, "MA Docs Stand to Lose Licenses Without Proof of EHR Ability."

89. "Overview of Final EHR/Meaningful Use Regulations," Massachusetts Medical Society, January 21, 2015, http://www.massmed.org/Advocacy/Regulatory-Issues/Overview-of-Final-EHR/Meaningful-Use-Regulations/#.VJmRkV4DaA.

90. Joshua Archambault, "60% of MA Docs Will Not Meet Ch224 Electronic Medical Record Mandate," Pioneer Institute, June 3, 2013, http://pioneerinstitute.

org/healthcare/60-of-ma-docs-will-not-meet-ch224-electronic-medical-record-mandate/.

91. Ibid.

92. Jessica Kim Cohen, "Paper Records Are Here to Stay: 4 Questions with Illinois Pain Institute's Dr. John Prunskis," Becker's Health IT & CIO Report, August 9, 2017, http://www.beckershospitalreview.com/healthcare-information-technology/paper-records-are-here-to-stay-4-questions-with-illinois-pain-institute-s-dr-john-prunskis.html.

93. Joanne Finnegan, "Why One Practice Ditched EHR in Favor of Paper Records," FierceHealthcare, August 14, 2017, http://www.fiercehealthcare.com/practices/unhappy-ehr-one-practice-ditched-it-and-went-back-to-paper-records.

94. Matt Kuhrt, "Team-Based Care Is Coming, and Doctors Must Adapt," FierceHealthcare, October 26, 2017, https://www.fiercehealthcare.com/healthcare/team-based-care-coming-and-docs-will-need-to-adapt.

95. Sophie Quinton, "Team Approach to Health Care Means New Role for Doctors," *Stateline* (blog), The PEW Charitable Trusts, October 25, 2017, http://www.pewtrusts.org/en/research-and-analysis/blogs/stateline/2017/10/25/team-approach-to-health-care-means-new-role-for-doctors.

96. Barbara Moran, "The Physician Assistant Will See You," *New York Times*, August 1, 2014, https://www.nytimes.com/2014/08/03/education/edlife/the-physician-assistant-will-see-you.html?_r=0.

97. "2016 Survey of America's Physicians Practice Patterns & Perspectives," The Physicians Foundation, September 2016, https://physiciansfoundation.org/wp-content/uploads/2018/01/Biennial_Physician_Survey_2016.pdf.

98. Keith Loria, "Physicians Leaving Profession Over EHRs," *Medical Economics*, January 24, 2018, http://medicaleconomics.modernmedicine.com/medical-economics/news/physicians-leaving-profession-over-ehrs?page=0,0.

99. Ibid.

100. Bernie Monegain, "Solving Physician Burnout: Interdependent Care Teams Beyond Hospital Setting Could Be Answer," *Healthcare IT News*, January 16, 2018, http://www.healthcareitnews.com/news/solving-physician-burnout-interdependent-care-teams-beyond-hospital-setting-could-be-answer.

101. Jonah Comstock, "Kaiser Permanente Colorado Finds There's More to Telemedicine Than Video," *Healthcare IT News*, February 1, 2018, http://www.healthcareitnews.com/news/kaiser-permanente-colorado-finds-theres-more-telemedicine-video.

102. Jennifer Bresnick, "Exploring the Use of Blockchain for EHRs, Healthcare Big Data," *HealthITAnalytics* (blog), n.d., https://healthitanalytics.com/features/exploring-the-use-of-blockchain-for-ehrs-healthcare-big-data.

103. DutchChain, "The Value of Bitcoin and Crypto Currency Technology - The Blockchain explained," YouTube, October 14, 2014, https://www.youtube.com/watch?v=YIVAluSL9SU.

104. Varun Gera, "Is Blockchain Paving the Way for Better Healthcare?" BW Disrupt, April 6, 2018, http://bwdisrupt.businessworld.in/article/Is-Blockchain-Paving-the-Way-for-Better-Healthc are-/06-04-2018-145668/.

105. Jennifer Bresnick, "Exploring the Use of Blockchain for EHRs, Healthcare Big Data."

106. "Will Blockchain Really Solve the Interoperability Problem?" *KLAS* (blog), November 3, 2017, https://klasresearch.com/resources/blogs/2016/11/03/will-blockchain-really-solve-the-interoperability-problem.

107. Jennifer Bresnick, "Blockchain Will 'Change the Physics' of Health Data Sharing," *HealthITAnalytics* (blog), February 27, 2017, https://healthitanalytics.com/news/blockchain-will-change-the-physics-of-health-data-sharing.

108. Jennifer Bresnick, "ONC Exploring Use of Blockchain in EHRs, Healthcare IoT Devices," *HealthITAnalytics* (blog), July 12, 2016, https://healthitanalytics.com/news/onc-exploring-use-of-blockchain-in-ehrs-healthcare-iot-devices.

109. Evan Sweeney, "Humana, UnitedHealthcare Launch Blockchain Pilot Focused on Provider Directories," FierceHealthcare, April 2, 2018, https://www.fiercehealthcare.com/tech/humana-unitedhealthcare-optum-quest-diagnostics-blockchain.

110. Susan Morse, "UnitedHealthcare, Optum, Humana, MultiPlan and Quest Diagnostics Launch Blockchain Provider Director Pilot," *Healthcare Finance*, April 2, 2018, http://www.healthcarefinancenews.com/news/unitedhealthcare-optum-humana-multiplan-and-quest-diagnostics-launch-blockchain-provider.

111. Lucas Mearian, "IBM Watson, FDA to Explore Blockchain for Secure Patient Data Exchange," *Computerworld*, January 11, 2018, https://www.computerworld.com/article/3156504/healthcare-it/ibm-watson-fda-to-explore-blockchain-for-secure-patient-data-exchange.html.

112. John D. Halamka, MD, Andrew Lippman, and Ariel Ekblaw, "The Potential for Blockchain to Transform Electronic Health Records," *Harvard Business Review*, March 3, 2017, https://hbr.org/2017/03/the-potential-for-blockchain-to-transform-electronic-health-records.

113. "Medicalchain—A Blockchain for Electronic Health Records," *Crypt Bytes Tech* (blog), November 16, 2017, https://medium.com/crypt-bytes-tech/medicalchain-a-blockchain-for-electronic-health-records-eef181ed14c2.

114. Jennifer Bresnick, "Exploring the Use of Blockchain for EHRs, Healthcare Big Data," *HealthITAnalytics* (blog), n.d., https://healthitanalytics.com/features/exploring-the-use-of-blockchain-for-ehrs-healthcare-big-data.

115. Bresnick, "Blockchain Will 'Change the Physics' of Health Data Sharing."

116. Jennifer Bresnick, "ONC Exploring Use of Blockchain in EHRs, Healthcare IoT Devices," *HealthITAnalytics* (blog), July 12, 2016, https://healthitanalytics.com/news/onc-exploring-use-of-blockchain-in-ehrs-healthcare-iot-devices.

117. "Medicalchain—A Blockchain for Electronic Health Records."

118. "Lightstreams to Launch New Protocol to Fix Blockchain Privacy Problems," CryptoNinjas, May 1, 2018, https://www.cryptoninjas.net/2018/05/01/lightstreams-to-launch-new-protocol-to-fix-blockchain-privacy-problems/.

119. An engaging video describing blockchain was published on October 14, 2014, by DutchChain and can be found here: https://www.youtube.com/watch?v=YIVAluSL9SU.

120. Ken Terry, "Patient Records: The Struggle for Ownership," *Medical Economics*, December 10, 2015, http://medicaleconomics.modernmedicine.com/medical-economics/news/patient-records-struggle-ownership.

121. Ibid.

122. Ibid.

123. Ibid.

124. Charles Safran, MD, MS, et al., "Toward a National Framework for the Secondary Use of Health Data," American Medical Informatics Association, September 14, 2016, https://www.amia.org/sites/amia.org/files/2006-Policy-Meeting-Final-Report.pdf.

125. Meryl Bloomrosen, MBA, and Don Detmer, MD, MA, "Advancing the Framework: Use of Health Data—A Report of a Working Conference of the American Medical Informatics Association," *Journal of the American Medical Informatics Association* vol. 15, no. 6 (Nov–Dec 2008): 715–22, https://www.ncbi.nlm.nih.gov/pmc/articles/PMC2585531/.

126. "Health Data Stewardship: What, Why, Who, How," National Committee on Vital and Health Statistics, US Department of Health & Human Services, December 2009, https://www.ncvhs.hhs.gov/wp-content/uploads/2014/05/090930lt.pdf.

127. "Interview for Woman's Own ('No Such Thing As Society')", Margaret Thatcher Foundation, September 23, 1987, https://www.margaretthatcher.org/document/106689.

128. "Health Data Stewardship: What, Why, Who, How."

129. Ibid.

130. Eric Just, "Healthcare Data Stewardship: The Key to Going from Information Poor to Information Rich," Health Catalyst,

SlideShare, November 11, 2014, https://www.slideshare.net/healthcatalyst1/healthcare-data-stewardship-41426531.

131. "Health Data Stewardship: What, Why, Who, How."

132. Leetaru.

133. Bloomrosen and Detmer.

134. Arthur Allen, "High Noon for Federal Health Records Program?" Politico Pro, December 28, 2014, http://www.politico.com/story/2014/12/federal-health-records-program-113787.

135. Pittman.

136. Arthur Allen, "Human Factor' Problems Persist in EHRs," Politico Pro eHealth, January 14, 2015, email received by author (subscription required).

137. Julie Spitzer, "Fairview CEO Bashes Epic, Calls for March on Madison," Becker's Health IT & CIO Report, January 17, 2018, https://www.beckershospitalreview.com/ehrs/fairview-ceo-bashes-epic-calls-for-march-on-madison.html.

138. Thomas W. Lagrelius, MD, "Computers Are Amazing, but Electronic Health Records Are Not," *The Hill*, March 26, 2018, http://thehill.com/opinion/healthcare/380381-computers-are-amazing-but-electronic-health-records-are-not.

139. Scot M. Silverstein, MD, "*Washington Post* Article: Electronic Medical Records Not Seen as a Cure-All," *Contemporary Issues in Medical Informatics: Good Health IT, Bad Health IT, and Common Examples of Healthcare IT Difficulties* (blog), Drexel University, n.d., http://cci.drexel.edu/faculty/ssilverstein/cases/?loc=cases&sloc=mostrous.

140. Shawn Martin, "EHR Market Needs Competition, Innovation," *In the Trenches* (AAFP blog), May 1, 2018, https://www.aafp.org/news/blogs/inthetrenches/entry/20180501ITT_ehrs.html.

141. Arthur Allen, "Why Health Care IT Is Still on Life Support," *Politico Magazine*, June 11, 2015, http://www.politico.com/magazine/story/2015/06/electronic-medical-records-doctors-118881.

142. Julie Creswell, "A Digital Shift on Health Data Swells Profits in an Industry," *New York Times*, February 19, 2013, http://www.nytimes.com/2013/02/20/business/a-digital-shift-on-health-data-swells-profits.html?_r=0.

143. Ibid.

144. "Information blocking," Section 4004, 21st Century Cures Act, Public Law No. 114-255, 130 Stat. 1033 (December 13, 2017), https://www.gpo.gov/fdsys/pkg/PLAW-114publ255/pdf/PLAW-114publ255.pdf.

145. "HIMSS Attendance Jumps By More Than 5,000 attendees to 43,129," Becker's Health IT & CIO Report, April 16, 2015, http://www.beckershospitalreview.com/healthcare-information-technology/himss-attendance-jumps-by-more-than-5-000-attendees-to-43-129.html.

146. "50 Things to Know about Epic and Judy Faulkner," Becker's Health IT & CIO Report, June 22, 2015, http://www.beckershospitalreview.com/healthcare-information-technology/50-things-to-know-about-epic-and-judy-faulkner.html.

147. "EHR Giants Rethink Interface, Sharing Fees," Connected Care Watch, n.d., http://www.hiewatch.com/news/ehr-giants-rethink-interface-sharing-fees.

148. Robert Moffit, "How Congress Mysteriously Became a 'Small Business' to Qualify for Obamacare Subsidies," The Daily Signal, May 11, 2016, http://dailysignal.com/2016/05/11/how-congress-mysteriously-became-a-small-business-to-qualify-for-obamacare-subsides/.

149. "Uses and Disclosures for Which an Authorization or Opportunity to Agree or Object is Not Required," 45 CFR 164.512, Legal Information Institute, Cornell Law School, n.d., https://www.law.cornell.edu/cfr/text/45/164.512.

150. Richard Sobel, "The HIPAA Paradox: The Privacy Rule That's Not," *Hastings Center Report* 37, no. 4 (July/August 2007): 47, http://pipatl.org/data/library/HIPAAparadox.pdf.

151. "Privacy Notice to Employees (Tennessen Warning)", Conway, Deuth & Schmiesing, PLLP, n.d., http://www.cdscpa.com/wp-content/uploads/2014/12/Tennessen-Warning.pdf.

152. Letter to President Donald Trump, House of Representatives, Commonwealth of

Pennsylvania, January 24, 2017, http://www.cchfreedom.org/files/files/PA%20Letter%20to%20Trump%20-%20REAL%20ID%20-%20Condensed.pdf.

153. "Unassigned Claim (Health Care) Law and Legal Definition," USLegal, n.d., https://definitions.uslegal.com/u/unassigned-claim-health-care/.

154. "HI 00801.002 Waiver of HI Entitlement by Monthly Beneficiary," Programs Operations Manual System (POMS), Social Security Administration, last reviewed April 7, 2015, https://secure.ssa.gov/apps10/poms.nsf/lnx/0600801002.

155. Arthur Allen, "Rucker Suggests ONC Policy," Politico Morning eHealth, June 12, 2017, http://www.politico.com/tipsheets/morning-ehealth/2017/06/12/rucker-suggests-onc-policy-220790.

156. Edmund H. Mahony, "Supreme Court Establishes Right To Sue Over Medical Record Breaches," *Hartford Courant*, January 11, 2018, http://www.courant.com/news/connecticut/hc-supreme-court-medical-rercords-20180111-story.html.

157. "UPDATE: Iowa Governor Signs Law Allowing Health Plans That Skirt ACA," *The Courier*, April 2, 2018, http://wcfcourier.com/news/local/govt-and-politics/update-iowa-governor-signs-law-allowing-health-plans-that-skirt/article_4a083b03-3bc1-5ed5-92ca-c303ecdeb3a9.html.

158. Joanne Finnegan, "Why One Practice Ditched EHR in Favor of Paper Records," FierceHealthcare, August 14, 2017, http://www.fiercehealthcare.com/practices/unhappy-ehr-one-practice-ditched-it-and-went-back-to-paper-records.

159. James Richard, comment on Howard Green MD, "EMR and EHR Buyers Beware Deceptive Sales," LinkedIn, December 9, 2016, https://www.linkedin.com/pulse/emr-buyer-beware-howard-green-md/.

160. Sharyl J. Nass et al., editors, *Beyond the HIPAA Privacy Rule: Enhancing Privacy, Improving Health Through Research*, 1st ed. (Washington D.C.: National Academies Press, (March 24, 2009), chap. 4, https://www.ncbi.nlm.nih.gov/books/NBK9573/.

161. Leetaru.

162. Associated Press, "Lawsuit Alleges Michigan Illegally Obtains Newborns' Blood," April 12, 2018, https://www.usnews.com/news/best-states/michigan/articles/2018-04-12/lawsuit-alleges-michigan-stole-newborns-blood.

163. Robert Gellman and Pam Dixon, "Paying Out of Pocket to Protect Health Privacy: A New but Complicated HIPAA Option," World Privacy Forum, January 30, 2014, http://www.worldprivacyforum.org/wp-content/uploads/2014/01/WPF_RightToRestrict_Jan30_2014_fs.pdf

How Patients Lost Control to Third-Party Payers

1. Robert B. Helms, "Tax Policy and the History of the Health Insurance Industry," American Enterprise Institute, February 29, 2008, 2, https://www.aei.org/publication/tax-policy-and-the-history-of-the-health-insurance-industry/.

2. "National Health Expenditure Projections 2017-2026," Centers for Medicare & Medicaid Services, n.d., 3, https://www.cms.gov/Research-Statistics-Data-and-Systems/Statistics-Trends-and-Reports/NationalHealthExpendData/Downloads/ForecastSummary.pdf.

3. Tom Miller, "Kill the Tax Exclusion for Health Insurance," *National Review*, August 19, 2014, http://www.nationalreview.com/article/385704/kill-tax-exclusion-health-insurance-tom-miller.

4. Ibid.

5. Gary Burtless and Sveta Milusheva, "Effects of Employer-Sponsored Health Insurance Costs on Social Security Taxable Wages," *Social Security Bulletin* vol. 73, no. 1 (2013), https://www.ssa.gov/policy/docs/ssb/v73n1/v73n1p83.html.

6. Associated Press, "Why Health Care Eats More of Your Paycheck Every Year," NBC News, November 4, 2016, http://www.nbcnews.com/health/health-news/why-health-care-eats-more-your-paycheck-every-year-n678051.

7. Sue A. Blevins, *Medicare's Midlife Crisis* (Washington D.C.: Cato Institute, October 25, 2001), 56, https://www.amazon.com/Medicares-Midlife-Crisis-Sue-Blevins/dp/1930865090.

8. Daniel R. Levinson, "Medicare Shared Savings Program Accountable Care Organizations Have Shown Potential For Reducing Spending and Improving Quality," Office of Inspector General, US Department of Health & Human Services, August 2017, https://oig.hhs.gov/oei/reports/oei-02-15-00450.pdf.

9. Twila Brase, RN, PHN, "Blame Congress for HMOs," Citizens' Council for Health Freedom, http://www.cchfreedom.org/cchf.php/171#.VuL-7lJeKvM.

10. Ibid.

11. Peter D. Fox, PhD, and Peter R. Kongstvedt, MD, FACP, *The Essentials of Managed Health Care*, 6th ed. (Burlington, MA, Jones & Bartlett Learning, April 20, 2012), chap. 1, 11, http://samples.jbpub.com/9781284043259/Chapter1.pdf.

12. Ibid., 26.

13. "Medicaid Managed Care Enrollment and Program Characteristics, 2015, Mathematica Policy Research, Centers for Medicare & Medicaid Services, Winter 2016, 8, https://www.medicaid.gov/medicaid/managed-care/downloads/enrollment/2015-medicaid-managed-care-enrollment-report.pdf.

14. H.R. 3600, Health Security Act, US Representative Richard Gephardt, November 20, 1993, http://www.gpo.gov/fdsys/pkg/BILLS-103hr3600ih/pdf/BILLS-103hr3600ih.pdf.

15. Health Insurance Portability and Accountability Act of 1996, Public Law No. 104-191, 110 Stat. 1936 (August 21, 1996), https://www.gpo.gov/fdsys/pkg/PLAW-104publ191/pdf/PLAW-104publ191.pdf.

16. "Summary of the HIPAA Privacy Rule," US Department of Health & Human Services, last reviewed July 26, 2013, https://www.hhs.gov/hipaa/for-professionals/privacy/laws-regulations/index.html; see also "Standards for Privacy of Individually Identifiable Health Information," 45 CFR Parts 160 and 164, US Department of Health & Human Services, *Federal Register* vol. 65, No. 250 (December 28, 2000): 82473, https://www.gpo.gov/fdsys/pkg/FR-2000-12-28/pdf/00-32678.pdf.

17. "Standards for Privacy of Individually-Identifiable Health Information, Final Rule," Part V, US Department of Health & Human Services, *Federal Register* vol. 67, no. 157 (August 14, 2002): 53211, https://www.gpo.gov/fdsys/pkg/FR-2002-08-14/pdf/02-20554.pdf. The consent requirements were stripped out by the Bush administration in 2002.

18. Fox and Kongstvedt, 25.

19. Senator William Frist, "Healthcare Research and Quality Act of 1999 (S. 580)" GovTrack, December 6, 1999, https://www.govtrack.us/congress/bills/106/s580; see also https://www.ahrq.gov/sites/default/files/wysiwyg/policymakers/hrqa99.pdf.

20. "Take Notice" Announcements, National Guideline Clearinghouse, Agency for Healthcare Research and Quality, April 30, 2018, https://www.guideline.gov/home/announcements; see also Dan Diamond, "Opioids, Opioids and More Opioids Today," Politico Pulse, April 24, 2018, https://www.politico.com/newsletters/politico-pulse/2018/04/24/opioids-opioids-and-more-opioids-today-181637.

21. Fox and Kongstvedt, 25.

22. Brian Biles et al., "Medicare Advantage's Private Fee-for-Service Plans: Paying for Coordinated Care Without the Coordination," Issue Brief, Commonwealth Fund, October 2008, 4, http://www.commonwealthfund.org/~/media/files/publications/issue-brief/2008/oct/medicare-advantages-private-fee-for-service-plans—paying-for-coordinated-care-without-the-coordinat/biles_medicareadvantageprivatefee forserviceplans_ib-pdf.pdf.

23. "Medicare Advantage," Kaiser Family Foundation, October 10, 2017, https://www.kff.org/medicare/fact-sheet/medicare-advantage/.

24. "Tax Relief and Health Care Act of 2006," Public Law No. 109-432, December 20, 2006, https://www.cms.gov/Medicare/Quality-Initiatives-Patient-Assessment-Instruments/PQRS/downloads/PQRITaxReliefHealthCareAct.pdf.

25. Medicare Improvements for Patients and Providers Act of 2008, Public Law No. 110-275, 122 Stat. 2494 (July 15, 2008): 2584, http://www.gpo.gov/fdsys/pkg/PLAW-110publ275/pdf/PLAW-110publ275.pdf.

26. American Recovery and Reinvestment Act of 2009, Public Law No. 111-5, 123 Stat. 115 (February 17, 2009), https://www.gpo.gov/fdsys/pkg/PLAW-111publ5/pdf/PLAW-111publ5.pdf.

27. Patient Protection and Affordable Care Act, Public Law No. 111-148, 124 Stat. 119 (March 23, 2010), https://www.gpo.gov/fdsys/pkg/PLAW-111publ148/pdf/PLAW-111publ148.pdf.

28. Health Care and Education Reconciliation Act of 2010, Public Law No. 111-152, 124 Stat. 1029 (March 30, 2010), https://www.gpo.gov/fdsys/pkg/PLAW-111publ152/pdf/PLAW-111publ152.pdf.

29. Byron York, "Obamacare's 2,700 Pages Are Too Much for Justices," *Washington Examiner*, March 29, 2012, http://www.washingtonexaminer.com/obamacares-2700-pages-are-too-much-for-justices/article/1204606.

30. John McDonough, "ACA vs. ObamaCare: What's In a Name?" *Health Stew* (blog), Boston, January 14, 2012, http://archive.boston.com/lifestyle/health/health_stew/2012/01/aca_vs_obamacare_whats_in_a_na.html.

31. Kevin Boland, "Confirmed: Obamacare Bureaucracy Unleashed," Speaker Paul Ryan, August 3, 2010, https://www.speaker.gov/general/confirmed-obamacare-bureaucracy-unleashed.

32. Medicare Access and CHIP Reauthorization Act of 2015, Public Law No. 114-10, 129 Stat. 87 (April 16, 2015), https://www.congress.gov/114/plaws/publ10/PLAW-114publ10.pdf.

33. "TO: Centers for Medicare and Medicaid Services, HHS" letter regarding CMS-5517-FC, Citizens' Council for Health Freedom, December 19, 2016, 2, http://www.cchfreedom.org/pdf/MACRA%20final%20comment%20Dec%2019,%202016.pdf.

34. Mary A. Majumder et al., "Sharing Data under the 21st Century Cures Act," *Genetics in Medicine* vol. 19, no. 12 (May 25, 2017), http://www.nature.com/gim/journal/vaop/ncurrent/abs/gim201759a.html?foxtrotcallback=true.

35. "Information blocking," Section 4004, 21st Century Cures Act, Public Law No. 114-255, 130 Stat. 1033 (December 13, 2016), 1176, https://www.gpo.gov/fdsys/pkg/PLAW-114publ255/pdf/PLAW-114publ255.pdf.

36. Consolidated Appropriations Act, 2017, Public Law No. 115-31, 131 Stat. 135 (May 5, 2017), https://www.congress.gov/115/plaws/publ31/PLAW-115publ31.pdf.

37. "Report Together with Minority Views and Additional Views [to accompany H.R. 5926]," US Departments of Labor, Health & Human Services, and Education, and Related Agencies Appropropriations Bill, 2017, U.S. House of Representatives, July 22, 2016, 110, https://www.gpo.gov/fdsys/pkg/CRPT-114hrpt699/pdf/CRPT-114hrpt699.pdf.

About the Author

Twila Brase, RN, PHN (public health nurse), is president and co-founder of the Citizens' Council for Health Freedom (CCHF). She was voted in as #75 on *Modern Healthcare*'s 2009 list of the "100 Most Powerful People in Healthcare." Working for CCHF, she initiated the nationwide "Refuse to Sign HIPAA" campaign; discovered state storage, use, and sharing of newborn DNA without parent consent (which led to parent lawsuits in three states); and in 2016 launched CCHF's patient and doctor freedom initiative called The Wedge of Health Freedom (JoinTheWedge.com).

She received the "Freedom of Informed Choice" award at the 2014 Sacred Fire of Liberty Gala in Maryland and the 2013 Eagle Forum's Eagle Award for Minnesota. Her "Health Freedom Minute" is heard weekdays on more than eight hundred radio stations in forty-seven states. Her commentaries have appeared in CNSNews, The Daily Caller, LifeZette, the *Pioneer Press*, the *Star Tribune*, *The Hill*, *Townhall*, the *Wall Street Journal*, and the *Washington Times*. Her article "Blame Congress for HMOs" is published online and in the *Congressional Record* of the US House of Representatives. She tweets @twilabrase. She graduated from Gustavus Adolphus College with a bachelor of arts degree in nursing and specialized in pediatric emergency room nursing.

About Citizens' Council for Health Freedom

CCHF was founded in 1998 as an independent 501(c)3 national donor-supported nonprofit organization. CCHF's patient-centered mission is to protect health care choices, individualized patient care, and medical and genetic privacy rights. CCHF can be found online (cchfreedom.org), on Twitter @CCHFreedom, and on Facebook (cchfreedom), where daily "Health Freedom Minute" radio broadcasts are available. CCHF information on "Baby DNA Warehousing" is found online (itsmydna.org). The *CCHF Health Freedom eNews* is emailed weekly: bit.ly/enews-letter.

CCHF provides education and information to the public on legislative, regulatory, and industry proposals, dissects health care news, publishes original research, and connects the dots between privacy and freedom.

CCHF is focused on building "escape hatches" back to patient and doctor freedom through direct payment, as found in The Wedge of Health Freedom, health sharing, lifelong health insurance (preferably purchased pre-birth), access to affordable indemnity (true) health insurance, tax equity to encourage individual purchase of health insurance, and securing the constitutional right of senior citizens to opt out of Medicare Part A (hospitalization) without losing Social Security retirement benefits.